C000180234

# Thinking Beyond the Brain

# Thinking Beyond the Brain

## A Wider Science of Consciousness

Edited by David Lorimer

Floris Books

First published in volume form in 2001 by Floris Books

© 2001 Scientific and Medical Network
All rights reserved. No part of this publication may
be reproduced without the prior permission of
Floris Books, 15 Harrison Gardens, Edinburgh.

British Library CIP Data available

ISBN 0-86315-357-7

Printed in Great Britain
by Bell & Bain, Glasgow

# Contents

# Introduction

## David Lorimer

*David Lorimer was Director of the Scientific and Medical Network from 1986–2000. He is now a consultant to the Network and continues to edit their Review. He is author of* Survival? Body, Mind and Death in the Light of Psychic Experience *and* Whole in One. *He is also editor of* The Circle of Sacred Dance — Peter Deunov's Paneurythmy; Prophet for our Times *and* Gems of Love. *More recently he has edited* The Spirit of Science *and* Wider Horizons. *He was educated at Eton and the Universities of St Andrews and Cambridge. After a spell in merchant banking, he spent a number of years teaching modern languages and philosophy at Winchester College. He is also Chair of Wrekin Trust, Vice-President of the International Association for Near-Death Studies (UK) and the current President of the Swedenborg Society.*

For years science paid little or no attention to consciousness, dominated as it was in the middle of the last century by behaviourism. It is symptomatic that Peter Fenwick, beginning his neurophysiological researches nearly fifty years ago, could not find the word 'consciousness' listed in the index of any of the textbooks he consulted. All this changed in the 1990s, the Decade of the Brain. Immense strides were made in neuroimaging but the so-called hard problem of the exact relationship between consciousness and the brain remained. Popular books began to appear, some with audacious titles like Daniel Dennett's *Consciousness Explained* (a wit suggested adding 'Away' to this title), the *Journal of Consciousness Studies* was founded and conferences on consciousness sprang up all over the globe. The majority of these meetings devoted little space to the kinds of human issues covered in this book, which question the premise of most modern science and psychology: that consciousness is based entirely in the brain and cannot exist apart from it. A number of people felt that something had to be done to counter the prevailing orthodoxy.

It was with this in mind that the 'Beyond the Brain' conference series (the title originating from a landmark book by Stanislav Grof) was conceived at the annual meeting of the Institute of Noetic Sciences in Chicago in 1993. Discussions with Willis Harman, President of the Institute, and Marilyn Schlitz, Director of Research, along with Barbara Hancock of the Lifebridge Foundation and Bob Lehman of the Fetzer Institute resulted in a plan for August 1995 to hold a joint conference at St John's College, Cambridge. This first meeting was preceded by a one-day symposium that explored Willis Harman's paper (printed in this volume) and around twenty written responses to it. The conference itself, subtitled 'New Avenues in Consciousness Research,' was attended by over three hundred people. The second conference, held in 1997, focused on 'Frontiers in Consciousness and Healing,' while the 1999 meeting examined the question 'Does Individual Identity Extend Beyond Birth and Death?' A fourth meeting, in August 2001, considers 'Scientific and Spiritual Perspectives on Meditation.'

## *Approaches to consciousness*

On looking back through the annals of the Mystics and Scientists conferences, now in their twenty-fourth year and featured in *The Spirit of Science,* a companion volume to this, one notes that the 1980 gathering was entitled 'A Science of Consciousness' at a time when the words were not often heard in conjunction. However, both the Scientific and Medical Network and the Institute of Noetic Sciences were founded in 1973. And the Religious Experience Research Unit was set up in Oxford in 1969 by the zoologist Sir Alister Hardy. The Centre has over 5,000 records of spiritual and religious experiences in its archives.

Hardy was strongly influenced by William James, whose classic *Varieties of Religious Experience* dates from 1903, being the text of his Gifford Lectures delivered in the University of Edinburgh in 1901–2 — almost exactly one hundred years ago. William James was at once a philosopher, psychologist and psychical researcher and coined the term 'radical empiricism,' signifying that science should take account of the whole range of human experience. A recent book by Eugene Taylor — *William James on Consciousness Beyond the Margin* — traces how James lost out to the experimental mode of psychology imported from Germany. After his death, Harvard refused an endowment for a chair of psychical research, and psychology embarked on its behaviourist agenda that arguably set consciousness studies back decades. Behaviourists took the third-person perspective to its logical (and self-contradictory) conclusion by declaring that consciousness did not exist. It seemed to escape them by that they had to be conscious in order to make such a statement. It is only in the 1990s that we once again picked up the threads that James was weaving a hundred years ago. James realized, as did Edwin Burtt in his classic 1924 *Metaphysical Foundations of Modern Science* that all science was undergirded by a metaphysical system, whether or not acknowledged: 'the juices of metaphysical assumptions leak in at every joint.' Burtt contends that the assumptions of Newton, shorn of their Deism and reduced to mechanistic materialism, were passed on implicitly and unconsciously down succeeding generations of scientists.

Among those currently involved in consciousness studies there are two basic orientations: those who follow the traditional Western method of looking from the outside in as detached observers — the third-person perspective; and those who look from the inside out — the first-person perspective — and who are interested in exploring the nature of their own consciousness. The Eastern meditative traditions fall into this latter category, but, as Ravi Ravindra points out, yoga has its own form of objectivity through rigorous self-observation and training of the mind. Ken Wilber and Willis Harman have also written eloquently about the need for a transformation of the knower. It is writers like Harman, Ravindra and Wilber who are pioneers of an emerging science of the spirit. The former group focus on experiment while the latter are concerned with experience. As Ken Wilber has repeatedly argued, a more adequate or integral science of consciousness requires a spectrum of complementary disciplines or approaches.

Another radical distinction of approach, not unrelated to the contrast between first- and third-person perspectives, can be drawn between those who assume that consciousness is entirely dependent on brain processes and those who contend that consciousness may in some sense be 'beyond the brain.' In his Ingersoll Lecture on Immortality that draws upon the ideas of F.C.S. Schiller, William James contrasts theories whereby consciousness is actually produced by brain processes with those positing that consciousness is in some sense filtered by or transmitted *through* the brain. The former 'productive' theories lead inexorably to the prediction that consciousness is extinguished at bodily death, while the latter 'transmissive' theories leave open the possibility that an aspect of the self may survive the death of the brain. 'Productive' theories necessarily regard brain processes as *causing* conscious experiences, while 'transmissive' theorists insist that this apparent causation may in fact represent no more than a *correlation* between brain processes and conscious subjective experience. Most of the best known and most influential philosophers and scientists such as Francis Crick and Daniel Dennett simply take it for granted that we are 'nothing but a pack of neurons' but they can only maintain this stance by ignoring the evidence from parapsychology and deep mystical experience that is presented in this volume. Dualists like Sir John Eccles and Sir Karl Popper are a rare and unfashionable breed. Their position is well defended here by John Beloff.

It is a curious feature of modern science and medicine that its proponents are interested in normal experience and abnormal (or subnormal) conditions but studiously ignore paranormal or supernormal experiences ('exceptional human experiences' or EHEs) that might widen their understanding and place it in a wider context. Willis Harman puts his finger on the underlying — and metaphysical — reasons for this neglect or denial. If one is wedded to a materialistic and brain-based philosophy that excludes the possibility of paranormal experiences, then one is very reluctant to accept the challenge that these experiences ostensibly pose to the established view. The research implications of this exclusion are strongly put in a book by the Estonian researcher Undo Uus entitled *Blindness of Modern Science.* If one bases one's research proposals on the premise that consciousness is a by-product of brain processes, the answers thrown up by the research are likely to reflect the original starting point; many interesting questions go unexamined and it is even hard to convince ethical committees of the practicality of NDE (near death experience) research that is testing the hypothesis that experiencers may have out-of-body experiences while unconscious.

The near-death experience provides a fascinating case study in attitudes towards the nature of consciousness. Conventional neurophysiological approaches stress such factors as cerebral anoxia (shortage of oxygen to the brain), hypercarbia (excessive $CO_2$ in the brain) and the neurochemical effect of drugs. They assume that these factors are causal and combine them if necessary with the assertion that all visual experiences are hallucinations. Veridical out-of-body experiences, or OBEs, as examined by Kenneth Ring in this volume, are the most interesting phenomenon since the subjective impression is in such cases verified by a third party so that the perceptions of the experiencer are deemed to be more or less accurate. It is hard — if not impossible — to account for this by means of conventional theories of visual perception, although attempts have been made, notably by Susan Blackmore in her book *Dying to Live.* The strength of Kenneth Ring's work is that it takes apparently visual experiences of the blind and applies a 'mindsight' theory to all cases.

As Peter Fenwick points out in his paper, the NDE shades into deep mystical experience in which the experiencer arrives at a knowledge — or gnosis — that leads beyond the division between subject and object, knower and known. The experiencer encounters a being of light who also emanates love, peace and joy, reporting back that the experience is more — not less — real that ordinary reality. They do not subsequently need to be convinced of the independent existence of a spiritual dimension or that their essence survives death — they know it first-hand. This kind of assertion leaves the third-person researcher in a limbo position since he only has his reason and the subjective reports to go on. He has not himself been initiated. It is worth remembering that the fundamental purpose of initiation into any mystery tradition was an experience of death and rebirth in such a way that initiates knew directly of their intrinsic immortality from first-hand experience without having to take it on trust. The third-person researcher can only go so far: if he is to acquire deeper self-knowledge, then he must undergo an spiritual transformation whereby he acquires the kind of knowledge that can only be derived from inner experience.

## *The need for a new science of consciousness*

This volume is divided into four parts: The Need for a New Science of Consciousness, Consciousness and Parapsychology, Frontiers in Consciousness and Healing, and A Wider Perspective on Consciousness. It begins with Willis Harman's question to the 1995 Cambridge symposium: is a new scientific epistemology required to make desired progress in research on consciousness? The question is philosophical rather than scientific and scientists may be tempted to ignore it on the grounds that (as Harman often used to say) 'philosophy of science is of as much interest to scientists as ornithology is to birds.' The answers given here not only consider this epistemological question to be fundamental, but answer it in the affirmative, as does Harman himself.

He singles out a number of subjective features of consciousness that need to be addressed: intentionality, attention, memory, creativity, subjectivity and synchronicity. He then asks 'what sorts of epistemology, conceptual frameworks and organizing metaphors can be used to help us understand the many facets and dimensions of consciousness *all considered together?'* He urges us, quite rightly, to take into account the effects of unconscious processes on our thinking, which may be '*a potentially major factor in the construction of any society's particular form of science.*' His central point is that the epistemological issue is arguably the most central and critical issue in consciousness research. Since we cannot agree about basic epistemological approaches we are unlikely to reach a consensus about the nature of any of the subjective features of consciousness mentioned above. He himself proposes a 'consciousness metaphor,' contending that this 'would allow us to gain insight from a vantage point resembling philosophical idealism without having to commit to an ontological position that insists consciousness is the ultimate reality.' He goes on to propose a number of features of a new epistemology for the study of consciousness that are taken up by other authors before dealing with the ontological questions raised by consciousness research. Here he raises the deeper issue of the nature of reality as seen by the perennial philosophy and explained in an essay by Ken Wilber. There is an important correspondence between epistemology — how we know, and ontology — what can be known: a wider and deeper participatory epistemology opens up our innate faculties to reveal subtle worlds behind physical appearances.

Peter Fenwick calls for a new science of so-called secondary qualities. He celebrates the advances in brain imaging that have vastly increased our detailed knowledge of brain function but argues that this leaves consciousness out of the picture and is therefore incomplete. He traces the mechanistic approach back to Galileo and Descartes with the resulting development of what he calls a 'primary quality science.' The major difficulty with our current mind-brain identity theory is that it offers 'no explanation of consciousness, which is the very basis of our perception of the world and our formulation of science itself.' A further problem is that such materialistic and deterministic views undercut any coherent notion of free will — a trend that has significant implications for the law, predicated as it is on the notion of individual moral responsibility.

Fenwick goes on to outline the 'downward causation' theory advocated by the Nobel Prize Laureate Roger Sperry as a way of salvaging this situation and points out how many of our responses to situations depend on the meaning that we subjectively attribute to them. His own research into the NDE has convinced him that experiencers do see into a deeper structure of the universe that is underpinned by love and light, so that a new grand unifying theory of consciousness must find some way of taking these insights into account. He argues that such a theory will have three components: 'a detailed role for brain mechanisms, an explanation for the action of mind outside the brain, and an explanation of free will, meaning and purpose. It should also give an explanation of wide mental states, including mystical experience and near-death experiences.'

Concluding this section, Brian Josephson counters theoretical approaches such as Daniel Dennett's which exclude 'ordinary thinking' and 'judgments of experience' as a basis for knowledge, and sees a genuine necessity to address consciousness in non-abstract and experiential ways.

## *Consciousness and parapsychology*

I have already mentioned Kenneth Ring's work in my discussion of veridical OBEs above. Ring is one of the most knowledgeable and careful of NDE researchers whose book *Lessons from the Light* sums up what he has learnt in twenty years of research. In this article he takes up a particular challenge, namely the question of whether blind near-death experiencers see anything and if the quality of experience resembles those of sighted subjects. In answering both questions in the affirmative he is careful to tease out the meaning of 'sight.' He asks if there is 'another form of awareness that comes into play when, *whether one is blind or not,* an individual is thrust into a state of consciousness in which one's sensory system is no longer functional?' His theory of 'mindsight' is in my view a most fertile one and is consistent with reports from mystics and visionaries down the ages: we are multidimensional beings who fall into *maya* if we take the physical world for the only reality available to us.

David Fontana brings a familiarity with Eastern spiritual traditions as well as extensive practical experience to his discussion of altered states in dreams and meditation. He introduces a variety of methods of inner exploration: enquiry, awareness, meditation and dream yoga. Like Charles Tart, Fontana places emphasis on non-separateness from life, reminding us that this is the true meaning of the Buddhist term *anatta,* frequently translated as no-self and associated with self-annihilation. It is a state beyond separateness so that 'when the opposites arise, the Buddha-mind is lost.' The practices that he introduces are not addressed to discursive knowing-about but rather the direct cognition of knowing or, more precisely, Delphic self-knowledge.

Erlendur Haraldsson's paper is concerned with the nature of memory and identity. Erlendur has been studying cases of the reincarnation type for two decades and gives us a clear and informative account of two cases that he has personally investigated, detailing their strengths and weaknesses. Readers who are encountering this kind of case for the first time are perfectly justified to be astonished as well as mystified by the accuracy of some of the statements that were later verified. Whatever one's view of these ostensible memories, the strongest cases prove beyond reasonable doubt that events are remembered that cannot by definition have been laid down in the brain of the person remembering them as they all took place before the subject was born. This finding raises intriguing questions about our current theories of memory as exclusively brain-based and which are investigated in Rupert Sheldrake's book *The Presence of the Past.* Readers may know that the classic work in this field has been carried out by Haraldsson's colleague Professor Ian Stevenson from the University of Virginia, whose books *Children who Remember Previous Lives* and *Where Reincarnation and Biology Intersect* can be strongly recommended.

In a succinct but telling contribution, John Beloff presents an analytical explanation of the relationship between physicalism and parapsychology, which he rightly regards as incompatible. He argues cogently that 'there exists, already, sufficient evidence for the existence of phenomena which are (a) incompatible with the known laws of physics and (b) mind-dependent.' He goes on to say that 'if (a) is correct, if there are such paranormal phenomena in this strong sense, it follows that the mind has powers and properties that defy any such physicalist analysis as implied by Crick's "Astonishing Hypothesis".' He then defends the necessity of a dichotomy or dualism of mind and body. Although this view is criticized by Mark Woodhouse in his piece (and not for the usual reasons) I am sure that Beloff is right to the extent that, if any part of the mind survives bodily death, it must be qualitatively distinguishable from the physical body. The next step is to argue, as Woodhouse does, that consciousness is in some sense fundamental. Beloff then proposes four ways to challenge the scepticism of scientists and philosophers. He does not hold out a great deal of hope that any of these stratagems will succeed, although he thinks the definitive the most likely candidate. I myself am not so sure, given the power of the unconscious and the rigidity of philosophical presuppositions; however, parapsychologists must persevere — and perhaps the best book to recommend to open-minded enquirers is Dean Radin's *The Conscious Universe.*

Michael Grosso raises some of the same philosophical issues as in Beloff's paper — for instance the question of survival — but his principal concern is to articulate the relationship between parapsychology and transpersonal psychology. He begins with the survival issue, explaining why he considers it important, introducing considerations about the spirituality and understanding the nature of reality. He conducts a thorough assessment of the strengths and weaknesses of the evidence for survival. Given the interest of the field he finds it surprising that so little of this research has created a stir and wonders about possible ways forward in the field. It is here that he introduces transpersonal psychology, focusing on three aspects of the NDE: the OBE, the apparitional encounter with deceased relatives and finally the experience of the light. The key here is the recognition through experience that there is more to the self than the surface personality and that this deeper nature is intimately related to light. Moreover, each of these features has a replicable counterpart that can be researched, lending itself to possible progress in the field. All this leads up to one of Grosso's central points, namely that parapsychology 'warrants belief that we inhabit a universe in which there is a basis for transpersonal experiences' and points towards a creative convergence of insights from the two fields.

## *Frontiers in consciousness and healing*

Charles Tart's piece retains the informality of his oral presentation, widely regarded as the high point of the 1995 conference. He coins the term 'endarkenment' to characterize the fact that modern Western psychology seems to know more about the obstacles to enlightenment than about enlightenment itself. Like Peter Fenwick vainly searching for the word 'consciousness' in the textbooks of the fifties, Charles Tart draws a similar blank when looking up 'enlightenment' in contemporary psychology textbooks. He then gives us a classic case of an enlightenment experience (compared later with the well-known experience of Richard Maurice Bucke), eliciting many interesting details before going on to state his assumptions about consciousness and enlightenment: that everyday consciousness is a subset of all the possibilities and is a relatively shrunken and even distorted state — Ravi Ravindra would agree with this statement. From this perspective we are caught in what he calls a bio-psycho virtual reality, which the Buddha would equate with *samsara,* itself a cause of suffering. If the sense of separation is related to suffering, then a move in the direction of enlightenment is a move towards wholeness, openness, compassion and humility. This can be achieved through meditative disciplines, which Tart himself practises. Again this requires participation rather than detachment, resulting in a gradual change in the quality of consciousness and therefore of life — this should surely be of interest to psychology.

Stan Grof gives a major summary of his work in non-ordinary states of consciousness over a forty year period. Along with Charles Tart, he was one of the modern pioneers of transpersonal psychology, following in the footsteps of C.G. Jung and Abraham Maslow. Grof has coined the term 'holotropic' for states that are 'oriented towards wholeness.' He traces these back through human history, in particular through shamanic traditions, and outlines their history in relation to psychiatry. He argues that 'if we study systematically the experiences and observations associated with NOSC (non-ordinary states of consciousness) or, more specifically, holotropic states, this leads inevitably to a radical revision of our basic ideas about consciousness and the human psyche and to an entirely new psychiatry, psychology, and psychotherapy.' This involves a new cartography of consciousness — and indeed of reality — a wider understanding of healing and of psychopathology, an expanded model of psychotherapy and a revisioning of the role of spirituality in life. The article then looks at one major area of his work — the transpersonal. He concludes, correctly in my view, that 'the observations from the research of NOSC represent a serious challenge to contemporary psychiatry and psychology and require a drastic revision of our thinking in these fields.' The challenge, as he sees it, is not to react dismissively but rather to welcome the new opportunities offered by such ideas in a spirit of true science: 'excitement about and intense interest in such anomalies combined with healthy critical scepticism.' As a result, he argues, 'it will also become clear to us that materialistic science has an incomplete and inadequate image of reality and that its ideas about the nature of consciousness and the relationship between consciousness and matter (particularly the brain) have to be radically revised.' Grof provides enough evidence in this article that we need such a radical revision.

Andrew Powell's essay brings out just the kind of participatory and insightful approach to medicine and healing advocated by Willis Harman and Marilyn Schlitz. Even his title: 'Beyond Space and Time: the Unbounded Psyche' suggests that he is operating beyond the normal confines of western biomedicine. Indeed Powell has been one of a small group within the Royal College of Psychiatrists to set up the College's Spirituality and Psychiatry Special Interest Group, of which he is Chair. He describes therapeutic encounters from his own personal and clinical experience involving past life regression, spirit release and soul recovery where the ordinary boundaries of space-time are transcended. These modalities demonstrate the need for a wider metaphysical view since a purely materialistic approach to conditions of this kind — if they really are what they seem to be — might be a major misdiagnosis due to the clinician's inability to think outside the physical box. The rejection of a framework within which influences from unseen realms might affect a patient is culturally conditioned. A Brazilian healer would not make the same mistake: if anything, he might attribute too great an effect to these influences, thus erring in the opposite direction.

The next piece, by Marilyn Schlitz and Willis Harman, shows how modern biomedical science is underpinned by the same metaphysical and epistemological assumptions as modern science in general. Central to these considerations as they apply to medicine is the causal efficacy of consciousness: is it just an epiphenomenal by-product of brain processes or can it intentionally intervene in the therapeutic process. Research on the placebo response suggests that it can and does intervene: patients are not simply passive recipients of treatment. The authors look specifically at a number of features of complementary medical models that do not seem to be compatible with the standard scientific world-view. Among these are 'subtle energies' (like *chi),* the action of homeopathy, intentionality in self-healing and intuitive diagnosis. They invite readers to consider some alternative ontological assumptions and suggest that the picture would look very different if biology rather than physics were regarded as the root science, especially Arthur Koestler's notion of the holon as elaborated by Ken Wilber as subsets of holarchies. They also advance a different set of epistemological assumptions that are participatory and experiential along with a metaphor derived from conscious experience itself. Nor should we neglect, as Willis Harman points out in his opening essay, the role and power of the unconscious. The authors hope for a 'whole-system' change but events in the past five years in the US suggest a more gradual process — an increasing openness to the role of spirituality in health and medicine led from the grass roots up.

Roger Woolger's ambitious paper argues for 'the presence of multiple worlds, spiritual and visionary, that interact with and inter-penetrate this one.' He considers energy field models of consciousness, moving on to theories that see matter as an emanation of spirit and propose a spiritual ontology that sees consciousness as ultimately real. It becomes clear that Woolger's own experiences and those of his clients are quite inexplicable on the basis of a materialistic bottom-up understanding. This means that '*the spiritual dimension is other than and of a higher order than the energy fields through which spirit manifests in the physical world.*' However, there are intermediary realms that are the realm of the 'imaginal' (*mundus imaginalis),* to use Henri Corbin's term. Woolger extends our view of the imagination towards its true creative meaning and draws parallels from the same kind of shamanic traditions referred to by Stan Grof above. He draws on a variety of visionary mystics and poets to illustrate his thesis — can one lightly dismiss the experiences and insights of those regarded as the finest human beings of their generation? They may not have known the exact details of the outer world but they were familiar with the intricacies of the inner realms which are perhaps less changeable even if dynamic. The timeless transcends the relativity of time.

## *Wider perspectives on consciousness*

Mark Woodhouse's multi-dimensional theory of energy monism seeks to integrate both scientific and spiritually oriented phenomena. It proposes that all things come from and are sustained by a common source; that they all have both conscious and energetic aspects; that 'all levels or dimensions are not merely interconnected, but "intersuffusing" in a hierarchical asymmetry;' that all objects and events are both wholes and parts; that 'change is implemented by, though not reducible to, the language of wave forms, frequencies, phase entanglements, entrainment, harmonic series, etc.' and that common sense reality occupies the lower levels of the spectrum. Woodhouse elaborates on the arguments for his theory, while criticizing other theories along the way and responding to criticisms of his own theory, before applying it to OBEs, clairvoyant healing, continuity of identity and psychoneuro-immunology. I find his approach enormously interesting and hope that his contribution here will encourage readers to look to his *Paradigm Wars* for a fuller exposition.

Ravi Ravindra's paper presents a perennial Indian perspective on the nature of self and identity. He places the emphasis on the transformation of the limited to a less limited and more integrated self: 'from an identification of oneself exclusively as the body to one closer to the supreme identity of oneness with the all.' The centre of being moves from the ego to God. The desired transformation is associated with a refinement of the self and subtle bodies towards an eventual liberation that precludes the necessity for reincarnation. Indeed, in this view we are condemned to reincarnate until we reach the freedom of this exalted state. Reincarnation is not the same as being born again; being born again, as Ravindra stresses, is being born from above. Nor is the eternal to be equated with the everlasting, which implies extension in time; the eternal is a quality of being that transcends time. The greatest fear of saints, observes Ravindra, is 'that of dying without being self-annihilated, without having died to their ego-selves.' In doing this they open themselves up and no longer 'restrict our consciousness to a small aperture in the vast spectrum of consciousness.' In all of this Ravindra reminds us of the primacy of the spiritual not only over the physical but also over the psychic and in doing so delineates the essential from the inessential in human life.

Anne Baring's contribution also draws on her personal experience while placing it within the wider picture of the evolution and awakening of consciousness, itself a process of exploration and discovery. As a backdrop to our present state she takes us back beyond the split between man and nature, masculine and feminine, mind and matter, arguing that such divisions represent a necessary phase in the evolution of consciousness (she illustrates this later with reference to the Fall). In answer to the question 'What is beyond the brain?' she responds: 'the lost realm of the soul,' which she proceeds to explore through the fairy tale of the Sleeping Beauty. She sees the story as an allegory for our time when we urgently need to marry heaven and earth, head and heart, the solar principle of consciousness with the deep instinctual wisdom. The soul is lost but can be recovered through the hero's journey in the course of which he relies on his own intuitive wisdom for guidance. Her next theme relates the evolution of the brain to the evolution of consciousness. She points out that we may think we act rationally while being driven by more archaic impulses emanating from more ancient parts of the brain: 'our belief systems, whether religious or scientific, as well as our ways of relating to each other as individuals and nations are profoundly rooted in unconscious instinctive responses which have their origins in earlier phases of our evolution.' This helps to account for our resistance to change as a threat to our existing belief systems. One creative way forward is to be found in the alchemical tradition, a process quintessentially embodying transformation and union of opposites into a new integration: 'in awakening to our soul, in discovering how to relate to it, transform it, to heal its wounds and listen to its guidance, to receive its dreams and acknowledge its visions, we help to bring about the marriage between the Sleeping Beauty and the Prince and eventually also, that sacred marriage with the ground of being which is the tremendous destiny of the human race.' Anne Baring's text is immensely evocative and her vision arguably constitutes the most profound task of our time. It is a fitting place to end the book.

David Lorimer
Fife, February 2001

# The Need for a New Science of Consciousness

# Towards a Science of Consciousness: Do We Need a New Epistemology?

WILLIS HARMAN

*Professor Willis Harman was President of the Institute of Noetic Sciences (IONS) from 1977 until his death in 1997. The Institute, which co-sponsored the first three 'Beyond the Brain' conferences, was founded in 1973 by astronaut Edgar Mitchell (for more details see Appendix). Prior to his appointment at IONS, Harman was a Senior Social Scientist at SRI International at Menlo Park, California, where he initiated a programme of research to explore national and global futures. He was also a founding board member of the World Business Academy and Emeritus Professor of Engineering-Economic Systems at Stanford University. He was a member of the Board of Regents of the University of California from 1980–90. His passion for the epistemology of science, reflected in the piece below, is evident in his last edited work* New Metaphysical Foundations of Modern Science (1994). *Among his other works were* An Incomplete Guide to the Future *(1979),* Changing Images of Man *(1982, with O.W. Markley),* Global Mind Change *(1988) and* Creative Work *(1990, with John Hormann).*

The symposium in which we will be participating asks a straightforward and important question, to which we expect fruitful response, although perhaps not a definitive answer: *Is a new scientific epistemology required to make desired progress in research on consciousness?*

This suggests other questions: what do we mean by 'scientific epistemology'? And what do we mean by 'consciousness'?

## *What do we mean by the epistemology of science?*

Epistemology, in essence, deals with the question: how do we know what we think we know? There is no single epistemology of science; the epistemology of physics is very different from that of cultural anthropology, for example. However, because the reductionist and positivist epistemology of the physical sciences has proven to be so powerful in terms of prediction, control, and the generation of technologies, it tends to dominate. In that dominant (mainstream) epistemology, consciousness is considered epiphenomenal — ultimately to be explained in terms of its presumed physical causes.

William James' (1912) concept of 'radical empiricism' implies a very different epistemology. Like any form of empiricism, it admits data from the senses, but it also encompasses the broad spectrum of inner realities articulated within the subjective life of the person. In his *Essays in Radical Empiricism* James defines his term thus: 'To be radical, an empiricism must neither admit into its constructions any element that is not directly experienced, nor exclude from them any element that is directly experienced. For such a philosophy, *the relations that connect experiences must themselves be experienced relations, and any kind of relation experienced must be accounted as "real" as anything else in the system* [since its effects are real].' (italics in original)

There are really two questions here. Is a new epistemology needed in order to carry out a scientific exploration of consciousness? If so, does that have implications for the biological and even the physical sciences?

## *What do we mean by consciousness?*

Among the many aspects of consciousness that need somehow to be dealt with are intentionality, attention, subjectivity, creativity, memory, and synchronicity:

*Intentionality.* Something like intentionality seems operative at all levels of life, from the smallest micro-organisms to those particular colonies of collaborating micro-organisms that make up our physical bodies. Mainstream science tends to think of intentionality as epiphenomenal — that is, caused by, and to be understood in term of, underlying physical and chemical processes. On the other hand, all of our practical experience implies intentionality as a *causal* reality.

*Attention.* Attention, William James in *The Principles of Psychology,* defined as 'the taking possession by the mind, in clear and vivid form, out of a number of possible objects or trains of thought.' Selective attention is a particular form of intentionality, and presents a similar puzzle.

*Memory.* All organisms seem to be capable of learning; which is to say, they exhibit some form of memory. We tend to assume that memory represents information stored in some fashion within the organism. But that kind of conceptualization does not seem to be able to account for all aspects of memory — memory, it seems, must be at least partially something beyond the physical organism, something other than states of a neuronal network.

*Creativity.* Naturalistic studies of organisms, from the micro-organisms on up, provide many examples of what appears to be creative-like behaviour. To the mainstream scientist, the appearance of creativity — like intentionality — is to be explained away, rather than being itself a causal factor.

*Subjectivity* (including consciousness of self). Mainstream science has tended to claim that it deals with *objective* data — with what is publicly observable. If we take into account that perception is culturally conditioned, this assumed sharp differentiation between subjective and objective breaks down. Although we are well aware of the extent to which all aspects of perception are affected by the contents and processes of the unconscious mind, the validity of the epistemology of Western science has never been systematically re-assessed in light of this fact.

Beyond that possibility of unacknowledged bias, lies a more profound epistemological issue. Some scholars (for example, the French philosopher Henri Bergson) have claimed that we have not one basic way of contacting reality (through the physical senses), but *two* — the additional way being subjectively, through inner experience and deep intuition. If that is assumed, it leads to an entirely different epistemology.

*Synchronicity.* Carl Jung introduced the term 'synchronicity' to refer to two or more events, separated by time or space, where there appears to be no possibility of physical connection in any known sense, and yet there seems to be *meaningful* connection. Jung is very clear about the fact that meaningfulness is not to be interpreted as merely a subjective feeling. Synchronicity, he insists, 'postulates a meaning which is *a priori* in relation to human consciousness and apparently exists outside man.'

*A choice of strategy.* It might seem a reasonable strategy to focus on the simplest and most tractable aspect of consciousness, proceeding to the more complex or recondite aspects as step by step progress is made. However there is an alternative strategy which also has precedent in the history of science. Consider the origin of the evolutionary hypothesis. In the mid-nineteenth century there was much to be learned from studying separately the great variety of micro-organisms, plants, and animals with which the planet is populated. But Charles Darwin boldly turned his attention to the synthesising question: How can we understand *all of these together?* The result was the concept of evolution, around which practically all of biology is now organized.

There is an analogous situation in the study of consciousness. We seem to need some sort of conceptual framework within which to understand a broad range of phenomena and experiences including the aspects mentioned above; imagery; states of consciousness; reports of awesome creative insight; out-of-body and near-death experiences; apparent memories of other lives; mystical experience; extraordinary psychic abilities; and so on.* Thus the alternative strategy suggests itself, namely to concentrate on the question: what sorts of epistemology, conceptual frameworks and organizing metaphors can be used to help us understand the many facets and dimensions of consciousness *all considered together?*

The above implies an intrinsic dilemma with regard to the epistemology of science which is too little noted. In order to have confidence in the scientific view of reality, we must answer the epistemological question: how do we know what we claim to know scientifically? Our view of reality is inevitably determined partly by that reality, and partly by the mental processes through which we arrived at the view we have. However, to know about those processes we need already a scientific study of the mind, for which we need a scientific epistemology — which with a frustrating circularity, leads us back to the initial question.

* This is not to suggest, of course, that all reports of anomalous phenomena or experience are to be believed, any more than everyone's every *sense* perception is to be trusted. But when reports are persistent enough, even when the phenomena appear erratic, a certain face validity must be granted.

This circularity implies that even if the results of generations of scientific inquiry appear to be convergent toward a particular picture of reality, a profound caution is advisable regarding how much faith is put in that picture. (This point has been made in another way by Thomas Kuhn, 1970.) In any case, this dilemma suggests that as we search for the appropriate epistemology for the study of consciousness, we need to pay particular attention to what is known about unconscious mental processes.

Research on perception, hypnosis, repression, selective attention, mental imagery, sleep and dreams, memory and memory retrieval, acculturation, etc. all suggests that the influence of the unconscious on how we experience ourselves and our environment may be far greater than is typically taken into account. Science itself has never been thoroughly re-assessed in the light of this recently discovered pervasive influence of the unconscious mind of the scientist. The contents and processes of the unconscious influence (individually and collectively) perceptions, 'rational thinking,' openness to challenging evidence, ability to contemplate alternative conceptual frameworks and metaphors, scientific interests and disinterests, scientific judgment — all to an indeterminate extent. What is implied is that we must accept the presence of unconscious processes and contents, not as a minor perturbation, but as *a potentially major factor in the construction of any society's particular form of science.*

Understanding that the influence of the unconscious on how we experience ourselves and our environment may be far greater than is typically taken into account, we now must re-assess the vaunted 'objectivity' of science. Research on perception makes it clear that science has been constructed on the basis of scientists' intersubjectively shared subjective experience, so that the difference between so-called 'objective' data (e.g. the read-out of a measuring instrument) and 'subjective' data (e.g. an inner image) is one of degree only. This point has been effectively made by Max Velmans (1993).

## *What are the critical issues in consciousness research?*

We are suggesting here that the epistemological issue is perhaps the most central and critical issue in consciousness research. Lack of consensus on the issue of epistemology leads to inability to resolve such issues as whether intentionality is caused or causal; subjectivity is epiphenomenal or revelatory; memory is exclusively stored information in the physical organism or is to some extent non-dependent on the physical organism; synchronicity is or is not mere accidental coincidence.

An unspoken issue is whether the centuries-long dream of a purely nomothetic science (that is, one in which all phenomena are governed by discoverable scientific laws that are never violated) is in truth a false goal. If intentionality can be causal (which we take for granted in all practical affairs), then this is a factor not taken into account by scientific laws. In that case, nomothetic science can only be a limited view, describing what happens under those conditions when consciousness (intentionality) as a causal factor is not interfering. That kind of science is still useful for prediction, control, and the design of manipulative technologies. But that science is in no way qualified to provide a worldview adequate to guide individual and societal decisions.

Selection of an appropriate epistemology is complicated by the extent to which epistemology implies ontology. Unspoken ontological assumptions in the Western view create resistance to the avowed goal of a science of consciousness. We explore this topic briefly in a separate section, below.

Another, related issue is what models and metaphors are permissible. In science, as in ordinary life, we use metaphors to understand or communicate about the unfamiliar in terms of the familiar. Great mischief results, however, when these models and metaphors are mistakenly taken to be the 'true' description of reality. When they are, people then feel driven to defend them, and to stamp out competing views. Many of the conflicts in the history of science (as in religion) have been battles between groups where each insists that *their* metaphors are 'really' how reality is.

It is a peculiarity of modern science that it allows some kinds of metaphors and disallows others. It is perfectly acceptable to use metaphors that derive directly from our experience of the physical world (such as 'fundamental particles,' acoustic waves), as well as metaphors representing what can be measured only in terms of its effects (such as gravitational, electromagnetic, or quantum fields). It has further become acceptable to use more holistic and non-quantifiable metaphors such as organism, personality, ecological community, Gaia, universe.

It is, however, taboo to use non-sensory 'metaphors of mind' — metaphors that tap into images and experiences familiar from our own inner awareness. I am not allowed to say (scientifically) that some aspects of my experience of reality are reminiscent of my experience of my own mind — to observe, for example, that some aspects of animal behaviour appear as though they were tapping into some supra-individual nonphysical mind, or as though there were in instinctual behaviour and in evolution something like my experience in my own mind of *purpose.*

The implicit or explicit epistemological position of the 'hard' scientist is that we know what we know through the empirical observation of quantifiable, replicable observations and interventions in the physical world. However, a less dogmatic attitude would hold that reality has many aspects, and is never fully captured in any model or metaphor. For example, admission of the consciousness metaphor would allow us to gain insight from a vantage point resembling philosophical idealism without having to commit to an ontological position that insists consciousness is the ultimate reality.

## *Toward an epistemology for researching consciousness*

Advocacy of an introspective or phenomenological epistemology to deal with the subjective aspect of consciousness is not a new development in science. In the past the proposal has been unequivocally rejected, for reasons that appeared adequate at the time. However, apparent cultural changes over the past few decades increase the likelihood that such an approach might now achieve gradual acceptance within the scientific community.

A recent effort to identify a suitable epistemology for the study of consciousness in the broadest sense resulted in the following nine proposed characteristics:*

1. The epistemology will be *'radically empirical'* (in the sense urged by William James) in that it will be *phenomenological* or experiential in a broad sense (that is, it will include subjective experience as primary data, rather than being essentially limited to physical-sense

* These nine characteristics emerged from a retreat at Tomales Bay, California, December 3–6, 1992, wherein fifteen scientists and philosophers attempted to explore the question of an appropriate epistemology for consciousness research. Contributions of Max Velmans, Eugene Taylor, Michael Scriven, and Ron Brady, in particular, are gratefully acknowledged. The retreat was convened by the Institute of Noetic Sciences, Sausalito, California. A fuller discussion will be found in Harman and De Quincey (1994).

data) and it will address the totality of human experience (in other words, no reported phenomena will be written off because they 'violate known scientific laws'). Thus, consciousness is not a 'thing' to be studied by an observer who is somehow apart from it; consciousness involves the interaction of the observer and the observed, or if you like, the *experience* of observing.

2. It will aim at being *objective* in the sense of being open and free from hidden bias, while dealing with both 'external' and 'internal' (subjective) experience as origins of data.
3. It will insist on *open inquiry* and *public (intersubjective) validation* of knowledge; at the same time, it will recognize that these goals may, at any given time, be met only incompletely, particularly when seeking knowledge that includes deeper understanding of inner experience.
4. It will place *emphasis upon the unity of experience.* It will thus be congenial to a holistic view in which the parts are understood through the whole, while not excluding a reductionistic approach that seeks to understand the whole through the parts. Hence it will recognize the importance of subjective and cultural meanings in all human experience, including experiences — such as some religious or interpersonal experiences — that seem particularly rich in meaning even though they may be ineffable. In a holistic view, such meaningful experiences will not be explained away by reducing them to combinations of simpler experiences or to physiological/biochemical events. Rather, in a holistic approach, the meanings of experiences may be understood by discovering their interconnections with other meaningful experiences.
5. It will recognize that science deals with *models and metaphors* representing certain aspects of experienced reality, and that any model or metaphor may be permissible if it is useful in helping to order knowledge, even though it may seem to conflict with another model which is also useful. (The classic example is the history of wave and particle models in physics.)
6. It will thus recognize *the partial nature of all scientific concepts of causality.* (For example, the 'upward causation' of physiomotor action resulting from a brain state does not necessarily invalidate the 'downward causation' implied in the subjective feeling of volition.) In other words, it will implicitly question the assumption that a nomothetic science — one characterized by inviolable 'scientific laws' — can in the end adequately deal with causality.

7. It will be *participatory* in recognizing that understanding comes, not alone from being detached, objective, analytical, coldly clinical, but also from cooperating with or identifying with the observed, and experiencing it subjectively. This implies a real partnership between the researcher and the phenomenon, individual or culture being researched; an attitude of 'exploring together' and sharing understandings.
8. It will involve recognition of the inescapable role of *the personal characteristics* of the observer, including the processes and contents of the unconscious mind. The corollary follows, that to be a competent investigator, the researcher must be *willing to risk being profoundly changed* through the process of exploration.
9. Because of this potential transformation of observers, an epistemology which is accepted now may in time have to be replaced by another, more satisfactory by new criteria, for which it has laid the intellectual and experiential foundations.

## *The possibility of different ontological assumptions*

If indeed something like the above epistemology were to be adopted as the scientific community attempts to construct a true science of consciousness, it would seem that serious attention would have to be paid to the inner explorations which have gone on for thousands of years within the world's spiritual traditions. The distillation of these explorations is sometimes termed the 'perennial philosophy,' and there are ontological implications, which are examined in a paper by Ken Wilber (1993).

Based on some very sophisticated (if prescientific) exploration, this ancient view centres around the following proposition: 'Reality, according to the perennial philosophy, is composed of different grades or levels, reaching from the lowest and most dense and least conscious to the highest and most subtle and most conscious. At one end of this continuum of being or spectrum of consciousness is what we in the West would call 'matter' or the insentient and the non-conscious, and at the other end is 'spirit' or 'godhead' or the 'superconscious' (which is also said to be the all-pervading ground of the entire sequence) ... The central claim of the perennial philosophy is that *men and women can grow and develop (or evolve) all the way up the hierarchy to Spirit itself,* therein to realize a 'supreme identity' with Godhead.'

A central understanding of this 'perennial wisdom' is that the world of material things is somehow embedded in a *living* universe, which in turn is within a realm of consciousness, or Spirit. Similarly, a cell is within an organ, which is within a body, which is within a society ... and so on. Things are not — cannot be — separate; everything is a part of this 'great chain of being.'

As Wilber observes, Western science became restricted to the matter end of the continuum only, and to 'upward' causation only. With that restriction came a faith that in the end, a nomothetic science can adequately represent reality — a faith that phenomena are governed by inviolable, quantified 'scientific laws.' From that restriction came both the power of modern science (basically, to create manipulative technology) and the limitation of its epistemology. From it also stem all sorts of classical 'problem' — the 'mind-body problem,' 'action at a distance,' 'free will vs. determinism,' 'science vs. spirit,' etc.

This restriction of science to only a portion of 'the great chain of being' was useful and justifiable for a particular period in history. The only mistake made was to become so impressed with the powers of prediction-and-control science that we were tempted to believe that that kind of science could lead us to an understanding of the whole: Fundamentally, *there is no reason to suppose that reductionist science can ever provide an adequate understanding of the whole.*

What must be done now, according to Wilber, is to retain the open-minded scientific spirit, and the tradition of open, public validation of knowledge (that is, abjuring any scientific priesthood), but to open up the field of inquiry to the entire continuum and to downward as well as upward causation. Whether that will be soon done within science is a good question. However, because of the cultural shift which appears to be taking place, attaching increasing importance to the transcendental, there may be increasing public insistence that some such development take place in science if science is to retain its present position as the only generally accepted cognitive authority in the modern world.

These sorts of consideration transform the original question to a far more radical and controversial one — namely, the question of whether the scientific exploration of consciousness can proceed far without a complete re-assessment of long-standing epistemological and ontological assumptions underlying defining aspects of modern science and society. Polish philosopher Henryk Skolimowski (1994) comes to a similar conclusion.

## References

Harman, Willis and Christian de Quincey. 1994. The scientific exploration of consciousness: towards an adequate epistemology. Report No. CP-6. Sausalito: Institute of Noetic Sciences.

James, William. 1912. *Essays in radical empiricism.* New York: Longman, Green. For a contemporary discussion, see Taylor, Eugene (1994).

Kuhn, Thomas. 1970 (2 ed.) *The structure of scientific revolutions.* University of Chicago Press.

Skolimowski, Henryk. 1994. *The participatory mind: a new theory of knowledge and of the universe.* London: Arkana.

Taylor, Eugene. 1994. Radical empiricism and the conduct of research. In *New metaphysical foundations of modern science.* Sausalito: Institute of Noetic Sciences.

Velmans, Max. 1993. A reflexive science of consciousness. In *Experimental and Theoretical Studies of Consciousness,* Ciba Foundation Symposium No. 174. Chichester: Wiley.

Wilber, Ken. 1993. The great chain of being. In *Journal of Humanistic Psychology,* 33:3.52–65.

# Brain, Mind and Beyond

PETER FENWICK

*Dr Peter Fenwick, FRC Psych, was educated at Trinity College Cambridge where he obtained an Honours Degree in Natural Science. His clinical medical training was carried out at St Thomas' Hospital in London. After obtaining experience in neuro-surgery he specialized in psychiatry. He is Senior Lecturer at the Institute of Psychiatry, Consultant Neurophysiologist at Radcliffe Infirmary in Oxford, and Honorary Consultant in Neurophysiology to Broadmoor Special Hospital. He has published numerous scientific papers on brain function and also several papers on meditation and altered states of consciousness. He is a Vice-President of the Scientific and Medical Network and also President of the UK branch of the International Association of Near-Death Studies, reflecting his special interest in this field. He lectures widely in England, on the Continent and in the United States on brain disorders and has made many appearances on radio and television. He has written a series of books with his wife Elizabeth:* The Truth in the Light, The Hidden Door *and* Past Life Memories.

## *Introduction*

At the age of fifteen, recognizing that I needed to know about consciousness, I hurried to the biology library to look it up in the largest textbook I could find. To my surprise, it was not mentioned in the index; 'unconsciousness' was the closest I could get. Nowhere was consciousness, as an entity, mentioned. Levels of alertness yes, consciousness, no. There were good descriptions of the neurone and how it fired but no mention of consciousness. Clearly nothing had progressed since the 1930s when Sherrington in his Gifford Lectures had said that the energy scheme describes how the light from a star strikes the eye, sets up an electrochemical reaction and is conducted to the cortex, but as to the way consciousness arises, in Sherrington's words, 'It puts its finger to its lips and is silent.'

## THE MODERN DILEMMA

To me, as a practising neuropsychiatrist, the current situation is in some respects very much better than it was when my interest in consciousness was first aroused in the 1950s. Current functional neuroimaging techniques have led to a much better understanding of the brain in action and have revealed a new phrenology of the mind. The brain appears to work as a set of interlocking modules, each one with a defined location on the cortex, and each with a specific function, all joined together in a magical way (the binding problem) to produce the unified world view of conscious experience.

It has become clear that a purely mechanistic view of the brain can lead to a fuller understanding of mind and the modification of mind by an alteration of its chemical and structural components. Nowhere within this picture does consciousness appear. It is worth pausing for a moment to examine why this is the case.

Our science is based on the rationalism of Descartes, Galileo, Locke, Bacon and Newton. Galileo defined a two-stuff universe: matter and energy. These stuffs, he said, had primary and secondary qualities. The primary qualities were those aspects of nature that could be measured, such as velocity, acceleration, weight, mass etc. There were also secondary qualities, the qualities of subjective experience, such as smell, vision, truth, beauty, love etc. Galileo maintained that the domain of science was the domain of primary qualities. Secondary qualities were non-scientific.

> To excite in us tastes, odours and sounds I believe that nothing is required in external bodies except shapes, numbers, and slow or rapid movements. I think that if ears, tongues and noses were removed, shapes and numbers and motions would remain but not odours or tastes or sounds.'

Clearly, our primary quality science has been outstandingly successful in examining and quantifying the world around us, and in producing our current technology, but it still puts its fingers to its lips and is silent when the question of consciousness arises. The reason for this is that consciousness, the view from the observer, is a secondary quality that has been removed, by definition. This leaves our science very lopsided, as only the physical aspects of any phenomenon — a 'view from nowhere' as it has been described — can be investigated by the scientific method. Yet a moment's thought, as Max Velmans has pointed out (Velmans 2000), shows that all phenomena are essentially psychological entities. It is the way that the evidence is obtained that makes the difference between 'objective' and 'subjective' qualities. Objective qualities are tested by asking individuals if their psychological concepts match, e.g. do we all see the same pointer readings when we do the same experiment? In the West the secondary science has yet to be evolved, which would ask whether we all have the same psychological state in the same circumstances. This form of science is very much an Eastern perspective used to investigate mind.

Two major philosophical schools currently attempt to explain brain function and tackle the nature of consciousness. Dennett's neurophilosophy characterizes one extreme. He argues that consciousness and subjective experience are just the functions of neural nets. Nothing is required to explain personal experience and wider states of consciousness except a detailed knowledge of neural nets. This is clearly a reductionist approach, a Galilean primary quality, equating subjective experience with neural mechanisms (Dennett 1991). The other extreme is characterized by the philosophy of Nagel (1974) who argues that it is never possible to learn from an objective third-person point of view what it is like to have a first-person experience. Subjective experience is not available to the scientific method, as it is not in the third person and cannot be validated in the public domain. Nagel argues that, however much we understand about the neurophysiology of the functioning of a bat's brain, we will never know what is it like to be a bat. This view suggests that the explanation of subjective experience requires a new principle that is beyond neural nets.

Searle (1992) argues from an intermediate position. He regards subjective experience as being a property of neural nets, but he does not agree with Dennett that a full understanding of neural net functioning is sufficient to explain subjective experience. Searle's view is that we need a Newton of neurophysiology to produce an entirely new principle — a synthesis between first- and third-person experience.

## *Postmodern science and its implications*

With the advent of postmodern science, a movement which started in the 1960s, it became recognized, a process started by Kuhn, that there were many different sciences and that the rational science of Galileo was only one science. He was the first to describe science as being culture bound, and that the fundamental discoveries of science about the structure of the universe were probably only relative to the metaphysical framework imposed on the world by Western thought. Thus, it can be seen that other sciences from other countries which postulate soul or spirit as being primary are just as likely to be correct as is our Western science which only emphasises materialism.

In 1994 Willis Harman, in a multi-authored book looking at the difficulties thrown up by the metaphysical foundations of our modern science, said:

> Scientists too quickly assume (or behave as though they do) that the philosophical premises underlying science are not at issue — but they are part of the definition of modern science ... Yet many debates that appear to be about scientific matters in fact centre around implicit ontological issues, about the ultimate nature of reality and the epistemological issues about how we might find out.

Thus it can be seen that reductionism or materialism are excellent when studying systems which do not involve subjective consciousness. But as soon as subjectivity becomes involved in the explanation, then our primary quality Galilean science is unable to provide a satisfactory framework for study.

We have a major difficulty with our current Western brain/mind identity theory which states that all qualities which flow from the brain are created by it: no explanation is provided of subjectivity, of the subjectivity of the senses, and there is no explanation of consciousness, which is the very basis of our perception of the world and our formulation of science itself. The most that can be claimed for Galilean science when looking at the details of brain activity, is that a correlation can be set up between subjective states and neuronal firing. However, one should note that many scientists slide from correlation to causation, claiming more than the evidence strictly allows as a result of their materialistic assumptions.

This insistence on the part of Western science that the primary qualities of Galileo are the only qualities that exist has led to an impoverishment in Western culture, as it is unable to incorporate moral values or ethics since they do not flow from a primary quality science.

An example of this is given by Gardener, in an article on miracles published in the 1983 Christmas issue of the *British Medical Journal.*

> When modern missionaries left some gospel books behind in Ethiopia and returned may years later, they not only found a flourishing church, but a community of believers among whom miracles like those mentioned in the New Testament happened every day — because there had been no missionaries to teach that such things are not to be taken literally.

Scientific missionaries have had much the same effect on our understanding of the world around us and the range of explanations that we may use to explain perfectly ordinary phenomena. Belief in parapsychology, for example, depends on how close you are to the scientific missionaries. In one survey in America, belief in parapsychological phenomena was highest in the general public (68%), lower in university professors (57%), lower still in Associates of the American Academy of Science (37%) and lowest of all in the prestigious scientific body, the National Academy of Science (4%).

In the last few years, however, with an expansion in postmodern thinking there has been a reversal in the dogmatic adherence to materialism, and the limitation that this had imposed on scientific study. Examples of the present trend are the formation in 1998 of a transpersonal (spiritual) section in the British Psychological Society, and the formation in 1999 of a spiritual section of the Royal College of Psychiatrists. Funding of complementary and alternative medicine, some of which used postmodern principles, by the National Institute of Health in America increased from $2 million to $66 million and it is estimated that this will soon have increased to $99 million. In Britain, The Wellcome Foundation is also considering the possibility of funding complementary medicine research.

Spiritual medical education in American medical schools is also increasing. In 1994 three of 125 US medical schools offered courses on religious and spiritual issues; in 1997 this had grown to thirty of 125 and in 1999 to sixty of 125. This year one hundred have expressed the desire to teach such courses.

## *Mind body interconnectedness and downward causation*

A major difficulty of the reductionist view relates to the question of control within the central nervous system. As an experiencing human being, I feel that I can, within limits, control my movements, attend to a specific sensory input, and to some extent control my thinking. However, the main thrust of reductionist science is that upward causation (neuronal functioning) is the prime cause of experiential control. If that were so, we would have to take a mechanistic view of the human being and there would be no question of free will or creativity.

Science has been concerned with upward causation for so long that it finds difficulty in seeing that macroscopic events within a biological system (in this case mind and meaning) may play a major part in the organization of (and may direct the physics, chemistry and biology of) lower order systems. This control by higher order systems of lower order systems within the body is called downward causation. Control is thought to go from mind (including social and cultural meaning) through the central nervous system to bodily function. Roger Sperry pointed out that downward causation within the central nervous system is a common property: 'things are controlled not only from below upwards but also from above downwards by mental ... and other macro properties (furthermore) primacy is given to the highest level control rather than the lowest.' (Sperry 1987).

This new view, giving prominence to downward causation, helps to redress the balance and allows the driver of the brain, in certain spheres, to be the conscious individual. But again, without a theory of consciousness which links brain directly to the possibilities of conscious experience, we remain immersed in a reductionist trap.

As remarked above, reductionism sees the lowest levels of the central nervous system, the cells and the dendrites, as being the fundamental aspects of the brain. Although in one sense this is clearly true, for if there were no functioning cells there would be no functioning brain, it is not true at the level of whole groups of cells acting together in response to meaning which has been imposed on the system. For example, the changes in brain function which are caused by the fear evoked by a dog can only be understood not in terms of the cells producing their graded response to the visual image in the visual cortex, but to the meaning of such an image which involves memory that this is a dog, and also the quality of the dog, which is dangerous.

This primacy of meaning in our interaction with the world is shown in a healing service in Worcester, Massachusetts. In this service, Father d'Amagio carries out his healing ministry and cures one of his parishioners of *myasthenia gravis,* an auto-immune disease of the motor endplates of the muscles. It is clear that the whole gestalt of the service, the patient's belief system, the charisma of the priest all provide a potent mixture leading to downward causation within the nervous system. Exceptionally, this can lead to marked change in bodily function, healing of the disease process, a process that we call a miracle.

The influence of psychological meaning on bodily processes has now been extensively investigated in the new science of psychoneuroimmunology. One of the first studies examined the infection rate amongst sailors on board ship and correlated this with life events. Those sailors who were most unhappy or stressed had the highest infection rates. Since then it has been recognized that stress (for example due to marital breakdown or death of a partner) can lead to reduced immune system functioning. Killer T cells, C4 and C8 cells are all reduced. It is thought that alteration in immune cell functioning may lead to infections, or even to cancer. Conversely, optimism is protective.

In a recent study at Harvard, students were shown a film of Mother Teresa ministering lovingly to the dying. The salivary IgA (an immune system marker) of the students increased. Imagining this healing scene had the same effect on salivary IgA.

Healing can be defined as an intentional influence of one or more people upon another living system without utilizing known physical means of intervention. A randomized double blind controlled trial of distant healing, prayer and advanced AIDS has shown that those patients who were prayed for showed significantly fewer AIDS illnesses ($p = 0.04$), lower illness severity ($p = 0.03$), had fewer doctor's visits (9 out of 13: $p = 0.01$), fewer hospitalizations ($p = 0.04$) and spent fewer days in hospital (5/3.4 $p = 0.04$). Interestingly, no correlation was found between clinical outcome belief in the power of distant healing (Targ, Moor and Smith 1998).

Another prayer study under way is examining the effects of prayer on 1200 patients undergoing coronary bypass surgery in three separate hospitals. No data for this study is yet available (Personal communication).

A video was made, with the subject's permission, of the following account of an exceptional experience that occurred during a hypomanic illness. He describes how during the experience he left his body and was taken on a trip through multiple universes. He came to understand the nature of the cosmos and our position in it. This teaching left him with total knowledge, and he then began his journey back into the body again. He finally returned to the room where his body was, and just prior to re-entering his body he saw a glittering, bejewelled structure which he came to recognize was his soul. There was information within this structure which suggested to him that he was a Time Lord, and ever since then he has called himself the Time Lord. This experience has left him marked and he feels convinced that it was true. He argues that he has truly seen the underpinning structure of the universe, which is absolute knowledge and total love.

The difficulty for those who have not had these experiences is that they can have little comprehension of their significance. The brain mind identity theory argues that these experiences can only be the abnormal firing of pools of neurones in the brain. As such the experience is termed pathological and is considered to be a hallucination. However, if a postmodern framework is used with a different metaphysics, then science can truly suggest that there may indeed be a structure underpinning the universe composed of knowledge and love. It is up to science to explore this rather than refuse to engage with it by arguing for only the brain mind identity theory.

The brain mind identity theory is quite specific. It argues that there is no experience that is not underpinned by a relevant brain state. For example, in lucid dreaming, when a dream arm moves, that part of the brain which initiates movement fires off impulses into the real arm, which may twitch but cannot move as the muscles are paralysed in REM sleep. Similarly, when auditory hallucinations are experienced the auditory cortex is found to be active (*Neuroimaging* January 2000), and when visual hallucinations are experienced the visual cortex is active. A recent functional MRI study carried out by Dominic ffytch and co-workers on patients who are having Charles Bonnet hallucinations shows that the visual cortical association areas are active during visual hallucinations. PET studies have shown that during imagined movements there is a change in cortical blood flow in the relevant cortical areas. There is thus no mind activity without an underpinning active brain state.

Recently, Dr Vollenweider and his team in Zurich have been looking at mystical states induced by drugs, and they have been able to show that there is an increase in cerebral blood flow and function in different areas of the frontal lobe, sensory cortex or thalamus, according to the nature of the mystical state that is being experienced. This work is important because it again stresses that even in the widest mystical states that can be experienced there is an underpinning brain pattern of activity.

## *Parapsychology and the near-death experience*

The current scientific view is that psychological processes are generated entirely within the brain and limited to the brain and the organism. Over the last fifty years, large numbers of parapsychological experiments have been carried out which suggest that mind is not limited to the brain and that it is possible to demonstrate directly the effect of mind on other minds (telepathy) and the effect of mind on matter (psychokinesis). For those interested in a more comprehensive review of this subject, the recent book by Dean Radin *The Conscious Universe* provides a wide range of references to the studies and examines some of the meta-analyses which have demonstrated these effects.

A common experience that raises questions that are in my view not adequately addressed by a reductionist approach is the near-death experience (NDE). Some NDEs appear to give the experiencer an insight into the underlying nature of the universe. In 1987 I took part in one of the first television programmes to examine this phenomenon, and afterwards received about 2,000 letters from people who had had such experiences, the majority of whom had not talked about what had happened to them or even heard of near death experiences. We took a sub-sample of 500 of those who wrote to us and sent them questionnaires asking about the details of their experience. 350 of these initially replied (Fenwick and Fenwick 1995), although the sample is now nearly complete with 420 replies.

It was found that the circumstances of the onset of the NDE were very variable:

| | |
|---|---|
| 28% | illness |
| 21% | operation |
| 15% | childbirth |
| 10% | accident |
| 9% | heart attack |
| 2% | suicide attempts |
| 20% | other |

*Table 1.*

Only 37% of the sample was receiving drugs at the time of the experience.

The most usual phenomena experienced were:

| | |
|---|---|
| Feelings of peace and calm | 82% |
| Out of body experience | 66% |
| Going down a tunnel | 49% |
| Seeing a bright light composed of love | 72% |
| Seeing a 'Being of light' | 33% |
| Making a decision to return | 72% |

*Table 2*

As can be seen from Table 1, the situations in which an NDE can occur are numerous, and many people who have the experience are not near to death. It is now recognized that there are three theories as to the causation of NDEs. Firstly that they are mystical experiences. This is certainly likely to be true in those experiences which do not occur near to death and often seem to arise spontaneously. Secondly, that they are due to psychological reasons, such as fear or anxiety in a dangerous or life-threatening situation. Finally, there are those experiences that seem to arise because of altered brain chemistry during unconsciousness.

We have been interested in those experiences which occur during cardiac arrest as they are the closest to death that can be recorded. Clinical death is defined by the following criteria: no detectable cardiac output; no respiratory effort; fixed dilated pupils. All three of these are present after a cardiac arrest. We decided to study near death experiences in the coronary care model, to see if we could determine the point at which they occurred; either before or during unconsciousness, during or after recovery. In order to do this we wanted to study the near death experience prospectively and so we studied their occurrence in a coronary care unit.

The results of the study were as follows. Of 63 cardiac arrest survivors, 55 had no memories during their arrest. Seven (11%) had memories, and of these four (6.3%) satisfied the criteria of true near death experiences. Three experiences (4.7%) did not meet the criteria, but two of these were on the same dimension as the near death experience, and only one was confusional. We concluded that near death experiences occur during unconsciousness. but that they occur less frequently than previous estimates have suggested.

We were fortunate in meeting one or two people who had had profound experiences. One was an ex-air-traffic controller whose experience was so profound that he was given in the experience total knowledge about the universe and felt himself changing into pure energy, consciousness and light. He felt that he was about to fuse with the basic consciousness of the universe when he had to come back to tell his wife that 'We never die.' His description of the experience was that it was highly moral and that each of us is responsible in a direct way for all the actions we have carried out. He also learned that the universe is a singular unity of which we are all a part.

The near death experience thus leads us to an altered state of consciousness in which we seem to be able to approach and experience the ground state of the universe. From the point of view of the near death experience, the universe is consciousness and love. This makes little sense within the framework of our Galilean science as we have to regard this as simply an altered brain state which is pathological and driven by altered brain chemistry. Fortunately, postmodern science comes to our rescue, and takes us outside the brain so that we can understand that a universe in which consciousness and love are basic is indeed a possibility. It is this universe to which we are led in the mystical experience.

## *The current position*

In my view, a satisfactory explanation of consciousness must include three vital components: a detailed role for brain mechanisms, an explanation for the action of mind outside the brain, and an explanation of free will, meaning and purpose. It should also give an explanation of wide mental states, including mystical experience and near-death experiences, when the experiencer sees through into the structure of the universe. Finally, it should provide a clear explanation for apparent downward causation (purpose) throughout the universe and in the brain, as well as some solution to the question raised, particularly in Eastern cultures, of the survival of aspects of consciousness after death.

The study of quantum mechanical effects suggests that the universe is highly interconnected and that particles interact with each other at a distance. Thus the idea that mind could also be interactive outside the skull is theoretically possible. The quantum mechanical theories of Chris Clarke and Mike Lockwood, and the quantum gravitational theories of Roger Penrose and Stuart Hameroff are all possibilities.

However, to my mind, the current most likely contender to link consciousness with brain function, as it has a wider explanatory power and leads to several testable predictions, is a theory by Amit Goswami (Goswami 1993). He argues that consciousness is a basic stuff of the universe and exists like energy. When a choice is involved, an observation made, the wave function is collapsed in consciousness and matter arises, the standard wave/particle duality theory. His contribution is that there is only one observer, and this is a universal, undivided consciousness. He argues that brains have evolved a special mechanism for 'trapping' consciousness, so that when consciousness interacts with brain processes the probability wave collapses, on the one hand producing the external object, and on the other, subjective experience of that object.

This theory has significant explanatory power, as it will link together the binding problem within the brain, parapsychological phenomena, and more particularly for the neuropsychiatrist, a possible explanation of the wide mental states when the individual sees through into the structure of the universe. Of further interest, in arguing for a field of possibilities (consciousness), the theory suggests a mechanism for creativity, as the consciousness field can be tapped directly by brain processes. This theory does not displace current neuroscience but leaves it as a valuable basis on which consciousness acts through the brain. Both are required. Of more importance, however, is the fact that this view heals science, adds meaning and purpose to life again, and links us to the primary creative force of the universe.

## *References*

Clarke, C.J.S. 1996. *Reality through the looking glass.* Edinburgh: Floris.

Dennett, Daniel C. 1991. *Consciousness explained,* London: Penguin.

Fenwick, Peter and Elizabeth. 1995. *The truth in the light.* London: Hodder Headline.

Goswami, Amit. 1993. *The self-aware universe.* New York: Simon & Schuster.

Harman Willis and Jane Clark (eds). 1994. *New metaphysical foundations of modern science.* Sausalito, CA: Institute of Noetic Sciences

Kuhn, Thomas. 1970. *The structure of scientific revolutions.* Chicago University Press.

Nagel, Thomas. 1974. What is it like to be a bat? *Philosophical Review* 83: 435–50

Penrose, Sir Roger. 1989. *The emperor's new mind.* Oxford University Press.

Radin, Dean. 1997. *The conscious universe.* Harper San Francisco.

Searle, John. 1992. The problem of consciousness. In P. Nagel (Ed) *Experimental and Theoretical Studies of Consciousness.* CIBA Foundation Symposium No 174. Chichester: John Wiley pp 61–80.

Sherrington, Sir Charles. 1940. *Man on his nature.* Cambridge University Press.

Sperry, Roger W. 1987. Structure and Significance of the Consciousness Revolution. *The Journal of Mind and Behaviour* 8,1. See also his *Science and moral priority,*

Targ, Moor and Smith. 1998. *Western Journal of Medicine* 169.356–63.)

Velmans, Max. 2000. *Understanding consciousness.* London: Psychology Press.

# First Person Experience and the Scientific Exploration of Consciousness

BRIAN D. JOSEPHSON

*Professor Brian D. Josephson, Ph.D., F.R.S. is Professor of Physics in the University of Cambridge and a Fellow of Trinity College. He was awarded the 1973 Nobel Prize for Physics for his work in tunnelling supercurrents, but since that time he has focused much of his attention on the limitations of conventional modes of scientific thinking and the creation of a paradigm which will overcome some of these limitations. His particular interests include higher states of consciousness, the organization associated with intelligence, and paranormal phenomena.*

## *Introduction*

What makes conscious experience a difficult or confusing subject for science to deal with is its personal or individualistic character (that is to say the fact that a given experience is an experience apparently tied to a particular individual). It is in this respect very different from the other phenomena studied by science, where while the phenomena may be observed by a particular individual they are considered to be in principle independent of that individual. To say that an individual's experience is merely the functioning of that individual's brain does not fully resolve the problem, since experiences are so very different in nature from brain processes.

The temptation for science is to ignore this first-person aspect of consciousness altogether, and treat it as no different in principle from any other natural phenomenon. A number of workers on consciousness would claim, furthermore, that as far as science is concerned, the presence of consciousness adds nothing new in principle: all the *behaviour* observed in conscious beings such as ourselves can be understood entirely in terms of brain function, without invoking any new laws or principles relating specifically to consciousness. There is a clear opposition between the point of view just stated, and the viewpoint taken in these chapters on consciousness, which presuppose the validity of a first-person point of view, and take it for granted that study of conscious experience can provide valuable input to our understanding of the mind.

Some such scientists seem to feel almost compelled to take a negative attitude in regard to everyday knowledge of consciousness and of mind (that utilizing everyday concepts such as believing, intending and desiring, and referred to in the scientific literature as 'folk psychology'). The psychologist Mandler (1984) for example, fairly typically dismisses folk psychology as 'convenient fictions that help our limited understanding,' while speaking of science on the other hand as a 'productive game,' namely the creation of models that enable one to understand and to predict; while Dennett (1991) puts forth strongly the idea that our everyday thinking is suspect, citing circumstances in which people are seriously wrong about what they are doing and why they are doing it. Specifically, they 'fill in gaps in what they know, guess, speculate and mistake theorizing for observing.' Although sincere in what they say, they are nevertheless 'unwitting creators of fiction.' Even when a person says he is (say) imagining a purple cow, or that he feels puzzled, we should not take these assertions as factual in nature, even if the speaker believes it to be true. The line followed by Dennett and Mandler appears to be this: only scientific method (as conventionally understood) can lead us to certainty, or to the facts of a situation; hence ordinary thinking leads us to something other than the facts; and if it leads to something other than the facts then what it leads us to must be non-fact, that is to say fiction.

## *An alternative perspective*

In what has been described above, one kind of thought is being used to cast doubt upon the validity of another, an interesting situation indeed. Should we trust such kinds of argument? Might a person not be equally entitled to argue that a kind of thinking whose conclusion is to doubt commonly accepted ways of thinking should itself be doubted?

To clear our minds in regard to such questions, it may be helpful to consider how it came about that scientific method attained to such an exalted status as it currently does obtain. The answer would seem to be a combination of two things, the great achievements of the scientific method, and the fact that, not infrequently in the past, commonly held opinions have been disproved by application of the methods of science. These facts would be evidentially more compelling if it were not for the converse facts that great achievements have come about in the past on the basis of methods other than science, while there have also been occasions where scientific beliefs have proved incorrect because faulty scientific assumptions were made. Thus both science and everyday opinion can be wrong as well as right, and it is up to the practitioners of each to minimize errors as far as they can.

The assumption may remain, however (as the above quotations indicate), that science, even if admittedly sometimes in error, has a unique ability to get at the truth that everyday analysis does not. I cannot myself help thinking that this assumption represents nothing more than a narcissistic attitude that the scientist has towards the products of himself and his companions in the scientific enterprise. In the context of understanding the mind, it entails the dogmatic assertion that people do not really understand their minds while scientific psychologists do. Is this actually so? The scientist's claim rests on the fact that models or theories are produced which can *predict in advance* the results that new experiments will produce. Can these theories, however, allow the scientist to cope well with the flow of real life situations in the way that people do? The answer here is no. Mandler's characterization of folk psychology as 'convenient fictions that help our limited understanding' can very well be countered by the assertion that the scientist's understanding of the mind, however good it may be in the realm of carefully chosen experiments, is extremely limited and fragmentary when applied to the context of ordinary life.

In conclusion, then, ordinary knowledge derived on the basis of introspection is good, if we look in an *appropriate* context, and is often better in such situations than is scientific knowledge. The question may be asked, what is meant by good knowledge, and how do we acquire it? In short, the answer is that knowledge is something that we *use,* and the good or bad outcomes of its use determine whether we judge the knowledge as being good or valueless. We may become expert at assessing knowledge by paying careful attention to the outcomes of acting upon various types of knowledge.

Studying the arguments of Dennett in depth one sees that they amount to the following: that the concepts that seem so clear in everyday use have no clear meaning *in science,* and they must therefore be dismissed as nonsense, or at least as unreliable. We should rather see this situation as implying a judgment on *conventional science's* inadequacies. More discussion of this point is given on page 52.

There are many alternative frameworks of thought to those of science, each with the potential to arrive at its own meaningful truths. In Josephson and Rubik (1992) many examples were listed: the humanities and the arts in general; spiritual or religious practices, creativity; the use of symbol, myth, and metaphor; the role of the feminine; the historical perspective; and cross-cultural aspects of knowledge.

## *Concrete experience vs. abstractions*

There are significant differences between the first-person, experiential approaches to the study of conscious experience and superficially similar approaches such as philosophy, differences that parallel the differences between science itself and the philosophy of science. These differences can be characterized as differences along the abstract/concrete dimension, or as differences in immediacy. There is a subtle difference between stating what one experiences and philosophizing about it, related to the difference between the idea of an experience and the experience itself, and the chapters of this book on consciousness focus on experience in a way that philosophy generally does not. In short, *experience is capable of teaching us things that words or symbolisms cannot.*

In connection with this last point, observe that in scientific discussions of consciousness it is commonly stated that the goal of investigations into consciousness is fully achieved if they can provide a full *abstract description* of the experiences concerned. One must question the terms on which such an understanding would be satisfactory. From the standpoint of abstractions itself (the usual scientific perspective), abstractions may be felt to give satisfactory accounts of experience, and yet from the point of view of experience itself or of life, abstractions seem inadequate substitutes.

We thus see the unbalanced consequences of excessive attachment to seeing things purely from a scientific perspective. There seems to be a genuine necessity, not addressed by the scientific, third-person perspective, for non-abstract ways of appreciating consciousness. Possibly everyday experience provides us with such non-abstract aids to interpretation, giving us a kind of knowing that is not quite an abstraction, but may nevertheless function as a source of the abstractions that we subsequently make. It may also be that literature, with its emphasis on metaphorical representation, can provide better contact with this kind of knowing than can the highly formal representations of knowledge that science utilizes.

In the case of investigations centred around a first-person perspective, one may admittedly be unable to accede to some of the usual demands of science such as the ability to attach an instrument and take measurements, and to obtain results independent of the individuality of the person whose experiences are being investigated; but rigour, and the evaluation of the significance of any hypotheses that may be proposed, need not be compromised because of this, and openness to the need to change one's ideas if contrary evidence should emerge is in no way excluded, any more than it is in the case of ordinary life. But the mere fact that a scientific argument says one thing and other approaches say something else does not provide sufficient grounds *in itself* for the abandonment of the non-scientific belief, as this conflict may merely represent alternative ways of thinking about the same thing. The case of the problem of the self, to be discussed in 'The concept of the self,' (p.54) provides a good illustration of this theme.

## *Working with the new perspective*

We now examine some of the ramifications of what has been discussed above, especially in regard to some of the claims of Dennett to which reference has been made previously. As we have seen, one of Dennett's claims is that since there is much confusion in people's minds concerning conscious experience then we should treat all people's utterances as if they were works of fiction. Note at work here a characteristic of the scientific approach, namely the demand for a uniform approach to all situations of a given kind (contrasting with the commonplace approach of forming one's own judgments with regard to the circumstances under which a given type of statement may reasonably be accepted). The alternative, developed on page 48 above, is to recognize that people's utterances or beliefs have practical uses, and to judge them in accord with how effective they are in such a context.

A simple example to illustrate this point is provided by the letters on the visual display units of most computers. Such letters are in reality not letter shaped at all, but are made up out of a number of conjoined rectangles (pixels). From one point of view (i.e. that of characterizing the geometrical shapes on the screen) it is incorrect, or a piece of fiction, to talk of there being letters, words, and sentences on the screen. But from another point of view (the wider context in which the screen is providing us with information that we require), our perceptions do not lie: they are providing us with the precise information that we need.

An interesting feature of everyday descriptions and everyday language is that, by taking into account some of the subtleties of the way our minds work, they are able to make effective distinctions of a kind that science currently does not make. An example is the case, discussed at considerable length by Dennett, of optical illusions. Dennett's discussion follows by now familiar lines: the illusory pink ring displayed on the jacket of the book is not actually there (as demonstrated by colorimetric measurements) and merely 'seems' to be there. It is not there as a fact, and must therefore be deemed fiction ('there's no such thing as a ring that merely *seems* to be there'). But ordinary thought has ways of transcending such apparent contradictions, for example by introducing the *concept* of illusion, clearly distinct from that of fiction (a ring which appeared to exist, but under closer examination was seen to be something else, would be an illusory one; while a ring that was said to exist but could not be discovered by a person who looked for it in the appropriate manner would be a fictional one). The holograms used for example on credit cards to deter forgery provide an interesting case of an illusory image that is effectively 'objective,' and has a very definite practical value.

The distinction to be made can be expressed in this way: science relies to a high degree on making its judgments mechanical, whilst everyday life makes freer use of 'judgements of experience' that cannot be readily mechanized. If we exclude 'judgments of experience' we are left with a void in our knowledge. Dennett and others erroneously deny the possibilities of developing sound judgments of experience, and optimistically assert that science can in the course of time fill the void that is left. But why deny ourselves the use and fruits of using the powerful tool for studying consciousness that we already have?

I must close by commenting that none of the above should be taken as an unconditional attack on being scientific. When science can show convincingly that opinions need to be adjusted since they do not hold up under close examination (concerning which kind of situation Dennett gives a variety of examples), the corresponding views should indeed be adjusted. It is however necessary to take into account, as previous examples have shown, that different descriptions suit different purposes, and that the localized purposes of scientific description may be different from those of the totality of life.

## *The reality of the field of consciousness*

A place where Dennett's arguments and the common-sense view of reality appear to be in collision lies in his claim to have proved that there is no specific field of consciousness (called by him 'Cartesian Theatre'), observed or possessed by a specific observer. Examination of his arguments shows that they depend on refuting particular formulations of the idea of an observer observing a field of consciousness, generally deriving from Descartes' proposal that the conscious self has a particular location in the brain. Once we extricate ourselves from such models and adopt a genuinely phenomenological/experiential approach, the alleged contradictions largely disappear. For example, there is no contradiction, as Dennett appears to believe, between his 'multiple drafts' picture (which does appear to be a necessary assumption in order to account for the results of certain experiments) and the detailed aspects of conscious experience, the latter of which may very well include such elements of a fleeting or provisional character as the multiple drafts picture requires. Contradictions come only from insisting on the metaphor of a theatre stage, on to which conscious images enter and depart like actors, requiring that a given entity be either 'in consciousness' (on the 'stage'), or not.

We do of course make judgments as to whether we are aware of something or not, and appear to arrive at definitive yes/no answers when we do so, apparently confirming the Cartesian Theatre idea. Going into the issue more deeply however, we recognize that in such cases our perceptions are subtly influenced by our judgments. Once we have decided the answer to a question concerning awareness of something (e.g. footsteps) is 'yes' we seem to be rather clearly aware of the percept of interest, while if on the other hand our judgment is that it is not there, our perception changes into one wherein the relevant percept is felt to be definitively absent. This discreteness in judged percepts is thus a consequence of our having decided to impose upon our perceptions a theory about those perceptions, thereby essentially vetoing perceptions of an intermediate nature, ones conforming less with our predetermined preconceptions. The mode of perception, in conformity with Dennett's ideas, where what we experience can be identified precisely with available descriptions of our experience, is not the totality of possibilities. There can be alternatively a receptive, non-judgmental state, that is open to experiences of a fundamentally (as far as one is concerned at the time of the initial encounter) elusive kind. Of such experiences Dennett argues that there is nothing we can do other than point to them saying 'that experience.' This is only partly the case. A new experience can gradually become linked to other experiences, and thereby acquire its own significance. Further, the significance of a given experience does not have to be closed or definite; it may be possible for it to augment itself indefinitely through accumulated experience of it.

## *The concept of the self*

Dennett's theory of the self, conceived as an agent that perceives and acts, is formulated on the basis of the third-person perspective. He sees it as a creative abstraction that helps survival by designating what should be given favourable attention. From the first-person point of view these can be perceived as interesting philosophical ideas that are not however particularly helpful from the point of view of getting on with life and are perhaps best left for the philosopher to enjoy himself with. For the purposes of life, the actual concrete experience I have of my perceiving things, deciding, and willing things to happen, is essential. Typically, I may have a recognizable experience of causing something to happen (e.g. making a car move faster by pressing down on the accelerator), or of programming myself to do certain things (such as to turn right at a particular place). Whether my 'I' is concrete in nature or an abstraction is generally not a matter of moment for me as a philosopher might think it ought to be: what really matters as far as I am concerned in ordinary life is simply the need to keep track by any means available of might be happening to the 'I,' so that experiences may be avoided of a kind that I wish to avoid. Other people (scientists: philosophers) may have other models for what is happening under such conditions; if for their own purposes they wish to think in these ways I may be content to let them do it, but my personal interest is (say) to drive to the beginning of a walk that I wish to go on, and experience indicates that it is more productive (to borrow Mandler's word) simply to use the 'myself' model than to analyse what state my brain might be need to be in for the achievement of my goal.

The actual experiences associated with the concept of myself or my soul are also of value in connection with personal development; however, this topic lies outside the scope of this chapter.

In this last section we have gained a glimpse into the pathology that is liable to attend over-reliance on the principles of the scientific, third-person approach. The concepts of 'myself' and 'I' that underlie our ordinary actions are simple ones, closely linked to actual experiences and thus to our reality. Science constructs its own, different version of reality that is extremely useful for its own purposes. However, when it starts to create explanatory models that purport to account for our experiences but do not fully fit with the totality of those experiences one may not unreasonably suggest that if the models are to be taken seriously than they should be adjusted to conform better to the latter. Otherwise, who is dabbling with fiction?

## Conclusion

This article was written primarily as a counter to attacks made by a number of scientists on experiential approaches to studying consciousness. Its main tenets are that there is nothing sacred or special about the scientific approach to knowledge, and that all knowledge-claims need to be judged in terms that are appropriate to the claims that might be made in any given case. With this understanding, many of the criticisms of the experiential approaches are seen to be inappropriate.

## Acknowledgments

This article is based on a talk given at the Second Gauss Symposium, 2–8 August 1993, Munich, and was first published in Ghista (1996).

The ideas contained in this article have been considerably influenced by discussions carried out over the course of a number of years with Prof. Steven Rosen and Dr Beverly Rubik. I should like to thank them for their inspiration.

## References

Dennett, D. 1991. *Consciousness explained.* London: Allen Lane.

Ghista, D.N. (ed.) 1996. *Biomedical and Life Physics,* Braunschweig/Wiesbaden: Viehweg, pp. 383–89.

Josephson, B.D. and B. Rubik. 1992. The challenge of consciousness research. In *Frontier Perspectives.* Center for Frontier Sciences at Temple University. 3:1.15–19. Electronic version available in the IPPE preprint archive: at URL http://phil-preprints.L.chiba-u.ac.jp/IPPE.html; ftp site Phil-Preprints.L.Chiba-u.ac.jp: directories Philosophy of Mind and /pub/preprints/Phil_of_Mind respectively).

Mandler, G. 1984. *Mind and body.* London & New York: Norton.

# Consciousness and Parapsychology

# Mindsight: Eyeless Vision in the Blind

KENNETH RING

*Professor Kenneth Ring, Ph.D., is Professor Emeritus of Psychology in the University of Connecticut. He is the Founding Editor of the Journal of Near-Death Studies and a past President of the International Association for Near-Death Studies. He is the author of* Life at Death: *a scientific investigation of near-death experiences;* Heading Toward Omega: *in search of the meaning of the near-death experience;* The Omega Project: *near-death experiences, UFO Encounters and Mind at Large;* Lessons from the Light *(with Evelyn Elsaesser Valarino) and* Mindsight *(with Sharon Cooper).*

*This life's dim windows of the soul*
*Distorts the heavens from pole to pole*
*And leads you to believe a lie*
*When you see with, not through, the eye.*

*William Blake,* The Everlasting Gospel

## *Vicki's experience and its implications*

In a recent study of near-death experiences (NDEs) that I conducted with Sharon Cooper (Ring and Cooper 1999), one of our respondents, a forty-five-year-old woman named Vicki, told us of the time she found herself floating above her body in the emergency room of a hospital following an automobile accident. She was aware of being up near the ceiling watching a male doctor and a female nurse working on her body, which she viewed from her elevated position. Vicki has a clear recollection of how she came to the realization that this was her own body below her.

> I knew it was me ... I was pretty thin then. I was quite tall and thin at that point. And I recognized at first that it was a body, but I didn't even know that it was mine initially. Then I perceived that I was up on the ceiling, and I thought, 'Well, that's kind of weird. What am I doing up here?' I thought, 'Well, this must be me. Am I dead? ...' I just briefly saw this body, and ... I knew that it was mine because I wasn't in mine.

In addition, she was able to note certain further identifying features indicating that the body she was observing was certainly her own:

> I think I was wearing the plain gold band on my right ring finger and my father's wedding ring next to it. But my wedding ring I definitely saw ... That was the one I noticed the most because it's most unusual. It has orange blossoms on the corners of it.

As twenty-five years of research into NDEs has shown, such reports of visual out-of-body perception are by no means rare among persons coming close to death, but are indeed so common that most readers of this article will already be familiar with them. Yet, there is something extremely remarkable and provocative about Vicki's recollection of these visual impressions, as her subsequent comment implied. 'This was,' she said,' the only time I could ever relate to seeing and to what light was, because I experienced it.'

In short, what is astonishing about Vicki's account is that she had never previously been able to see at all. She was born blind, her optic nerve having been completely destroyed at birth because of an excess of oxygen she received in the incubator. Yet, she appears to have seen during her NDE.

Vicki was just one of the more than thirty persons we interviewed at length during a two-year study we carried out of near-death and out-of-body experiences in the blind. As we shall recount, Vicki is hardly a unique case among our respondents: as our findings show with unmistakable clarity, reports of seeing during such episodes are very common among the blind, even those, like Vicki, who have never had any previous visual experiences in their life and could well attest, as Vicki did to us, that they have 'never been able to understand even the concept of vision.'

But before describing some of these astonishing cases of what we call mindsight in the blind, we need to return to Vicki's, for her experience didn't end with her perception of her body. Indeed, her story is a particularly clear instance of how NDEs in the congenitally blind can unfold in precisely the same way as do those of sighted persons. As you will see, apart from the fact that Vicki was not able to discern colour during her experience, her account of her NDE is absolutely indistinguishable from those we have been hearing about for twenty years from individuals with intact visual systems. How the blind can 'see' during these experiences is a mystery we will try to unravel at the end of this article, but that they can do so will be apparent from what follows.

Now, to continue with Vicki's narrative, she then told us that following her out-of-body episode, which was very fast and fleeting, she found herself going up through the ceilings of the hospital until she was above the roof of the building itself, during which time she had a brief panoramic view of her surroundings. She felt very exhilarated during this ascension and enjoyed tremendously the freedom of movement she was experiencing. She also began to hear sublimely beautiful and exquisitely harmonious music akin to the sound of wind chimes.

With scarcely a noticeable transition, she then discovered she had been sucked head first into a tube and felt that she was being pulled up into it. The enclosure itself was dark, Vicki said, yet she was aware that she was moving toward light. As she reached the opening of the tube, the music that she had heard earlier seemed to be transformed into hymns and she then 'rolled out' to find herself lying on grass.

She was surrounded by trees and flowers and a vast number of people. She was in a place of tremendous light, and the light, Vicki said, was something you could feel as well as see. Even the people she saw were bright. 'Everybody there was made of light. And I was made of light.' What the light conveyed was love. 'There was love everywhere. It was like love came from the grass, love came from the birds, love came from the trees.'

Vicki then becomes aware of specific persons she knew in life who are welcoming her to this place. There are five of them. Debby and Diane were Vicki's blind schoolmates, who had died years before, at ages 11 and 6, respectively. In life, they had both been profoundly retarded as well as blind, but here they appeared bright and beautiful, healthy and vitally alive. And no longer children, but, as Vicki phrased it, 'in their prime.' In addition, Vicki reports seeing two of her childhood caretakers, a couple named Mr and Mrs Silk, both of whom had also previously died. Finally, there was Vicki's grandmother — who had essentially raised Vicki and who had died just two years before this incident. In these encounters, no actual words were exchanged, Vicki says, but only feelings — feelings of love and welcome.

In the midst of this rapture, Vicki is suddenly overcome with a sense of total knowledge:

> I had a feeling like I knew everything ... and like everything made sense. I just knew that this was where ... this place was where I would find the answers to all the questions about life, and about the planets, and about God, and about everything ... It's like the place was the knowing.

And then she is indeed flooded with information of a religious nature as well as scientific and mathematical knowledge. She comes to understand languages she doesn't know. All this overwhelms and astonishes her:

> I don't know beans about math and science. It's like things that I all of a sudden understood intuitively almost, things about calculus, and about the way planets were made. And I don't know anything about that ... I felt there was nothing I didn't know.

As these revelations are unfolding, Vicki notices that now next to her is a figure whose radiance is far greater than the illumination of any of the persons she has so far encountered. Immediately, she recognizes this being to be Jesus. He greets her tenderly, while she conveys her excitement to him about her newfound omniscience and her joy at being there with him.

Telepathically, he communicates to her: 'Isn't it wonderful? Everything is beautiful here, and it fits together. And you'll find that. But you can't stay here now. It's not your time to be here yet and you have to go back.'

Vicki reacts, understandably enough, with extreme disappointment and protests vehemently, 'No, I want to stay with you.' But the being reassures her that she will come back, but for now, she 'has to go back and learn and teach more about loving and forgiving.'

Still resistant, however, Vicki then learns that she also needs to go back to have her children. With that, Vicki, who was then childless but who 'desperately wanted' to have children [and who has since given birth to three] becomes almost eager to return and finally consents.

However, before Vicki can leave, the being says to her, in these exact words, 'But first, watch this.'

And what Vicki then sees is 'everything from my birth' in a complete panoramic review of her life, and as she watches, the being gently comments to help her understand the significance of her actions and their repercussions.

The last thing Vicki remembers, once the life review has been completed, are the words, 'You have to leave now.' Then she experiences 'a sickening thud' like a roller-coaster going backwards, and finds herself back in her body.

As we have indicated, such reports, replete with visual imagery, were the rule, not the exception, among our blind respondents. Altogether, 80% of our entire sample claimed some visual perception during their near-death or out-of-body encounters. Although Vicki's was unusual with respect to the degree of detail, it was hardly unique in our sample. Here, by way of comparison, is a summary of another of our cases, this time involving a young man named Brad who had his NDE when he was an eight-year-old child.

## *Brad's experience*

Brad's NDE took place during the winter of 1968 when Brad was living at the Boston Center for Blind Children. At this time, Brad developed pneumonia and eventually had severe breathing difficulties. Afterwards, he was told by nurses that his heart had stopped, apparently for at least four minutes, and that resuscitation (CPR) had been necessary to bring him back.

Brad remembers that when he couldn't breathe any longer, he felt himself lifting up from the bed and floating through the room toward the ceiling. He saw his apparently lifeless body on the bed. He also saw his blind roommate get up from his bed and leave the room to get help. (His room-mate later confirmed this.) Brad then found himself rapidly going upward through the ceilings of the building until he was above the roof. At this point, he found that he could see clearly.

He estimates that it was between 6:30 and 7 in the morning when this happened. He noticed that the sky was cloudy and dark. There had been a snowstorm the day before, and Brad could see snow everywhere except for the streets which had been snowploughed, though they were still slushy. (He was able to give us a very detailed description of the way the snow looked.) Brad could also see the snow banks that the ploughs had created. He saw a streetcar go by. Finally, he recognized a playground used by the children of his school and a particular hill he used to climb nearby.

When asked if he 'knew or saw' these things, he said: 'I clearly visualized them. I could suddenly notice them and see them ... I remember ... being able to see quite clearly ...'

After this segment of this experience was over (and it went very fast, he said), he found himself in a tunnel and emerged from it to find himself in an immense field illuminated by a tremendous, all-encompassing light. Everything was perfect.

Brad could clearly see in this domain, too, though he commented that he was puzzled by the sensation of sight. He found himself walking on a path surrounded by tall grass, and also reported seeing tall trees with immense leaves. No shadows were visible, however.

While in this field, Brad became aware of beautiful music, like nothing he had ever heard on earth. Walking toward the sound, he came to and climbed a hill, eventually encountering a glittering stone structure so brilliant that he thought it might be burning hot. But it wasn't, and he entered it. The music continued here as well and, to Brad, seemed to be praising God. In this structure, Brad encountered a man whom he didn't recognize but from whom emanated an overwhelming love. The man, without a word, gently nudged Brad backward, initiating a reversal of his experience, ending with his finding himself in bed gasping for air, attended by two nurses.

Brad, like Vicki, has been blind from birth.

In general, as illustrated by the cases of Vicki and Brad, what we found in our study is that blind persons normally report seeing both 'things of this world' and otherworldly scenes once they transit into the transcendental realm of the NDE. Once they discover themselves in that domain, seeing is often described as 'perfectly natural' or 'the way it's supposed to be.' However, sometimes the initial onset of visual perception of the physical world is disorienting and even disturbing to the blind. This was true for Vicki, for example, who said:

> I had a hard time relating to it [i.e., seeing]. I had a real difficult time relating to it because I've never experienced it. And it was something very foreign to me ... Let's see, how can I put it into words? It was like hearing words and not being able to

> understand them, but knowing that they were words. And before you'd never heard anything. But it was something new, something you'd not been able to previously attach any meaning to.

Later, in commenting on the shock of these initial visual impressions, she even used the word 'frightening' to characterize them.

Now, what we must note here is that this period of disorientation mirrors, in some ways, the experience of persons born with congenital cataracts who have their sight restored in later life. In such cases, the newly sighted have trouble distinguishing between even simple objects and shapes and it often takes some time and training before they adapt to the visual environment. Similarly, visual perception in the blind during NDEs may require a period of adjustment before it becomes self-organizing and coherent. But once it does, it is as if the individual has been seeing his or her whole life. As Brad commented on the naturalness of his own perception in the otherworldly domain:

> It was like it was always there ... It was so natural it was almost as if I should have always been able to see like that ... I could never understand why I never could do that back in my own body, yet it was so unbelievably natural ... I thought to myself I should be able to carry this right back with me. It's just something I've always had ... I was very comfortable with it.

How well do our respondents find they can see during these episodes? We have of course already noted that the visual perceptions of Vicki and Brad were extremely clear and detailed, especially when they found themselves in the otherworldly portions of their near-death journeys. While not all of our blind NDErs had clear, articulated visual impressions, nevertheless enough of them did, so that we can conclude that the prototypic NDE cases we have presented in this article are fairly typical in this regard.

For instance, one of our interviewees whose sight perished completely as a result of a stroke at age 22 and was near-sighted before that told us in connection with seeing her body, her doctor and the operating room during her NDE: 'I know I could see and I was supposed to be blind ... And I know I could see everything ... It was very clear when I was out. I could see details and everything.'

Another man who lost his vision in a car accident at the age of 19 had a comforting vision of his deceased grandmother across a valley during his NDE. In commenting on his clarity, he said: 'Of course I had no sight because I had total destruction of my eyes in the accident, but [my vision] was very clear and distinct ... I had perfect vision in that experience.'

Still another man, this one blind from birth, found himself in an enormous library during the transcendental phase of his NDE and saw 'thousands and millions and billions of books, as far as you could see.' Asked if he saw them visually he said, 'Oh, yes!' Did he see them clearly? 'No problem.' Was he surprised at being able to see thus? 'Not in the least. I said, 'hey, you can't see,' and I said, 'Well, of course I can see. Look at those books. That's ample proof that I can see.'

As common and sincere as these claims of seeing seem to be, how can we be sure they do not represent some kind of fantasy or complex hallucination on the part of the blind or simply an expression of wish fulfilment? In our study, whenever possible, we attempted to gather corroborative evidence from independent sources in order to be able to document that our respondents' perceptions did have some basis in fact. Here, for example, is a summary of one such case, and probably our most persuasive instance that what the blind report seeing cannot be written off as purely subjective experience.

## *Veridical perceptions*

A forty-one-year-old woman underwent a biopsy in 1991 in connection with a possible cancerous chest tumour. During the procedure, the surgeon inadvertently cut her superior *vena cava,* then compounded his error by sewing it closed, causing a variety of medical catastrophes including blindness — a condition that was discovered only shortly after surgery when she was examined in the recovery room.

At that time, she was rushed in a gurney down the corridor in order to have an angiogram. However, the attendants, in their haste, slammed her gurney into a closed elevator door at which point the woman had an out-of-body experience.

She told us she floated above the gurney and could see her body below. However, she also said she could see down the hall where two men — the father of her son and her current lover — were both standing, looking shocked.

In trying to corroborate her claims, we interviewed the two men. The first man could not recall the precise details of that particular incident, but the second witness — her lover — did and independently confirmed all the essential facts of this event. (It should be noted, by the way, that this witness has been separated from our participant for several years and they had not even communicated for at least a year before we interviewed him.) Furthermore, even if she had not been blind at the time, the respirator on her face during this accident would have partially occluded her visual field and certainly would have prevented the kind of lateral vision necessary for her to view these men down the hall. But the fact is, according to indications in her medical records and other evidence we have garnered, she appears already to have been completely blind when this event occurred.

So if the blind do indeed 'see' during these NDEs, how is it possible for them, at least under these extreme conditions, apparently to transcend the sensory restrictions that have hitherto imprisoned them in a sightless world?

## *Mindsight*

Does seeing really depend on the eyes, after all? Or, alternatively, is there another form of awareness that comes into play when, whether one is blind or not, an individual is thrust into a state of consciousness in which one's sensory system is no longer functional?

In exploring such questions, we were forced to consider a gamut of alternative interpretations for our findings. These ranged from conventional psychology (e.g., dream-based explanations of NDEs or sensory-cuing hypotheses) through little known studies of blindsight and skin-based theories of vision to perspectives based on esoteric and metaphysical systems, which postulate the existence of subtle bodies and spiritual senses. In the end, however, we found that none of these potential interpretations could provide an adequate explanation for the results of our study.

What ultimately proved more availing for us involved a reframing of our findings in the form of a question: is what we discovered in our blind respondents truly a form of seeing? That is, is it in any sense something that might be conceived of as an analogue to physical sight? We were led to ponder this question because a brace of telling considerations continued to draw us back to it ineluctably. For one thing, a close reading of our transcripts frequently revealed a multifaceted synaesthetic aspect to the experiencer's perception that seems to transcend simple sight. Some of our interviewees, for example, were hesitant to assert that what they were able to describe was incontestably visual either because they were blind from birth and didn't know what vision was like or because they knew they couldn't possibly be seeing with their physical eyes. The following comments were typical of this vein:

> It wasn't visual. It's really hard to describe because it wasn't visual. It was almost like a tactile thing, except that there was no way I could have touched from up there. But it really wasn't visual because I just don't have vision any more ... It [was] sort of a tactile memory or something. It's not really like vision is. Vision is more clear.

> I think what it was that was happening here was a bunch of synaesthesia, where all these perceptions were being blended into some image in my mind, you know, the visual, the tactile, all the input that I had. I can't literally say I really saw anything, but yet I was aware of what was going on, and perceiving all that in my mind ... But I don't remember detail. That's why I say I'm loath to describe it as a visual.

> What I'm saying is I was more aware. I don't know if it's through sight that I was aware ... I'm not sure. All I know is ... somehow I was aware of information or things that were going on that I wouldn't normally be able to pick up through seeing ... That's why I'm being very careful how I'm wording it, 'cause I'm not sure where it came from. I would say to you I have a feeling it didn't come from seeing, and yet I'm not sure.

Even Brad, whose initial testimony seemed so clear on this point, in a subsequent interview eventually qualified and clarified his earlier remarks about his memory of seeing snow on the streets outside his school:

> I was quite aware of all the things that were physically mentioned in there [i.e., his earlier description]. However, whether it was seen visually through the eyes, I could not say ... I mean, you have to remember, being born blind, I had no idea whether those images were visual ... It was something like a tactual sense, like I could literally feel with the fingers of my

> mind. But I did not remember actually touching the snow ... The only thing I can really state about those images was that they came to me in an awareness and that I was aware of those images in a way I did not really understand. I could not really say that they were visual *per se* because I had never known anything like that before. But I could say that all my senses seemed to be very active and very much aware. I was aware.

A second clue came from our gradual realization that the blind often use vision verbs far more casually and loosely than sighted persons do. Vicki, for example, says that she loves to 'watch' television and uses phrases such as 'Look at this,' which clearly cannot be taken literally. Although this observation does not of course necessarily invalidate our reports, it does send up another amber flag of caution when it comes to the interpretation of the narratives of our blind respondents.

As this kind of testimony builds, it seems more and more difficult to claim that the blind simply see what they report. Rather, it is beginning to appear it is more a matter of their knowing, through a still poorly understood mode of generalized awareness, based on a variety of sensory impressions, especially tactile ones, what is happening around them. The question that immediately confronts us now, however, is as unavoidable as it is crucial: Why is it, then, that these reports, when casually perused, nevertheless often seem to imply that the blind do see in a way that is akin to physical sight?

By this point, the answer, we believe, should be fairly obvious. However these experiences may have been coded originally, by the time we encounter them they have long come to be expressed in a particular linguistic form. And that form is a language of vision, since our ordinary language is rooted in the experiences of sighted persons and is therefore biased in favour of visual imagery.

Because the blind are members of the same linguistic community as sighted persons, we can certainly expect that they will tend — indeed will be virtually compelled — to phrase their experiences in a language of vision, almost regardless of its appropriateness to the qualities of their own personal experience. Now, this is not to say that as part of this multifaceted synaesthetic awareness there will not be some sort of pictorial imagery as well; it is only to assert that it must not be understood as anything like physical vision *per se.*

Even if we cannot assert that the blind see in these experiences in any straightforward way, however, we still have to reckon with the fact

— and it does seem to be a fact — that they nevertheless do have access to a kind of expanded supersensory awareness that may in itself not be explicable by normal means. Perhaps, as we have suggested, although these reports may not in the end represent an analogue to retinal vision as such, they clearly represent something that must be reckoned with. In our view, we are inclined to believe that the blind — as well as others who experience an NDE or OBE — enter into a distinctive state of transcendental awareness that we would like to call mindsight. When sensory systems fail, mindsight becomes potentially available to us and affords direct access to a realm of transcendental knowledge to which our normal waking state is barred. Under these conditions, 'with the doors of perception cleansed,' things present themselves in true Blakean fashion, 'as they are, infinite.' Thus it is that the blind can perceive what they could not literally see, and can know what was hitherto hidden to them. Clearly, this is not simple 'vision' at all, as we commonly understand it, but almost a kind of omniscience that completely transcends what mere seeing could ever afford. In mindsight it is not of course that the eyes see anything — how could they? Instead it is the 'I' that sees and suddenly beholds the world as it appears to eyeless vision.

## *References*

Ring, Kenneth and Sharon Cooper. 1999. *Mindsight: near-death and out-of-the body experiences in the blind.* Palo Alto: William James Center for Consciousness Studies at the Institute of Transpersonal Psychology.

# Altered States through Meditation and Dreams

DAVID FONTANA

*Professor David Fontana, Ph.D., is currently Distinguished Visiting Fellow at the University of Wales, Cardiff, and holds professorships at the universities of Alagarve and of Minho in Portugal. He is also the UK's first Professor of Transpersonal Psychology at Liverpool John Moores University. He is the author of numerous research publications and of twenty books which have been translated into 22 languages. For many years he has studied the relationship between Western and Eastern psychological systems, together with methods for deepening and expanding consciousness, and has written widely on dreams, meditation and psycho-spirituality. Among his recent books are* The Secret Power of Dreams; The Lotus in the City; *and* Know Who You Are: Be What You Want. *He is a Chartered Psychologist, a Chartered Counselling Psychologist, and a Fellow of the British Psychological Society. He is also President of its Transpersonal Section.*

## *Introduction*

The term 'Beyond the Brain' presupposes that psychological events are not bounded by the neuro-physiological processes that take place inside the cerebellum. I would dearly like to explore the nature of this presupposition, and the mind/brain dichotomy that it introduces. However, this is not my brief, so for present purposes I intend to accept this dualistic hypothesis, and go on from there. I am not unhappy to accept it, because it is axiomatic that human beings do not experience themselves as a brain — that is as a series of electrical-chemical events taking place within a mass of grey matter — but as a mind — that is as a series of thoughts, emotions, perceptions and sensations taking place within some non-determinate inner space, and arising in large measure from some non-determinate inner source.

Thus whether we think of the mind as operating through the brain or as a consequence of the brain, we need to maintain a definitional dualism between the two. The mind is a living, thinking, feeling inner experience which is directly accessible only to the experiencer him or herself; the brain, by contrast, is a physical organ in the public domain and only directly observable to others. Thus, in the sense that it is functionally distinct from it, one could argue that the whole of our psychological life takes place 'beyond' the brain, and cannot be understood by any examination *of* the brain.

## *What is the experience of the mind?*

My focus, then, is upon the mind, as a domain of inner experience. And the first question that arises is what, as psychologist, we know about this mind. The answer, in fact, is very little. We have of course our cognitive models, and our theories on the nature and function of consciousness. But these, for all their sophistication, have a curiously arid quality. They are, like descriptions of love or of mountains in summer, distinct from the experience itself. For all the glamour of language, and for all its definitional sophistication, they curiously miss the point, like arrows fired with strength and skill but at the wrong target.

For the mind is a direct, lived experience, and no second-hand description can capture its essential flavour. Thus in any real science of mind, we must start not with theories and descriptions but with practices. To experience one's own mind is to experience the strange mystery of life itself, something that can be known only from the inside, and which by its subjective nature cannot reveal itself to Western scientific, objective methodology.

To look beyond the brain, therefore, requires not the middle language of other people's theories, but the ability to look into oneself with a particular kind of precision, a precision which has long been the concern of what we might call Eastern psychologies, that is the psycho-spiritual traditions of Buddhism, Hinduism, Taoism and certain branches of Islam. Let us introduce this by undertaking a simple practical experiment.

> I am going to pause for a moment, and in that moment I want you to close your eyes, and sit in silence and watch the emergence of thoughts in your mind. Pay no attention to the content of each though, or to the associations that appear to

> have set it in motion. Look instead at the place from which the thought arises. What is that place? Can you identify it? Where, in short, does the thought come from? Like a spring arising from the ground it must have a source. Can you identify that source? Like a fish jumping from water a thought arises, but where does the fish come from?

The answer is probably — 'I'll have to think about it'!

We can try another exercise. This time: Close your eyes and try to stop thinking.

Very few people are able to do this even for the length of one minute — and sitting there thinking to oneself 'I am not thinking, I am not thinking' does not count! This raises the important question — how effective are we at examining our own consciousness, and at controlling it?

If we look at the great traditions of the East, and indeed at those associated with the mystery traditions in the West, we find that there are four, closely inter-related techniques that are taught as means towards the achievement both of self-understanding and of consciousness control. These are *enquiry, awareness, meditation* and *dream yoga.* The practice of these techniques, at a research level, raises the problem for our Western science in that the experiences derived from them are difficult to put into words, and not generalizable — in the sense that one person's experience necessarily provides definitions applicable to that of another.

And herein lies part of the challenge, a challenge which in my view extends to much of psychology — how can we use scientific methods which rely upon sameness, replicability and generalizability to human beings who are manifestly not identical with each other, who do not necessarily replicate their own inner experience, and who in many instances cannot be the subject for generalized comment. Thus there is no substitute for each person working upon him or herself, and becoming his or her own experiment. And this of course was the way of the Buddha and of many other teachers in the Eastern tradition — most recently Krishnamurti — namely take nothing on trust, place no blind faith in gurus, check up for yourself. Here is a method to help you in this checking, use it, see what comes up, and if it doesn't work for you abandon it and try something else.

For teachers of this persuasion, dogma — the ideas of others forced upon us as if they are our own — is actively harmful, in that it interrupts the process of self-enquiry. We take on trust what others tell us, and cease to explore for ourselves.

Let us now turn briefly to each of the four methods: *enquiry, awareness, meditation* and *dream yoga.*

## *Enquiry*

By enquiry, I mean the act of engaging the mind in a certain inner process, rather than an attempt to come up with answers to specific questions, or even to make the presumption that there are such answers. Socrates used a method known as the *elenchus* which provides an example of this, namely an activity of mind which in itself led towards wisdom, irrespective of whether this wisdom could be expressed in the form of an identifiable solution (the Oracle of Apollo at Delphi pronounced Socrates the wisest man in all Athens, as he was the only one who knew that he did not know).

In Zen Buddhism we have the koan — the best known of which is 'what is the sound of one hand clapping?' This performs the same function of engaging the mind in a particular inner process. There is, quite literally, no logical, rational, linear answer to a koan. One could suggest for example that the answer to the koan 'what is the sound of one hand clapping?' is silence, but this is self-defeating, as the koan asks for a *sound.* Koans therefore frequently contain a paradox. At other times, they are open-ended in that almost any number of answers are possible — for instance, 'Why did Bodhidharma come from the West?' Each time the pupil comes up with an answer and takes it to the master, he is told that it is wrong, largely because he is trying to solve it with the rational mind, instead of allowing a certain level of inner experience to speak — or to act — through him.

All koans are variants in fact of the fundamental existential questions which we can render as 'Who am I?' or 'What is the nature of life? And as Ken Wilber tells us, the question 'Who am I?' is at the heart of the practices taught by all the great spiritual traditions. A Chinese Ch'an master once instructed me to keep this question always poised in the mind, as a sort of wordless enquiry, a pressing energy to know the true nature of my own existence.

In recent times, Krishnamurti used a similar method of rigorous enquiry, a method that probed and probed at the conditions and the presuppositions with which we face life, and that condition not only the answers we give to life questions, but even the way in which these questions are put. Krishnamurti in fact reminded his listeners that the known can never be true. All that we know consists simply of memories carried over from the past — useful in their way, but not truth in the sense in which life is true. The only trust is to be totally in touch with each moment as it arises (there are interesting parallels here with the philosophical method of empiricism, which reminds us that everything we know is concerned with the past, and therefore there is no guarantee that it will hold good in the present or in the future, since neither of these things has yet been experienced).

In effect, what is being said is that if we would know the nature of the mind, if we would know what is beyond the brain, then we must look for ourselves. It is no good taking on the theories — Whitehead called them inert ideas — of other people, no matter how erudite they may appear to be. We must find out for ourselves. The Buddha put this clearly when he said that no one should take anything he said upon trust. They must try it out for themselves, and accept it only if it was found to work for them. Krishnamurti said much the same thing when he refused to have followers, or to start a cult or a movement of any kind. In his words, 'trust is a pathless land,' which means that each person must find his or her own truth if they wish fully to know the nature of the mind.

## *Awareness*

The first technique in this knowing is the one that I have already mentioned, namely the observation of the mystery of one's own thinking. The second is awareness, awareness, awareness not only of one's own thinking, but of each perception of the outer world. When it is necessary to carry previous knowledge into the present in order to deal with experience we must of course do so, but we should not allow past knowledge to become our habitual way of defining new experience. The world arises afresh each moment in our own experience. No scientist would any longer doubt that we are literally co-creators of the world, creating through the channels of our programmed perception a world of meaning from the flux of subatomic energy which actually goes to make up the world. But if we always create this world in terms of the lessons learnt from past perceptions, then we soon cease to see our creation in its beauty and its strangeness, and thus cease to recognize the beauty and the strangeness of our own minds.

We can never experience life as the poet experiences it, or hear it as the musician hears it, because the shutters of our prior conditioning descend and rob us of proper contact with what is. To be aware is to be awake, to be unaware is to be asleep. *The Dhammapada* puts it that he who is awake never dies, while he who is asleep is as if dead already.

## *Meditation*

The third technique (and each of these techniques are closely linked — so much so in fact that they are various applications of the same technique rather than different techniques in themselves) is meditation. Much has been written about meditation, but it is only comparatively recently that we in the West have come to recognize the extraordinary power of meditation as a psychological tool. A tool which, perhaps above all others, has the power to open our minds to ourselves, and to allow us to witness what being beyond the brain actually means.

There are many techniques of meditation, but nearly all have one thing in common, namely the focus upon a single point of concentration to the exclusion of mental distractions. The mind, consciousness, is usually a chatter of associations, memories, desires, feelings, emotions, hopes, etc. which distract it from dwelling in what Eastern traditions call its own self-nature. In other words, it rarely experiences itself as anything other than thoughts or feelings — to such an extent, in fact that it has come to believe that thoughts and feelings represent its reality. In a Cartesian sense, it has come to believe that it is thinking that gives it its identity and its meaning.

In meditation, as the mind develops its powers of one-pointed concentration, a different level of awareness gradually develops, only glimpsed at first, but progressively becoming more and more established. This is the mind in its self-nature, just as clarity, rather than muddy opaqueness, is the self-nature of water.

Let me give an example of an experience of the self-nature of the mind, taken not from an Eastern practitioner but from a Western devotee of Ch'an Buddhism, that is the Chinese (and original) form of Zen.

> One night my body and mind dropped away ... there was a burst of light into which the whole cosmos dissolved (and with it) came an incredible sense of bliss. This was the dropping of the ego. Their was a sense of interweaving of the atoms of the cosmos with the energy that seemed to be the consciousness

> that was aware of it ... At this last point consciousness itself dissolved into Oneness ... (After the experience), although I could say I was conscious of myself as being, this sense was no longer located in this or any body. It was as if the whole world was conscious, was a living moving body of energy ... My mind ... was simply reflecting what was around and objective without any subjective choice or selection or attachment. It was certainly like having no head at all. (Luk 1975.12f)

D.T. Suzuki, one of the main interpreters of Zen describes the meditative experience as leading to the dissolution of the boundaries of self, and likens this dissolution to a circle whose centre is everywhere and whose circumference is nowhere (e.g. Suzuki 1982).

Far from being psychotic, the meditative state appears to be correlated with improved psychological and physical health (e.g. West 1987). It is not an escape from the world, as some people suppose, but a way of increasing one's effectiveness within it. The more clearly we know and understand the workings of our own consciousness, the more we can be open to consciousness as expressed by others. Indeed, many of the great Eastern traditions, such as Buddhism and the Advaita philosophy within Hinduism, teach that at the deepest level all consciousness is one — that is that we can express a unified underlying reality (there are interesting parallels here with Jung's collective unconscious). Just as there is a single life force that animates the whole of humanity (and perhaps the whole of creation), so there is a single force that activates consciousness. Meditation brings us closer and closer to this force, whose reality is usually obscured by the busy workings of our individual thought and feeling processes.

Thus, meditation leads not to self-annihilation, but to what in the East is called self-realization (or the Buddha or wisdom mind or enlightened mind), which as far as it can be described would seem to be the state that underlies all other states. The confusion among some writers in the West about the Buddhist teachings on the nature of this state stems from the fact that they take the Buddhist doctrine of *anatta* (no permanent self) to mean nihilism. In fact *anatta,* as Humphreys and other experts in the field make clear (Humphreys 1962), is the doctrine of the non-separateness of all forms of life. As applied to man it states that there is no permanent ego or self in the five *skandhas,* the five causally conditioned elements of existence (form, sensation, perception, volition and consciousness) that go to form the personality, and which thus give rise to the temporal or phenomenal nature of man. See for instance the *Anattalakkhana Sutra,* in which the Buddha says the soul cannot be in anything that is impermanent, painful and transitory: 'These are not mine, these I am not, these are not my soul' (*The Buddha and his Teachings* p.101f; later he says, 'Which is better, seeking a woman or seeking oneself?' (p.111).

Consciousness, *vijnana,* is what arises out of contact between the object and the corresponding organ — that is, of sight, sound, smell, taste, touch and thought. The deeper stages of meditation involve *content-less awareness,* in which the awareness is not occupied by any one of the five *skandhas.*

The Buddha nowhere denies the existence of an ego or soul, but taught that no permanent entity, not subject to *anicca* (impermanence) and *dukkha* (suffering), can be found in any of the human faculties. That which pertains to any human being is not immortal; that which is immortal and unchanging is not the possession of any one human being, but the common possession, like the life force, of us all. And yet this common possession contains the potential for all things, including individuality, so it is a state that transcends and yet contains all diversity. So it is said in Buddhism that when the opposites arise, the Buddha-mind is lost. When we become caught up in concepts of this or that — *either* this or *that* — we are no longer grounded in our self-realized nature.

## *Dreams*

The fourth of the practices, dream yoga, refers to the ability not just to use dreams as a path towards greater self-understanding, but as a method firstly for uniting the conscious and unconscious parts of the mind, and secondly for preparing oneself for the act of dying (for particularly in the Tibetan Nyingma tradition, sleep is seen as a dress rehearsal for death, and dreams as a glimpse of the after-death state).

Leaving aside for the present the various theories advanced in the West as to the function of dreams, we can accept from personal experience that in dreams our consciousness is experientially located in other times and other places. In addition, sensations come to us in dreams. We touch and feel things as if they are real. We see things. We hear things. We smell things. All the senses appear to be operating, and operating within experiences which are novel and not simply memories of events in waking life. In both Eastern traditions and the Western mystery traditions, these dream experiences are seen as ultimately controllable and usable if one follows certain clearly-defined practices.

The most accessible example to illustrate this is the so-called lucid dream, in which the dreamer knows he is dreaming, and can take certain apparently fully conscious decisions within it. Lucid dreams typically occur when the dreamer notices an anomaly of some kind in the dream, something that does not fit with taking reality, or finds himself practising some skill which is not usually associated with dreaming. In my own case, an early instance of the former was when I found myself walking down a street in what I knew to be Britain, and noticed that the signs above all the shops were written in French; and deduced from this odd experience that I must be dreaming. An early instance of the latter was when I found myself looking at a clock tower with some wording around the face of the clock, and discovered that I could read the wording. As a result I said to my dreaming self: 'That's odd; usually you can't read the wording in dreams,' and this not surprisingly was followed by the realization that I was in fact dreaming.

When a dream becomes lucid, there is at once an intensity of the dream experience. Colours become more vivid, and there is a sense of great excitement (see for instance, Green 1968). Dream events become apparently as real as in waking life, and the sense of participating in a real existence outside the physical confines of the body becomes greatly heightened. Somewhat similar to lucid dreaming is the phenomena known as 'false awakening.'

In Tibetan Buddhist traditions, particularly the Nyingma, all the dreaming of the advanced practitioner reportedly is of the lucid kind. Even in dreamless sleep, he or she is said to remain conscious (a state that must be akin to deep meditation), and is apparently able to travel to teach his students and so on. (I have also met examples of this in Hindu traditions in India, where among many people the existence of skills of this kind is taken for granted.) By developing this continuity of consciousness, one is said not only to be able to live this life in a vastly more unified way (just imagine being able to rove at will through the contents of one's own mind), but to remain fully conscious throughout the act of dying, thus allowing oneself to recognize fully the clear light of ultimate reality, instead of being taken in by the dream-like images with which the mind personifies this divine energy.

## Conclusion

Let me end by re-emphasising what I said in my opening remarks, namely that these four practices involve a methodology very different from that of Western science. They are concerned with a *knowing* rather than with a *knowing about,* direct knowledge based upon personal experience, rather than indirect knowledge based upon the experience of others. In the East there is always a certain amount of amusement at the idea that Western psychologists base their work upon the examination of the minds and behaviours of others rather than upon the minds and behaviours of oneself.

Certainly, there is nothing wrong in pooling experiences and looking for patterns, provided that we remember that the act of reducing these patterns to language misses their essence. Descriptions of things can never be the same as the things themselves, and this holds good for inner experience even more vividly than it holds good for the experience of the outer world. A science of consciousness should therefore differ from other forms of knowledge in that it teaches a methodology rather than applies a methodology to others, and in that it prizes this methodology above the accumulation of knowledge based upon that methodology. The Oracle of Apollo at Delphi had the words 'Know Thyself' above the portals, and these should be the watchwords of our science.

## References

Broughton, R. 1992. *Parapsychology: the controversial science.* London: Rider.
Crookall, R. 1964. *More astral projections.* London: Aquarian.
Green, C. 1968. *Lucid dreams.* London: Hamish Hamilton.
Humphreys, C. 1962. *A popular dictionary of Buddhism.* London: Arco.
Kermani, K. 1992. *Autogenic training.* London: Thorsons.
Luk, C. 1975. *The transmission of the mind outside the teaching.* New York: Grove Press.
Luhrmann, T.M. 1994. *Persuasions of the witch's craft.* London: Picador.
Muldoon, S. and H. Carrington. 1968 (4 edn.) *The projection of the astral body.* London: Rider.
Ring, K. 1985. *Heading towards Omega.* New York: Morrow.
Solé-Leris, A. 1986. *Tranquillity and insight.* London: Rider.
Suzuki, D.T. 1982 (3 edn.) *Living by Zen.* London: Rider.
Tart, C.T. 1988. *Waking up.* Shaftesbury: Element Books.
Walker, B. 1974. *Beyond the body.* London: Routledge & Kegan Paul.
West, M.A. (ed.) 1987. *The psychology of meditation.* Oxford: Clarendon.

# Children and Memories of Previous Lives

*Erlendur Haraldsson*

*Professor Erlendur Haraldsson, Ph.D., is Professor of Psychology in the University of Iceland at Reykjavik, where he has been teaching since 1974. He has been an active researcher, having written four books, published numerous articles in parapsychological journals and been visiting professor at the Institute for Borderline Areas of Psychology in Freiburg and at the University of Virginia. Among his books are* Deathbed Visions *(with Karlis Osis); and* Sai Baba, or Miracles are my Visiting Cards, *both translated into many languages).*

In some parts of the world we may come across parents who believe that their children are speaking about events that must have happened to them in a previous life. And why? Because they know that the events the child is talking about did not take place in the two to four years that the child has lived when it begins to make these statements. Hence, the child must be speaking about a previous life. Such an explanation seems more plausible to the parents not only due to the prevalent belief in reincarnation that is found in the countries where these cases are generally found, but also to the fact that between two-thirds and three-quarters of the children speak of events that lead to their death. Most common are accounts of fatal accidents (such as in traffic, drowning, bomb blasts), murders, or dying in war related activities.

The child will also often express the wish to go back to his or her previous home and family. In some instances the child will state the name of the locality where he or she lived previously. If the child's account is divided into individual statements, they may vary in number as much as from 5 to 50. In most cases, the centre of the account features events that lead to a tragic premature death, usually at a young age. In most instances the child describes events that seem to have occurred only a few years back, like one, two or three years before the child was born, and apparently took place not far from the locality where the child is now living. Never do we find the children speaking about events that appear to have occurred in past centuries, to famous, historical personalities, and rarely do they occur in distant countries.

On average, the child will start to make these claims around two and a half years old and it may continue to speak about them until it reaches the age of five, or even longer. Then these alleged memories usually seem to fade away to such an extent that if the child is asked about them a few years later, he/she may have forgotten them completely. In a few instances knowledge about the core event seems to live on in the mind of the child.

Many cases of this kind have been carefully recorded and investigated by interviews with available witnesses, the child, the parents and other relatives who have witnessed the child's statements, so as to ascertain what statements the child has been making and how persistent these statements have been. A pioneer in this field is Professor Ian Stevenson at the University of Virginia, who has meticulously investigated a great number of these cases and published numerous detailed reports on individual cases as well as overviews of cases in individual countries or on particular kinds of cases (Stevenson, 1987, 1997a, 1997b). More recently others have published findings of independent investigations (Mills, Haraldsson & Keil, 1994).

When the investigator comes to the scene, the parents (or someone who has come to know the case) may have become interested in testing the veridicality of the child's claims. Did the events the child speaks about actually take place? Can the statements made by the child be verified? In some instances a person has been traced who lived before the child was born and lived a life that corresponds to the claims of the child. Then that person becomes identified as the child's previous personality, which may lead to contact with the previous family. In other instances the case has remained within the wall of the family and no attempt has been made to 'solve' it. Then the investigator will attempt to find a deceased person whose life events correspond to the child's statements.

In other instances attempts were made to find a person that fitted the account but none was found, sometimes in spite of extensive efforts.

In Sri Lanka the author has investigated some sixty cases over a period of twelve years (Haraldsson, 1991, 2000a, 2000b; Haraldsson & Samararatne, 1999). These cases are rare by any standard as only about five children could be found each year in a population of 18 million. In about one third of the cases a person was found that to a varying degree fitted the previous life description made by the child. In two-thirds of the cases, no person could on the basis of the child's account be identified as a potential previous personality. This raises the question of the role of pure chance in the so-called solved cases. Here statistics cannot help us to discern real from apparent relationships as can be done in the biological sciences. We are left to make a subjective judgment about what may be considered a solved case and what is not, all the more so because in all of them we find some statements that do not fit. Let us look at three widely different recent cases that the author investigated in Sri Lanka. This involved the interviewing and re-interviewing of numerous witnesses.

## *The case of Purnima Ekanayake*

According to her parents, Purnima started to speak of a previous life in 1990 when she was three years old (for a full report see Haraldsson, 2000a). Three years later they took some interest in her account and an attempt was made to check the correctness of her statements.

In Table 1 (p. 84), I have listed all twenty statements that Purnima made before a previous family was traced. This list is based on several interviews with her parents and Purnima. I will comment on some of her statements.

*I died in a traffic accident.* The first unusual statement that Purnima repeatedly made as a small child was: 'People who drive over people in the street are bad persons.' Sometimes she would ask her mother: 'Do you not also think that persons who cause accidents are bad people?' Purnima also spoke about a fatal accident with a big vehicle. Her mother thinks that this statement first came about (or she started to pay attention to it) when a traffic accident occurred near their home. Purnima's mother was upset about the accident. Then Purnima tried to soothe her by saying: 'Do not think about this accident. I came to you after such an accident.' She told her mother how she closed her eyes after the accident and then she came 'here.' Purnima told that after the accident she floated in the air in semi-darkness for a few days. She saw

| Statement | |
|---|---|
| 1. I died in a traffic accident and came here | + |
| 2. My family was making incense and had no other job | + |
| 3. We were making Ambiga incense | + |
| 4. We were making Geta Pichcha incense | + |
| 5. The incense factory is near a brick factory and near a pond | + |
| 6. First only our family worked and then two people were employed | ? |
| 7. We had two vans | + |
| 8. We had a car | + |
| 9. I was the best manufacturer of incense sticks | ? |
| 10. In earlier birth I was married to a sister-in-law, Kusumi | + |
| 11. The owner of the incense factory (I) had two wives | + |
| 12. My previous father was bad (present father is good) | ? |
| 13. Previous father was not a teacher as present father | + |
| 14. I had two younger brothers (who were better than present brothers) | + |
| 15. My mother's name was Simona | + |
| 16. Simona was very fair | – |
| 17. I attended Rahula School | + |
| 18. Rahula School had a two storeyed building (not like in Bakamuna) | – |
| 19. My father said: You need not go to school, you can make incense | – |
| 20. I studied only up to 5th grade. | + |
| *+ verified (14) – incorrect (3) ? indeterminate (3)* | |

*Table 1 Statements made by Purnima (according to her parents) before first contact with her alleged previous family, and how they fit the life of Jinadasa Perera.*

people mourning for her and crying, and saw her body until and including at the funeral. There were many people like her floating around. Then she saw some light, went there and came 'here' (to Bakamuna where she was born).

*My family was making Ambiga and Geta Pichcha incense and had no other job* Sometimes Purnima spoke of incense making and said that she had been making Ambiga and Geta Pichcha incense. Purnima's parents thought that she might be speaking of Ambiga because a jeweller firm of that name was advertising on television. Her mother assumed she was mixing something up. They also thought that she might be speaking of Geta Pichcha as there were a few 'geta pichcha' flowers (a variety of jasmine) in their garden. Purnima had also stated that members of her family as well as some outsiders were working for them making incense sticks. She used to walk around with her hands behind her back imitating how she had examined the way they were doing their work. We checked the shops in Bakamuna and only found two brands of incense, one made in Kandy and one from India, no Ambiga or Geta Pichcha incense.

*In earlier birth I was married to a sister-in-law, Kusumi.* Her parents inferred that she had been a man in her previous life.

Further statements will be listed and discussed below.

At the age of four Purnima saw a television programme on the Kelaniya temple that is some 145 miles away from her hometown and said that she recognized the temple. A little later her father, who is principal of a secondary school, took a group of school children to the temple, which is a place of pilgrimage among Buddhists in Sri Lanka. Purnima was allowed to join the group. In Kelaniya she said that she had lived on the other side of the Kelaniya river which flows at the side of the temple compound.

In January 1993 W.G. Sumanasiri, was appointed a teacher in Bakamuna, and he and the principal became acquainted. Sumanasiri spent his weekends in Kelaniya where he had married. They decided that Sumanasiri would make inquiries across the Kelaniya river and the principal gave him the following items to check:
— She had lived on the other side of the river from Kelaniya temple.
— She had been making Ambiga and Gita Pichcha incense sticks.
— She was selling incense sticks on a bicycle.
— She had a fatal accident with a big vehicle.

Accompanied by two local friends Sumanasiri inquired about incense makers on the other side of the Kelaniya River. This area is like a spread-out town with fields in between and village-like clusters of houses. They were told of three incense-makers, all small family businesses. One of them named his brands Ambiga and Geta Pichcha. The owner was L. A. Wijisiri. His brother-in-law and associate, Jinadasa Perera, had died in an accident with a bus in September 1985 as he was bringing incense to the market on a bicycle. This was about two years prior to Purnima's birth. Wijisiri's and Jinadasa's home and factory had been 2.4 miles from the ferry and 5–10 minutes walking distance from the Kelaniya river. Sumanasir informed Purnima's father about his findings. A week or two later Purnima, her parents, and Sumanasiri made an unannounced visit to the Wijisiri family.

When they arrived, Wijisiri was not in. Wijisiri's two daughters were in the house and Purnima met them first. When Wijisiri came walking towards the house Purnima told those around her: 'This is Wijisiri, he is coming, he is my brother-in-law.' He heard her say this just as he was entering the house. When Purnima said that she had come to see her brother-in-law and sister, he was puzzled and did not realize that she was talking about a previous life. Wijisiri wanted to send them away saying that those they were asking for were not here. Then, when he thought about it and the little girl started to ask about various kinds of packets and such things, only then was he inclined to believe her story. She alone spoke, no one else said anything. This is how Wijisiri remembered her visit. This account was confirmed by Purnima's father.

Purnima said to Wijisiri that she used to sell these incense sticks. She asked: 'Have you changed the outer cover of the packets?' Wijisiri used to change colour and design every two years or so. She seemed to realize that the packets looked different from the time Jinadasa was working with Wijisiri. Then she told about the various packets, about an accident that Wijisiri had many years ago. Also that Jinadasa (she) had applied medicine to his knee after the accident. She asked about Jinadasa's friends, like Somasiri and Padmasiri. Padmasiri is Wijisiri's brother and had gone with him on business on the day Jinadasa met with his accident. They had left home together and then split and gone different places. She mentioned their names. These were the things that convinced Wijisiri.

Purnima also asked about her mother and her (Jinadasa's) previous sister who is Wijisiri's wife. The sister was abroad working in Saudi Arabia, and the mother was absent at her ancestral home. Purnima expressed concern when she learnt that the mother had gone alone to a distant place. Wijisiri's family was still confused.

Purnima was born with a prominent cluster of birthmarks on her lower chest, left of the midline. Someone in Wijisiri's family mentioned that Jinadasa had been injured on the left side of his trunk. Then Purnima showed her birthmark and said: 'This is the mark I received when I was hit by a bus.' This additional feature of the case convinced both families that Purnima was Jinadasa reborn.

Jinadasa had in fact had two wives. After several years of living together he had disagreements with his first wife (Wijisiri's sister). In the south Sri Lanka he became acquainted with a lady by the name of Nanda, and left his former family. There he lived for five years and produced incense with a friend, M. Somasiri. During a visit to Colombo Jinadasa learnt of Wijisiri's accident, which rendered him bed-ridden for several months. He then went to his earlier home to help. A few days later he met with the accident.

Did Purnima say anything that was wrong and that did not fit Jinadasa's life? She had said that two vans and a car had belonged to her (Jinadasa). This was a family business, so in a way this was correct but formally the vehicles had belonged to Wijisiri. This is the essence of Wijisiri's account of his first meeting with Purnima.

We had been told that Purnima had recognized an old co-worker, Somasiri. He told us that he had come to see her at her first visit. He stood there among a group of people. Then she pointed to him and said: 'This is my friend.' When Purnima's father asked who that man was, she answered: 'This is Somasiri, my friend.' Apparently she also recognized Jinadasa's younger sister, G. Violet. She and Somasiri told us that she had pointed to her and said: 'This is my younger sister.' These were the only names that Somasiri and Violet heard her say during the first visit.

## *Further verification of Purnima's statements*

Of the 20 statements listed in Table 1, 14 fit the life of Jinadasa (1–5, 7, 8, 10, 11, 13–15, 17, and 20), three are indeterminate (6, 9, 12,) and three statements (16, 18, 19) are incorrect. Let us first consider the incorrect items. We learnt independently from his mother and younger sister that Jinadasa had attended Rahula School. However, our inquiries revealed that this school did not have a two-storeyed building until in the 1980s. According to his family, Jinadasa attended school only up to 5th grade. However, he was doing odd jobs until his sister married Wijisiri. Then that he took up incense making, and two years later 'married' Wijisiri's sister. Hence the statement that Jinadasa's father had told him to leave school to earn money by making incense cannot be true. The statement of Jinadasa's mother being very fair is not true now, and it seems unlikely that she was so earlier.

Some of the correct items have already been described. Regarding item 5: there is a pond within 200 yards of Jinadasa's old residence. The old factory that was some 100–150 yards down the road had been demolished and close to it, a neighbour told us, there had been a kiln (brick-making facility), and another kiln is still close by. Item 13:

Jinadasa's father had been a poor farmer (hence not a teacher). Item 14: Jinadasa had indeed two younger brothers (and two sisters).

We had no way of checking the indeterminate items 9 and 12 (best maker of incense sticks, and his father was a bad man). Items 6: first our family worked, then two people were employed. This was primarily a family business but soon they employed people who worked in the factory or in their homes. We could not ascertain exactly when they started to employ people, but gradually up to thirty people came to work for them in the time of Jinadasa, who was an industrious and popular man.

Most specific are items 3 and 4 stating that the family was making the brands Ambiga and Geta Pichcha. According to Wijisiri, this is correct and they showed us packages of both brands. Since the time of Jinadasa the family has started to make two additional brands. We inquired in several shops in Sri Lanka about the brands of Ambiga and Geta Pichcha. We only found those made by Wijisiri and they were not widely distributed.

## *Purnima's knowledge of incense-making*

It occurred to us to ask Purnima if she knew how incense is made. She gave us a detailed reply. There are two ways to make it. One is through cow dung, the other is from ash from firewood (charcoal). A paste is made, and then a thin stick is cut from bamboo and some gum is applied on the bamboo stick. Then the stick is rolled over the paste and then something is applied to obtain a nice smell. As far as she can remember they made their incense from charcoal powder.

What is charcoal made from and how is it produced? 'When firewood is burnt you get charcoal.' We asked Purnima's parents if they knew how incense is made. The father had heard that it is made from cow-dung, and hears now for the first time that it can be made from firewood. Her mother knows even less. My interpreter had never heard how incense is made. We later asked Wijisiri to show us how they make their incense. Wijisiri did it the way that Purnima had described.

## *Jinadasa's fatal injuries*

Jinadasa died immediately at the accident. His brother Chandradasa was called into the mortuary to identify his brother. He saw massive injuries from the lower ribs on the left side and up and obliquely across the body, caused by the wheel of the bus as it ran over Jinadasa's body. We were able to obtain the post-mortem report. It gives a detailed description and a sketch of injuries. They had been massive, particularly on the left side of the chest, where several ribs had been broken. The post-mortem report describes the internal injuries thus:

Fracture of the ribs, 1 and 2, 8, 9, and 10, laterally on the left.
1 to 5 anteriorly and 6 anteriorly and laterally, and 7 laterally.
8 and 9 anteriorly and posteriorly. 10 and 11 anteriorly.
The liver was ruptured.
The spleen was ruptured.
Lungs were penetrated by broken ribs.
Externally there was a 'grazed abrasion running obliquely from the right shoulder across the chest to the (left) lower abdomen.' There were lesser injuries on legs and face.

## *The strong and weak points of the Purnima Case*

Let me summarize the strong points of this case. The locations of the two families were far apart, and the two families were complete strangers. A third party succeeded in finding the person that matched Purnima's statements. Fourteen of 17 statements that could be checked were found to match the life of Jinadasa who had died two years before Purnima was born. Purnima's cluster of birthmarks was found to fall within an area of fatal injuries suffered by Jinadasa. Her birthmarks are on the left side of the chest where most of the ribs broke, and where Jinadasa is likely to have felt most pain. There is also some evidence of knowledge of incense making that is highly unusual for a child, and which Purnima explains as stemming from her previous life. This is a good example of a case with different characteristics that fall into a pattern and must be viewed as a whole; memories, birthmarks and, perhaps technical knowledge. Overall, one can state that the case of Purnima Ekanayake is of unusual quality among cases of children who speak of remembering a previous life.

The principal weakness of the case is the fact that no record was made of Purnima's statements before the case was solved, which occurred three years before the author started his investigation. A second weakness concerns the chance hypothesis. Can it be that through pure chance an incense maker is found across the Kelaniya river near the Kelaniya temple that was making Ambiga and Gita Pichcha incense and died in a traffic accident before Purnima was born, and whose principal injuries had been in the left side of his chest?

Incense makers are not very numerous in Sri Lanka. We made our own inquiries across the Kelaniya river. Sumanasiri made fairly thorough inquiries. However, of the three incense makers he learnt about, only one was in fact making incense, namely Jinadasa. The second one turned out to be only a wholesaler of incense, and the third had just died at that time as a result of alcoholism. The probability of finding in this locality through pure chance a person who fits Purnima's statements seems extremely unlikely. The problem is that we can only assess this subjectively, as no statistics can be applied to give us an estimate of the odds against chance.

Purnima's case has some features that are uncommon among Sri Lankan cases. She speaks of memories of a life between death and birth that the author has only found in one Sri Lankan case. Purnima's memories have lasted much longer than they generally do as she spoke freely of her previous life at the age of ten. Purnima's case also has many of the typical features. Purnima started to speak of her memories at a very early age, and spoke persistently about them. She spoke of a life close in time and in the same country that ended in a violent death at the early age of 36. One aspect of her memories also gets reflected in play.

Finally, Purnima displays prominently some characteristics that my formal psychological studies have shown to distinguish between ordinary children and children speaking of previous-life memories. She is highly gifted, has excellent vocabulary and memory, is the best pupil in her class, shows some tendency towards dissociation, and is less suggestible than most children. She is a demanding child for her parents, is argumentative and independent-minded, wants to be perfect, is much concerned with neatness and cleanliness, and is at times hot tempered and boastful; in short a vivid and memorable personality.

It is not easy to find a satisfactory natural explanation for the case of Purnima. It is one of the most impressive among the so-called solved cases, as it has features that few cases match. I stated earlier that about two-thirds of the cases in Sri Lanka remain unsolved. Let me briefly describe one such case.

## *The case of Chamalsa Ratnaweera*

Chamalsa had just had her fifth birthday when we met her in 1995 in one of the suburbs of Colombo. Her mother tells that Chamalsa was not fully two years old when she started to speak of a previous life. She repeatedly spoke about being picked up by the police in a three-wheeler (auto-rickshaw), from it they were brought to a lorry and thereafter there was a 'great noise' (shooting, she died). Then she added, 'I am still alive.' Chamalsa got tears in her eyes when she described what had happened. She spoke very vividly about this, more than one would expect from a child. Chamalsa is afraid of three-wheelers: she goes down on the floor when she hears the sound of one, so as to seek shelter. She also has a phobia of black clothes and police uniforms. One day her grandfather wore a black shirt. She became afraid when she saw it and covered her face with her hands.

Chamalsa also often speaks of her boyfriend Mithrachandra, even gesticulates with her hands on her chest to express the beautiful feeling she had for Mithrachandra. Sometimes she will sit in a corner and speak on the phone with Mithrachandra. If she behaved badly her mother would sometimes say to her, 'I will tell Mithrachandra.' Then she would immediately behave better.

Chamalsa's case remains unsolved. None of her 15 or so statements are specific enough to test their truth or falsity. It is interesting though that in the two years preceding Chamalsa's birth (1988–90) there was a major civil strife in Sri Lanka when often up to 30 people (politicians, civil servants, military men and police in their homes) apparently got killed every night. In the end, during a state of emergency, this brought on the death of hundreds of young people who formed the bulk of the extreme-left terrorist movement JVP (Janatha Vimukthi Peramuna, which means Peoples Liberation Front) or were suspected of being members of it. They were rounded up by the police and security forces and killed without being brought to justice. This sad period in the modern history of Sri Lanka is not much spoken of in public, being something of a taboo. Could Chamalsa have heard about these events?

Chamalsa's case is rich in behavioural features. How did she develop her phobia of three-wheelers, black clothes and police uniforms? Phobias are common among children who speak of a previous life and they are often associated with their accounts of events that lead to their death.

## *The case of Ushan Gunasekera*

Ushan is the four year old son of well-to-do educated parents living near Colombo when we first met him. About the age of two and half he started to speak about having lived in the city of Galle (the largest city in the south of Sri Lanka) and having worked in the Ruhunu Cement Factory that is to be found on the main road out of the city. One night there was a big party in the factory, he bought whisky and wine for a girl there. They drank a lot. A driver who drove them away crashed into a train (a railway line runs between the factory and the main road). Ushan gave his previous name, the name of his father and mother and his brother who was in the army. He spoke of his sister who worked in the law court inside the old Fort section of the city, and of having known some nice girls. Ushan was speaking of a life as a young man.

Several of Ushan's statements were specific enough to permit verification. Ushan's father tried and had no success in identifying the persons mentioned by Ushan, but made no inquiries in the Ruhunu Cement Factory. We met Mr Palliagara, the personnel director of the factory. He told us that few employees had died in the last ten years but none fitted the description given by Ushan. He promised to make a search for us of all employees who had died since the factory was founded. The result regarding accidental deaths: one security guard, married with three children, died as he collided on his bicycle with a bus close to the gate of the factory. No one had died in an accident inside the factory. One young single employee, Vidana Patharana, had left the factory ten years ago to work in Saudi Arabia. There he died in a car accident. When working in the factory he had lived nearby with a lady relative. She told us that he had been travelling in Saudi Arabia with some friends in a jeep when the accident happened. The names Ushan had given did not fit his family and none of his relatives had lived or worked in the Fort. It must be mentioned that before Ushan started to speak about his alleged previous life Ushan's father with his wife and son had passed Galle and the large and highly visible Ruhunu Cement Factory on their way to the extreme south of Sri Lanka.

## What do we make of the accounts?

When a child starts to speak about past life events in a country with widespread belief in reincarnation, the traditional interpretation is that the child is remembering a past life. Obviously there are also other interpretations, both transcendental-survivalistic and naturalistic. The former include possession or overshadowing of the child by a deceased spirit who experienced the events described by the child. Possession seems rather far-fetched as the children keep their present identity, although they may occasionally refer to themselves in the third person (namely as the previous person).

There are several potential naturalistic interpretations, such as the anthropological, the psychological, the psychic and the chance interpretations. First the anthropological: about the time when children are learning how to speak they may make unclear statements that are hard to understand. In verbal interaction between the child and the parents an account may be formed about a previous life. What speaks against this interpretation, in many cases, is the fact that some of the statements made by the children are disliked by their parents, such as that the present mother is not the child's real mother, that the child wants to go back to its old home, that it repeats his/her account persistently and repeatedly so that it may become a bore to the whole family.

There may be psychological reason for a child to come up with a previous life account, such as if a child with rich fantasy lives in much isolation or in very difficult circumstances. It may seek refuge in a fantasy creation of a more pleasant life. There is some support from psychological studies for these children reveal as a group high scores for dissociative tendencies and considerable daydreaming (Haraldsson, 1997; Haraldsson, Fowler & Periyannanpillai, 2000). Additionally, the child frequently speaks of a life in more comfort and of socially higher status than the present life. Against this interpretation are the facts that the great majority of children give accounts of violent deaths, and that phobias are a common feature of the cases, along with signs of post-traumatic stress disorder. Little of this imagery or fantasies can be considered pleasant or enjoyable. However, this theory might explain a few cases. What about outstanding cases, like that of Purnima, particularly the birthmark aspect? Her massive birthmark that corresponds to the location of Jinadasa's wounds will have started to form in the embryo, and before environmental and psychological factors came into play. Hence, a psychological explanation will not suffice. A possible third interpretation would be the chance hypothesis that was briefly discussed above. I leave it to the reader to ponder that possibility. In my view, such an interpretation is obviously possible but can hardly been seen as satisfactory when we consider the relatively good fit between the two main aspects of the case, namely imagery/memory and the birthmarks and facts in the life of Jinadasa.

The main purpose of this chapter has been to acquaint the with some of the data that have been collected by briefly presenting some cases. It is beyond the scope of this contribution to attempt a detailed analysis of various possible interpretations but these cases have hopefully stimulated the reader to ponder on the various possible explanations.

## *References*

Haraldsson, E. 1991. Children claiming past-life memories: Four cases in Sri Lanka. *Journal of Scientific Exploration,* 5:2.233–62.

—. 1997. Psychological comparison between ordinary children and those who claim previous-life memories. *Journal of Scientific Exploration.* 11.323–35.

—. 2000a. Birthmarks and claims of previous life memories (I). The case of Purnima Ekanayake. *Journal of the Society for Psychical Research.* 64.16–25.

—. 2000b. Birthmarks and claims of previous life memories (II). The case of Chatura Karunaratne. *Journal of the Society for Psychical Research.* 64:859.82–92.

Haraldsson, E. and G. Samararatne. 1999. Children who speak of memories of a previous life as a Buddhist monk: Three new cases. *Journal of the Society for Psychical Research.* 63:857.268–91.

Haraldsson, E., P. Fowler, and V. Periyannanpillai. 2000. Psychological Characteristics of Children Who Speak of a Previous Life: A Further Field Study in Sri Lanka. *Journal of Transcultural Psychiatry.* 37.525–44.

Mills, A., E. Haraldsson, and H.H. Jurgen Keil. 1994. Replication studies of cases suggestive of reincarnation by three independent investigators. *Journal of the American Society for Psychical Research.* 88.207–19.

Stevenson, I. 1987. *Children who remember previous lives,* Charlottesville: University Press of Virginia.

—, 1997a. *Reincarnation and biology. A contribution to the etiology of birthmarks and birth defects.* 1 & 2. Westport, Conn.: Praeger.

—, 1997b. *Where reincarnation and biology intersect.* Westport, Conn.: Praeger.

# Physicalism and Parapsychology

JOHN BELOFF

*John Beloff, Ph.D., is an Honorary Fellow of the Department of Psychology in the University of Edinburgh. He has had an abiding interest in parapsychology and its implications for the philosophy of mind. He has served as President of the Parapsychological Association and the Society for Psychical Research. He is author of* The Existence of Mind; Psychological Sciences; The Relentless Question; Parapsychology: a Concise History; *and co-editor, with J.R. Smythies, of* The Case for Dualism.

## *Definitions*

By the term 'physicalism,' I shall mean that doctrine which holds that everything that ever happens in the real world can, in principle or ultimately, be explained conclusively and exclusively in terms of the motion of particles in space and time. Physicalism, so defined, is also sometimes referred to as 'reductionism,' 'materialism,' 'monism,' and so on. As applied to mental phenomena, that is to say, our awareness, our thoughts, feelings, desires, etc., physicalism becomes equivalent to 'epiphenomenalism,' that is the doctrine that all such phenomena can be fully explained in terms of the operations of the brain, their subjective residue being of no consequence for behaviour. It is precisely this doctrine that Francis Crick (1994) calls his 'Astonishing Hypothesis' (the title of his book) which he there defines as: 'The hypothesis that a person's mental activities are entirely due to the behaviour of nerve cells, glial cells, and the atoms, ions, and molecules that make up and influence them.' Whether or not you find this hypothesis 'astonishing,' the fact is that it has for some time been the accepted, orthodox position not just for scientists or neurophysiologists, like Crick, but indeed for some of our most influential philosophers who today make a show of disdaining anything that to them smacks of 'folk psychology' and who take their cue from the neurosciences.

I come now to my second key term the 'paranormal.' A 'paranormal phenomenon' is one that, quite simply, cannot be explained in physicalist terms. In principle, any kind of a physical anomaly that defied such a reductive explanation would rank as 'paranormal' but, in practice, the only phenomena that are ever cited as being paranormal are those associated with a living creature or, if we include so-called 'hauntings,' with a discarnate entity. In other words, the only kind of paranormal phenomena that need concern us are those that are in some sense mind-driven or mind-dependent. It follows from our definition of the term paranormal' that physicalism is incompatible with the existence of genuine paranormal phenomena and hence that anyone wishing to uphold physicalism or epiphenomenalism, is constrained to deny the existence of such phenomena.

Most physicalists recognize this incompatibility and, if they deign to mention 'parapsychology' at all, shrug it off as a 'pseudo-science' or, at best, an 'empty science.' If pressed, they may resort to what we may call a 'promissory physicalism,' that is to say a plea that, even if we cannot provide a physicalist explanation *now* for such phenomena, we can expect such an explanation to be forthcoming in the fullness of time. At this point some appeal is often made to the cutting edge of quantum theory where the exuberant array of paradoxical or counter-intuitive phenomena seem to mimic on the subatomic level what, at the macroscopic level we would call paranormal. Indeed, physicalists are to be found even among the parapsychological community. The so-called 'observational theories' of Helmut Schmidt and others were just such a bid to reconcile experimental parapsychology with quantum theory. The scientific community, however, remained obdurately aloof. More to the point, however, is the fact that such a reconciliation could be achieved only at the cost of ignoring or repudiating all the so-called 'strong phenomena' characteristic of spontaneous paranormal events in real life.

## *Attitudes to consciousness and psi*

Having now made clear, I hope, what I mean by 'physicalism' and what I mean by 'paranormal' we can proceed to consider the thesis that I propose to defend in this paper. This may be expressed as follows:

There exists, already, sufficient evidence for the existence of phenomena which are (a) incompatible with the known laws of physics and (b) mind-dependent. Furthermore, inasmuch as they are 'mind-dependent,' not just 'brain-dependent,' there is no reason to think that they will ever become compatible with any laws of physics yet envisaged even by those who talk glibly of new paradigms or of a post-modern outlook (see Krippner 1995). Hence, if (a) is correct, if there are such paranormal phenomena in this strong sense, it follows that the mind has powers and properties that defy any such physicalist analysis as implied by Crick's 'Astonishing Hypothesis.' It follows, further, that we have no option but to come to terms with an essential mind-body dichotomy. Dualism has been out of favour for a long time and has suffered from a bad press, philosophically speaking, but, whatever problems philosophers may have had with a dualist metaphysic, truth, in the end, is more important than fashion and an acknowledgment of the paranormal would force a return to some form of dualism even though not necessarily to the original Cartesian formulation.

It may well be that dualism can be upheld *without* ever invoking the paranormal. The late Karl Popper and his ally, John Eccles (1977), certainly thought so — although they failed to carry the philosophical community with them. It can certainly be argued that there are features of perception and memory that defy a physicalist analysis. Nevertheless, the paranormal, by definition, leaves one with *no option* but to acknowledge that if such phenomena exist, they are mind-driven as distinct from brain-driven.

It is not surprising, therefore, that most physicalists prefer simply to deny that there *are* any genuine as distinct from putative 'psi phenomena' (as we parapsychologists call them) or, preferably, refrain from even mentioning this possibility. Crick, for example, never once so much as mentions a psi phenomenon in the course of his book. Nor, likewise, and with even less excuse, does the philosopher John Searle. Searle's case is especially revealing since his book, provocatively titled *The Rediscovery of the Mind* (1992), is ostensibly a vindication of subjectivity as against the all-out materialism of radical behaviourists, mind-brain identity theorists or functionalists of the 'Strong A.I.' persuasion, all of whom contrive to deny the very existence of consciousness. Yet Searle is surely right when he exclaims, 'if your theory results in the view that consciousness does not exist, you have simply produced a *reductio ad absurdum* of the theory.'

But, having salvaged consciousness from the assaults of contemporary philosophers, Searle clings tenaciously to the epiphenomenalist view of consciousness as when he dubs his position 'biological naturalism' and insists that: 'Mental events and processes are as much part of our biological natural history as digestion, mitosis, etc.' Searle's 'gimmick' (if I may call it that) is to insist that consciousness is an emergent property of the brain in just the same way as 'liquidity' is an emergent property of an assembly of $H_2O$ molecules. His analogy, however, ignores a crucial difference. For, whereas, given the laws of physics, water could *not* be other than wet there are no *conceivable* laws of physics which tell us that certain brain-processes *must* generate consciousness. It follows that Searle's attempt to salvage epiphenomenalism by invoking the emergent properties of physical objects, must be dismissed as a sham. The mind-brain dichotomy cannot be downplayed in this way. If consciousness performs no function in the life of the individual that is not already catered for by the brain then we cannot escape what I call the critical epiphenomenalist paradox, namely that, but for this useless and unintelligible accident of evolution, the whole of human history could have unfolded exactly as it has done without anyone *ever* being conscious of anything that ever transpired. Surely a belief in the paranormal is a trifle compared to our having to contemplate such a preposterous fantasy!

## *Challenging the sceptics*

However, no theory in philosophy or science has ever been overthrown by calling it absurd. Hence the importance of finding facts that may contravene the doctrine in question. Parapsychology purports to purvey just such facts. Indeed, the annals of psychical research over the past hundred years or so represent a mountain of such facts. The reason offered by the guardians of scientific orthodoxy, if, indeed, they deign to offer a reason, for rejecting these alleged facts, is that none of the phenomena has so far been reliably demonstrated to order in an accredited laboratory to the satisfaction of impartial observers. Sure enough, there *have* been numerous replications of all the principal psi phenomena, as the many published meta-analyses testify. It remains true, nevertheless, that one can never depend on a particular psi effect showing up exactly when and where it may be required.

Is there any prospect of meeting the sceptic's insistence on repeatability on demand? If not is there any other way whereby the deadlock can be broken? While one can never know what the future may hold, past experience must make one doubtful about the possibility of a truly reliable phenomenon. Even the most successful procedures, such as the Ganzfeld technique, cannot claim a success rate of more than fifty percent and it is so time-consuming and laborious that no sceptic would have the patience to try it for themselves. PH tests on random-event generators, on the other hand, while easy to conduct, seldom reach a significant level of scoring. Indeed, all our experience so far points to the fact that psi is, for whatever reason, inherently elusive and evasive — it is as if nature actively rejected all such attempts to bypass her regular workings.

Another hypothetical possibility for overcoming the sceptical objection depends on finding an exceptional individual whose psi ability is so pronounced and so secure that it would be possible to stage a *definitive demonstration.* There have, of course, been a number of such exceptional individuals during the past hundred and fifty years or so since paranormal phenomena were the object of serious study. There are, however very few such individuals at the present time to the best of my knowledge although reports from various parts of the world suggest that they still do crop up here and there from time to time. At all events, the goal of a definitive demonstration is currently being actively pursued by at least one person I know in the United States. Such a definitive demonstration would be attended not only by eminent scientists but, since it is sometimes alleged that scientists are easy to fool, by conjurors and professional sceptics. However, given present day technology, it would not matter much who was actually present during the demonstration since every detail of the proceedings would be minutely recorded on video-tapes and so on, and the media would ensure that the outcome received mass publicity.

A third hypothetical scenario for overcoming scepticism is what I have called the 'permanent paranormal object' or PPO. The classic example is that of two interlocking wooden rings each cut from a different timber. There have been reports of such objects in the past but none, so far as I know, are now extant. Sceptics would no doubt still suspect trickery but the onus would then be on them to replicate the PPO by normal means and persistent failure to do so would inevitably consolidate the case for the paranormal.

A fourth and final possibility is that some reliable practical demonstration of paranormal powers might arise, whether in healing, forecasting, detection or whatever. In that case, sceptical objections would simply be bypassed and treated as pedantic nonsense.

Here, then, are four hypothetical ways for overcoming scepticism about the paranormal and thereby refuting physicalism. I cannot say, however, that I have much faith that any of them will be realized in the foreseeable future. Hence we must, I think, resign ourselves to the indefinite continuance of physicalism and epiphenomenalism whatever we may personally think about their plausibility.

## Conclusion

To recapitulate, there may be all kinds of reasons for rejecting physicalism as false or absurd: intuitive, ideological, metaphysical and so forth. Those, however, who regard universal explanation as the ultimate goal and glory of science, who seek what Stephen Hawking has called a 'Theory of Everything' will remain unperturbed by all such objections. What physicalists cannot tolerate, however, are claims for the existence of phenomena which, by definition, defy a physicalist analysis, i.e. 'paranormal phenomena.' Hence the deep suspicion which the scientific community in general harbour with regard to parapsychology. Whether, in the face of such suspicion, parapsychologists can succeed in demonstrating that there actually are paranormal phenomena remains to be seen. Four hypothetical stratagems were mentioned: (1) the discovery of some set-up that can be relied upon to produce a psi phenomenon where and when required; (2) a once-for-all definitive demonstration of just one blatantly paranormal phenomenon which would then be recorded for posterity in a permanent form; (3) the production of a permanent paranormal object or PPO which would then shift the onus of explanation onto the physicalist; and (4) the development of a reliable practical application of a psi phenomenon. It remains to be seen, however, whether any of these four solutions will be forthcoming even if we grant the existence of the paranormal. Personally, however, as one who takes seriously the paranormal, I would reckon that the second stratagem, the definitive demonstration, is the most hopeful.

## References

Crick, Francis. 1994. *The astonishing hypothesis: the scientific search for the soul.* London: Simon & Schuster.

Krippner, Stanley. 1995. Psychical research in the postmodern world. In *Journal of the American Society for Psychical Research,* 89.1–18.

Popper, K.R., and J.C. Eccles. 1997. *The self and its brain.* Berlin: Springer.

Searle, J.R. 1992, *The rediscovery of the mind,* Cambridge, Mass.: MIT.

# Psi Research and Transpersonal Psychology: Some Points of Mutual Support

MICHAEL GROSSO

*Professor Michael Grosso, Ph.D., is Chair of the Department of Philosophy and Religion at New Jersey City University. He studied classics and received his doctorate in philosophy from Columbia University. His chief interest lies in exploring the interface between psychical research and transpersonal psychology, with applications to counselling and studying the creative process. His books include* The Final Choice; Frontiers of the Soul; Soulmaking; The Millennium Myth; *and the forthcoming* Consciousness and Life After Death.

## *Introduction*

In this paper, I want to underscore the complementary relationship between parapsychology and transpersonal psychology. That relationship is subtle and complicated, so I plan to stick to making two main points. The first deals with the most contentious yet most practical parapsychological question: is there an afterlife? Although work here is slowly advancing — see, for example, the latest research of Stevenson (1997) and Ring and Cooper (1999) — even sympathetic investigators sense something unsatisfying about the knowledge so far acquired. What's lacking, in my opinion, is knowledge that is immediate, intuitive. Some of the evidence may be strongly suggestive; but the gut feeling that one survives death is something else.

As things stand, the evidence for life after death is indirect, based on inferences many hold to be suspect. This inferential quality of the evidence is an epistemic shortcoming. I will argue that certain experiences called 'transpersonal' could supplement the shortcomings of afterlife research. To remove the irritant of uncertainty certain kinds of direct experience might be induced in prepared subjects. The idea I want to discuss is related to what Charles Tart has called 'state-specific science' or Rhea White characterizes as 'exceptional human experiences.' Another link I would exploit is William Roll's (1974) idea that we study life after death through certain kinds of experiences of living people. I would put it like this: if we do survive death in a meaningful and personal way, it will clearly have to be in a radically altered state of consciousness. For one thing, our consciousness will not be mediated by the stabilities of sense experience. But radically altered, presumably expanded states of consciousness are the domain of what is often called transpersonal psychology.

The second point: transpersonal psychology gains an ally from the fundamental findings of parapsychology. In my experience, the response of mainstream sceptics to transpersonalism is more often humane tolerance than thoughtful agreement. It sounds good, but what's really at the bottom of it all? In the ruling cultural climate, transpersonal experiences are typically reduced to subjective states; the most exalted are seen as interesting, perhaps benign, but at bottom second-class citizens in the realm of the real. At worse they are regarded as indicative of psychosis. Parapsychology prompts us to question this; psi phenomena support an ontology of independent spirit, which is assumed by the transpersonal vision in most of its guises. Forerunners of contemporary transpersonalists such as Frederic Myers, William James, and Aldous Huxley were also students of parapsychological phenomena. In my opinion, the drifting apart of the two fields of study is a mistake; my aim in this paper is to lobby for their reunion.

## *Search for the immortal soul*

Ever since the founding of the English Society for Psychical Research (SPR) in 1882, a small but steady band of maverick scientists and scholars have tried to use scientific method to solve the riddle of human destiny. One question seems fundamental, and points to a dividing line between realms of the possible. The question is: what are the limits, the powers of human consciousness? To drive a wedge into the possibilities, we ask: could consciousness survive the death of the body? This relates to root concerns of transpersonal psychology. While not often directly discussed, it is an assumption of the great spiritual traditions that human beings are more than complex physical objects; that they have, or are, souls, minds, spirits, forms of consciousness distinct from and functionally independent of brains and bodies. This is true for Buddhism, although it denies there is such a thing as a unified and changeless self, and it is true for most indigenous worldviews. An independent consciousness is tacitly assumed by all the great faiths and perennial philosophies. On the strength of this fact alone, afterlife research and transpersonal psychology are logically interdependent. A few words now about why afterlife research is *important.*

*Afterlife and Spirituality* — first, as I just said, there is the close link between the transpersonal vision and the spiritual nature of human beings. Many concepts of spiritual practice such as prayer, divine modes of being, the freedom of conscious personality to transcend the constraints of physical existence, all presuppose an extraphysical essence to human reality.

*Ontology and the Mind-Body Problem* — afterlife research forces us to ask about the basic question concerning *what there is.* A case for postmortem existence would show in a uniquely compelling way that human beings are more than their physical elements. Until recently it was widely believed that persons were indeed more than their bodies, but modern scientific materialism denies this. Survival, it seems to me, would clearly rule out materialism.

*Healthy worldviews* — are some worldviews healthier than others? Worldviews determine values and attitudes, which influence choice and behaviour and therefore health. A stressful way of looking at life, for example, may damage the cardiovascular system. Feelings of helplessness and hopelessness weaken the immune system and have been linked to the onset of cancer. Since the idea of death is the most aversive stimulus, a worldview that helped us cope with that idea would have health benefits. The case for life *after* death has therapeutic implications for life *before* death. For the medical materialist, death can only signify final defeat: the polar opposite of health. In a perspective that affirmed continuity after death, the view would widen. Instead of terminal, death would be viewed as transitional; another stage of development, an episode in a larger history.

*Consciousness, politics, and death anxiety* — Ernest Becker's Pulitzer Prize winning *The Denial of Death* is one of several books that detail the difficulties that post-traditional people have in psychologically integrating the idea of their mortality. He writes:

> To be sure, primitives often celebrate death ... because they believe that death is the ultimate promotion, the final ritual elevation to a higher form of life, to the enjoyment of eternity in some form. Most modern Westerners have trouble believing

> this anymore, which is what makes the fear of death so prominent a part of our psychological make-up. (Becker 1973.ix)

Becker's thesis is that this 'difficulty' has occasioned wholesale denial that deeply distorts the human personality. The denial of death affects the way we relate to our bodies; it affects our capacity to feel; for defensive reasons, we anaesthetize ourselves; fear of death makes us obsess over power, wealth, celebrity — countermeasures to the terror of death. Before Becker, the Spanish philosopher Miguel de Unamuno (1921) wrote of the need that drives people to 'singularize' themselves, to stand out at all costs and make their mark on the world. This hunger for immortality fuels the nightmare of history, according to Unamuno, and is the psychic engine that drives the will to power. An expanded, less death-haunted, view of human potential would, I believe, blunt the dynamics of this desperate dialectic.

## *A story crying out for closure*

Despite the importance of the subject, afterlife research nowadays seems to be at an impasse. For one thing, there is very little work being done in the field. Mainstream culture, including medical science, is under the spell of scientific materialism. Thousands of scientists are working with billions of dollars to study the human genome, for example, but there are just a handful of survival researchers working with pathetically small budgets. One reason for the impasse in research is the data's ambiguity; conceptual issues confound interpretation. Very concisely now, I want to summarize the strengths and weaknesses of the evidence. Mainly, I want to point a way beyond the impasse that this evidence gives rise to.

### STRENGTH OF THE EVIDENCE

The first thing to note about evidence suggestive of an afterlife is its antiquity, persistence, variety, and surprising abundance. Whatever it is that causes all these afterlife manifestations, something deep in human nature recurrently gives the impression, and tends to produce the conviction, that human personalities survive death. Four types of data need to be reckoned with: out-of-body experiences, apparitions of the dead, mediumistic behaviours, and reincarnation effects.

*Out-of-body experiences* (OBEs) — it is a fact that substantial numbers of people claim to have the experience of being conscious at a location distant from their physical bodies. These experiences are interesting when they involve out-of-body perceptions that are later verified. In one case I recorded, a man named Dave, a professional scuba diver for the US Navy, got entangled underwater, was temporarily deprived of oxygen, and lost consciousness. He reported to me that while he was trapped underwater he found himself out of his body and observing his wife at home miles away; he noticed what she was doing in the kitchen, heard the phone ring, and watched his wife speak on the phone with a co-worker from the scene of her husband's accident. Somehow Dave remained with his wife as she drove to the scene where his body was located. By the time she arrived, he had been rescued and found himself back in his body. Dave's wife was so confused when he described what she was doing while he was trapped underwater that she believed he had hired someone to spy on her.

In another case, I challenged a student, who claimed she could leave her body on occasion, to visit me and make her presence known the next time it happened. She succeeded during an OBE to visit my home, accurately observed my behaviour, and moved a music stand from one part of the room to another (Grosso 1997.156–62).

Such experiences give vivid impressions of being able to interact with the environment independently of one's bodily organism. Veridical OBEs have in a few cases been induced experimentally (Tart 1968.3–27; Osis 1974.110–13). A case has recently been reported by cardiologist Michael Sabom (1998), in which a woman operated on for an aneurism had the blood drained from her head, her eyes and ears sealed from all incoming stimuli, and suffered clinical death with a flat EEG; none of this stopped her from having a veridical OBE. Such reports suggest that consciousness appears able to function not just apart from the body but during temporary brain death. This points to the possibility of postmortem survival.

*Apparitions* — hauntings and ghostly apparitions of the dead are as old as history. Most are worthless as evidence for life after death. But some cases have features that support survival. 'Pact' cases, for example; two people agree that whoever dies first will try to prove to the other his or her survival. Pact cases are important because they suggest that one may survive, remember, and act voluntarily after death. Researchers value cases where there is evidence of purpose (Richmond 1938). Most apparitions show no evidence of purpose, and consist of phantasmal images of unknown persons. In a strong case, there is evidence of the identity of a known deceased person *and* evidence of purpose. Even stronger cases are on record in which the evidence imparted is unknown to any living person, for example, the whereabouts of a missing object, a will or lost manuscript.

An old, but intriguing example, is the story told by Boccaccio about the last cantos of Dante's *Divine Comedy,* which were lost after the poet's death. Dante is said to have appeared in a dream to his son and correctly described the location of the cantos. Some apparitions are collectively perceived. Apart from torturous accounts of contagious hallucinations, collective percipience plus evidence of identity and purpose seem to imply that *some* intelligent agent is present at the apparitional scene.

Another class of apparitions is worth noting: those seen near or at the moment of actual death. People on the threshold of death tend to see deceased relatives, sometimes even people not known to them to be dead. Moreover, recent work has shown that some people, blind from birth, report having visual impressions during their near-death or out-of-body experiences (Ring, Cooper 1998). Such experiences are hard to reconcile with what is known of the brain. I hope there are follow-up studies to confirm and enrich our understanding of this remarkable phenomenon.

*Mediumship* — mediumship is a source of quasi-experimental evidence for postmortem survival. A medium is somebody whose organism temporarily becomes a human telephone through which deceased personalities presumably communicate. Great mediums like Leonora Piper were closely monitored to reduce the risk of fraud; careful records were made of proceedings; sittings were held and analyzed by more than one investigator; and types of experiment performed became increasingly more inventive and stringent. Some seemed to have originated from the side of the presumed communicators.

There were the so-called cross-correspondence cases, in which Myers and some of his scholarly compatriots, after they died, apparently tried to communicate coherent messages through *different* mediums. The point was to bolster the confidence of the living researchers that the messages were indeed coming from the other side. Another type of procedure presumably started on the other side was the so-called book tests; here the communicator revealed through the medium some specific passage in a book intimately related to himself but unknown to anyone else. A third development involved so called 'drop-in' communicators; during a seance persons unknown to medium or sitters break in, identify themselves, and give evidence of purpose and identity, which is later confirmed. These cases strengthen the impression that intelligent beings external to any living person have communicated from another world.

*Reincarnation effects* — centring around the work of Ian Stevenson (1987; 1997), the number of case histories has been growing since the 1960s that suggest the reality of reincarnation. Stevenson and his associates have produced a data base of about 2,600 cases. Children seem to retain verifiable memories from previous lives; in some cases, the reincarnated person shows birthmarks or birth defects that seem causally related to previous lives.

It is difficult to read some of these reports without concluding that the best explanation is that aspects of human personalities survive death and are reincarnated (Almeder 1992). However, in most Eastern traditions, reincarnation, not a desirable goal, is viewed as the failure to achieve enlightenment. To a Westerner, reincarnation may also seem unsatisfactory since few remember their past lives, and if they do, it's only for the early years of their lives, rarely past age eight. 'Survival' is brief, partial, and virtually equivalent to annihilation.*

Nevertheless, should this reincarnation data hold up, an expanded model of human personality is in the offing. Ever since the early mesmerist the Marquis de Puységur discovered the secondary personality of Victor Race, our image of the nature of the self has been expanding and complexifying; the simple unity of the self has been called into question, and multiple layers of the unconscious mind have been mapped (Ellenberger 1972). Reincarnation research continues this process of complexification. Stevenson, for example, argues that the reincarnation hypothesis may explain unusual talents, unexplained phobias, confusion over gender, and so forth. If reincarnation were proven, we would have to conclude that (at least some) persons are composites of numerous layers of successively incarnated individuals. The breadth, depth, and multiplicity of the human self would be further ratified. Moreover, it may be possible in more evolved states of consciousness to tap into the incredibly rich fund of our normally subliminal selves.

* Past life regression therapy may be valuable as therapy, but is rarely accompanied by evidence in support of the claimed previous life.

## The weak points in the evidence

Now let's look at some of the weak points in the afterlife data. In the first place, all narratives must pass muster before a host of preliminary objections. They have to establish their authenticity; reports must be corroborated; testimony made credible, and so on. Errors springing from malobservation, mistakes and distortions of memory, and the possibility of fraud or prank must be ruled out. Even when these preliminary obstacles are removed, and one is confronting an authentic case, there is another disturbing problem that has to be dealt with. In view of the fact that no one knows the limits of psychic ability, even strong cases suggestive of survival may be explained by the paranormal abilities of living people. What looks like an instance of somebody surviving death may actually be an illusion simulated by the unconscious of living people. This extrapolation of mental power has been dubbed *superpsi*. In theory, the simpler the explanation the better, and psi from the living will seem to many a simpler explanation than survival of the dead. Hope in survival is slashed by Occam's razor.

The superpsi explanation is something to reckon with. A full statement must take into account: 1) motivation; 2) the multiple nature of the self, and 3) certain automatic, mythopoetic tendencies of the unconscious mind. The first item, motivation, prevents us from applying superspi wholesale. Absence of motivation at first glance makes superpsi unlikely. In one case, reported early in the English SPR Proceedings, a man renting a hotel room saw the apparition of another man. He later accurately described this person to people who knew him and identified him in a photograph. It turned out that the apparition was of a man who died in the room some weeks earlier.

According to the superpsi hypothesis, the subject must have retrocognized the past or telepathically fished the image of the person who appeared to him from the hotel manager's mind. But what would motivate the percipient to use this extraordinary psychic power just once in this particular instance? Since he had never known the person whose apparition he saw, it is hard — apart from *ad hoc* speculation — to see superpsi at work here. Of course, superpsi might work spontaneously without prior motivation; but this would imply that some people possess extraordinary capacities that operate in purely arbitrary ways.

The early psychical researchers were aware of the notion of secondary personality; they knew, for example, that so-called 'controls' employed by mediums usually gave no evidence of their independent terrestrial history and were in all likelihood derivative from the medium's personality. But this raises the possibility that any self-declared persona of a deceased person might be what Flournoy (1911) called 'the fiendish by-play of the subliminal mind.' We are familiar with the histrionic capacities of our own minds from the evidence of our own dream life. Now, combine credible motivation and dramatic power with what may be unlimited psi, and the ability to simulate the appearance of surviving entities seems far more likely.

We have yet to confront the most damaging component of the non survival hypothesis. According to Anita Muhl's (1963) study of automatic writing, once a subject slips into what she calls 'the automatic zone,' there is a tendency to tell fabulous stories, imagine fairies, and evoke spirits and entities of the 'other' world. This 'zone' is similar to what has been called the mythopoetic mind. In the automatic zone or mythopoetic world, the fabrication of spirits and supernatural entities are routine expressions of a deep need. In the mythopoetic world, the idea, the image is its own truth. It has its own kind of truth, symbolic not literal. In the subliminal world of the automatic zone we honestly believe we are immortal and seem to feel our timeless nature.

So at some level of our mental life we may be programmed to produce an entire array of images and narratives full of meaning and psychological purpose but literally false. We may not only need to believe in life after death but be able to fabricate what looks like good evidence. In the youth of our species this arrangement may have served psychological needs. In the course of our mental evolution, the sceptic might say, we seem to have stumbled upon this well-tried ploy of the unconscious, unmasked our internal support system, and exposed it for what it is — a device for producing healing fictions.

## *The way out*

Afterlife research — however momentous — has with few exceptions failed to capture the public imagination. Now and then a popular book (often the worst by literary or intellectual standards) creates a stir; but nothing takes hold. Something seems to be missing, a unifying myth, a solid platform, programme, vision. Perhaps we need to take a fresh look at the whole problem. Historically, there have been several approaches.

*Way of the shaman* — Shamanic and mythical thinking on life after death flourished in the beginning. Exceptionally sensitive types fasted, drummed, chanted, ingested psychoactive drugs, sometimes even physically tortured themselves until they underwent altered states of consciousness, psychically travelled to what seemed like other worlds, and brought back practical insights. Part of the overall impact was to produce conviction of an afterlife.

*Way of the mystic* — Nearly as old is the way of the mystic who combines powerful self-discipline with philosophical and psychological analysis of the conditions of enlightenment. Conviction of immortality is here a by-product of experiencing the eternal aspect of the human personality.

*Way of the philosopher* — Let's not forget the appeal of pure argument. Plato, Leibniz, Descartes, and others of the Western philosophical tradition tried to prove the immortality of the soul without appealing to matters of fact. Then Kant came along and showed how pure reason will never solve what he wrongly fancied was a purely speculative question. There are always arguments for and against metaphysical claims, Kant said, so we might as well deal with the afterlife strictly by faith.

*Way of the spiritualist* — Another phase of this long quest was nineteenth century spiritualism, which grew out of mesmerism, and corrected Kant by looking at the empirical side of the question. In the end, however, spiritualism became more religious than scientific; it did, however, pave the way for the next approach.

*Way of the psychical researcher* — psychical research, beyond intuition and theology, sought to use impartial scientific and empirical method. Out of that effort modern parapsychology emerged. Psychical research has pursued a trace approach to afterlife research; one investigates traces, signs, signals of beings once alive who have presumably survived death. One attempts to determine if the best explanation of these traces is that some person actually survived death. However, as I tried to show above, the trace approach, despite its empirical riches, has led to a kind of Kantian antinomy where arguments for and against survival always seem possible. Thanks to the indirect nature of the inquiry — indirect as long as we are alive — we may never resolve the question by rational means. So let's consider another possible stage; call it the integral way to afterlife research.

## *An integral perspective on afterlife research*

Supposing survival research needs a fresh approach, how can transpersonal studies help? One type of survival data overlaps transpersonal studies: the near-death experience (NDE). As evidence for life after death, the NDE is valuable but far from compelling (Cook, Greyson & Stevenson 1998). To one who has the experience, however, the experience can be a revelation. Near-death-experiencers seem, like shamans, mystics, or visionaries, temporarily to visit another world. To them their experience is not a dream but something infinitely more real than waking life. They become convinced that they *know* there is another world, have talked with dead relatives, seen God, angels, heaven, and hell. They know these things, they say, because they have been there.

Something about the sense of being there, right on the scene, is what I believe people need, and are drawn to, even as they pull back with understandable fear: an experience that supplements rational knowledge achieved through survival research. I did not say *supplant.* Experience without rational grounding would be shaky; rational grounding without experience is shallow. Survival research in the next century needs a more integral approach.

The NDE suggests enticing avenues of experiment and exploration. In *Lessons From the Light* (1999), Kenneth Ring shows how we might gain the wisdom of the NDE by entering sympathetically into the images, language, and internal environment described by experiencers. Consistent with, but different from, Ring's approach, the following also seem possible. It is not as extreme as the idea in the movie *Flatliners* (Schumaker 1990) in which medical students stop their hearts hoping to snatch a preview of the next world. My idea is more manageable, and a lot safer. I would focus on three specific features of NDEs, each being an inlet to personal experience and discovery:

**1.** The first is the *out-of-body experience,* a prominent NDE feature. The experience is transformative, as known from the famous case of St Paul's conversion on the road to Damascus. Note the odd, third person way Paul put it in the Second Letter to the Corinthians (12:2–4.): 'I know a man in Christ, who, fourteen years ago, was caught up — whether still in the body or out of the body, I do not know, God knows — right into the third heaven ... into paradise and (who saw) things which must not and cannot be put into human language.' In this description, it is hard to weed out the psychic from the spiritual. Out of the body, paradise, the third heaven, vision, the ineffable: what is parapsychological and what is transpersonal here?

The prophet Joel predicted a day would come when people from all walks of life will have transformative experiences: 'And it shall come to pass afterwards, that I will pour out my spirit upon all flesh' (Joel 2:28). I have always seen Joel as a prophet of democratized spiritual consciousness. One thinks today of people claiming to have near-death or out-of-body experiences, angelic encounters, alien abductions, psychedelic epiphanies, Marian visions, and the like. Is it possible for ordinary people to learn to induce functionally similar experiences? The shift from accidental recipient to proactive explorer would be a step toward Joel's democracy of higher consciousness.

There is a small literature on the subject, based on gifted out-of-body travellers and experimental studies. As far as I can see, the main techniques described involve the use of intention, concentration, and imagination. A recent book by Robert Peterson (1997) shows how dogged effort can awaken and train the ability to leave the body. D. Scott Rogo's *Leaving the Body* (1983) summarizes methods used by well-known practitioners such as Oliver Fox and Sylvan Muldoon. There is the resource of the Monroe Institute and the books of Robert Monroe (1970). It is clear from the Sutras of Patanjali that practice in the art of out-of-body projection is a real possibility. Whatever the benefits of such experiments, they would be based on one's own experience; the knowledge gained would be personal, inwardly felt, and authentic, in the sense of being 'one's own.'

The out-of-body side of the near-death experience corresponds to the ecstatic function of shamanism (Eliade 1970). Traditional shamans, according to Eliade, are masters of ecstatic flight, explorers of the higher and lower realms of consciousness. As more people pursue this form of experimentation, a new consensus might form about the probability, value, and meaning of life after death.

**2.** A second replicable aspect of the NDE is the *visionary or apparitional encounter*. People report meeting with deceased relatives during NDEs, and they claim to see archetypal religious figures and supernatural landscapes. Various traditions give hints for conducting personal experimentation. Consider an example from the ancient world. For two thousand years the ancient Greeks conducted elaborate rites at Eleusis (a town near Athens) with the purpose of inducing a vision of Persephone, Goddess of the Underworld (Kerenyi 1967). Fasting for nine days and drinking a psychoactive brew *(kukeon)* was preceded by much internal preparation. A well orchestrated rite, an expensive and elaborate procedure, based on consistent testimony, produced an experience with profound, transformative effects. It is clear from records from Plato, Cicero, Sophocles, Aeschylus and many others, that the Eleusinian experience was transformative. Like the NDE, it made an indelible impression on the celebrant's consciousness of one's intrinsic immortality. What the modern equivalent of Eleusis might be remains for some enterprising researchers to discover. Unfortunately, the laws proscribing use of the crucial entheogens are stupid and draconian.

An ancient technique for inducing visionary experience is scrying or crystal gazing. Moody (1992) has attempted to revive the practice of mirror gazing as a way of inducing visionary encounters with departed spirits. Another technique, known for its psi-conduciveness, that could be used for visionary induction purposes is the *Ganzfeld:* by restricting sensory experience to uniform inputs (a form of sensory deprivation) it is possible to facilitate ESP (Honorton 1977.459–64). The same experimental setup could be used for inducing visions of the dead. We could think of this as a distillation of the traditional vision quest, a procedure less clumsy than the sensory isolation tank. I have also heard much informal discussion of using lucid dreaming as an entrée to visionary encounters with discarnate entities. So, whether by mirror gazing, hypnotic or *Ganzfeld* procedures, vision questing, psychedelics, or lucid dreaming, methods abound for exploring visionary and apparitional experiences. Again, as more subjects learn to record and share their experiences critically with others, changes in the consensus about an afterlife may emerge, a consensus more intuition-and-experience based than the current one that is based on theory and dogma.

**3.** Perhaps the central aspect of the NDE is *experiencing the light.* The light experience, essential to the archetypal NDE, cuts across a wide range of transpersonal phenomena (Eliade 1965.19–77; Williams 1992). Eliade has compiled reports of experiencing the 'mystic light': in dreams and other spontaneous episodes, Eskimo shamanism, Tibetan tantrism, Hindu yoga, Chinese Taoism, Iranian and Christian mysticism, and aboriginal dreamtime. The mystic light is a universal feature of transpersonal experience. Paediatrician Melvin Morse (1992) has stated that experiencing the light is central to transformation in the near-death experience. Experiencing the light — so often described in the most powerful NDEs — is what changes people, convinces them of the reality of another world, and touches them with an all-embracing love. The evidence suggests that this widely reported light experience, so powerful and so universal, is available to all. The remarkable thing about the modern near-death experience is its wide distribution. In keeping with Joel's prophecy, it has democratized mystical opportunity. People of all ages, culture, and mental development may experience this, no doubt uniquely in each case. Nor must you literally be near death.

## *Misgivings about the paranormal*

I want now to turn to the second main point of this paper and discuss one key way in which psi research supports transpersonal psychology. But I first want to address the fact that some people concerned with spiritual things seem reluctant to deal with parapsychology. Their reasons vary. Talking with a well-known Christian theologian, I once mentioned the possibility that there could be evidence for life after death. I was solemnly warned that this was 'self-serving' and would encroach upon the domain of faith; I replied that in a more catholic view knowledge complements faith. Another misgiving voiced by religious fundamentalists is that to study the paranormal is to court the diabolic (a view I discount as absurd); while a Buddhist friend genially dismissed afterlife research on grounds that no self exists that could conceivably survive. However, Buddhists do believe in reincarnation, and nirvana is not annihilation (Johansson 1969). A deep ecologist once told me in no uncertain terms how 'selfish' it was to fuss over the puny consideration of my afterlife when the environment was going to pieces.

More serious objections have been raised against interest in *siddhis,* charisms, or paranormal powers as distractions from spiritual practice and enlightenment. Prelates within the Catholic church attacked Padre Pio during his life because his fame as a healer, bilocator, and stigmatist was creating a cult of personality (Boniface 1971). Then there's that story of the Buddha rebuking a disciple for wasting time learning how to levitate across a river when a ferry was available for a pittance. Much to my surprise, I notice that people sworn to a spiritual outlook are often as bitterly opposed to the paranormal as hard core materialists.

While granting some merit to these objections, my stress in this paper is on the theoretical support that parapsychology offers transpersonalism. It seems, moreover, a mistake to separate paranormality (a term relative to dogmatic materialism) from the transpersonal. In other words, transpersonal experiences always entail, or at least strongly suggest, the kinds of experiential extensions beyond doctrinaire materialism implied by the term *paranormal.* The paranormal, however, challenges mainline materialism more sharply than the transpersonal, which is why it rouses more critical ire from the official watchdogs. Look closely now at some ways the paranormal is implicit in the transpersonal vision.

## *Psi and the transpersonal vision*

### THE MEANING OF THE TRANSPERSONAL

We need a working definition of the word *transpersonal.* '*Transpersonal experiences* may be defined as experiences in which the sense of identity or self extends beyond *(trans)* the individual or personal to encompass wider aspects of humankind, life, psyche, and cosmos' (Walsh & Vaughan 1993.3). This is a useful definition that stresses the subjective sense of transcending ordinary ego-bound existence. The definers leave open the question of how to interpret the experience. However, I would hesitate to say, as Walsh and Vaughan do (p. 4), that the transpersonal is neutral with regard to ontology. Transpersonalism is kin to ontologies that affirm the autonomy and logical independence of spirit and consciousness. More on this shortly.

### HISTORICAL FORERUNNERS

As I have already pointed out, the alliance of psi research and transpersonal studies may be seen in the work of William James (1913) and Frederic Myers (1903). Both men studied experiences nowadays called peak, transcendent, or transformative *as well as* supernormal and paranormal phenomena. James wrote the *Varieties of Religious Experience,* a phenomenology of transpersonal experiences; also a lifelong student of psychical research, he discovered one of the greatest mediums of the day, Eleanora Piper.

Myers' *Human Personality and its Survival of Bodily Death* is a model for thinking about the connections between psychical research and transpersonal psychology. It covers states of consciousness nowadays discussed under the rubric of 'transpersonal' such as genius, inspiration, madness, mysticism, prayer, multiple personality, hypnosis, trance, possession, ecstasy, and so forth. For Myers the spectrum of our conscious states formed a graded, interlaced system that pointed toward complete transcendence of the brain. Myers saw psi abilities as evolutionary indicators of humanity's postmortem spiritual potential. Far from seeing the paranormal as a misleading side effect of spiritual life, he saw it as integral to our whole evolutionary project.

Interest in personal survival is not at odds with the transpersonal. 'The passion for Life is not selfish weakness, it is a factor in the universal energy.' Myers saw in 'telepathic law' the basis of our real membership in a spiritual community. Evolution invites the endless deepening of our capacity for transpersonal love. 'Love,' he said, 'is a kind of exalted but unspecialized telepathy' (Myers 1903.1.282), suggesting that in all intimate, empathic, and compassionate relationships there is an element of telepathy, literally, of 'distant feeling.'

A similar, comprehensive ordering of a spectrum of extraordinary *physical* phenomena reported of mediums, saints, yogis, mystics, shamans, and athletes has been described by Michael Murphy in *The Future of the Body* (1992). Murphy marshals an immense array of evidence, as did Myers, demonstrating a continuum of extraordinary physical capacities that reflect various afterlife-related phenomena. They all suggest potentials for what are called subtle bodies, bodies midway in range of property between the physical and the spiritual.

## Psi, Materialism, and the Transpersonal Vision

A strictly materialist view of mind cannot authenticate mystical raptures, near-death visions, and most transpersonal experiences. If materialism is true, an air of humbug must hang over the transpersonal vision. A materialist could say: enjoy your sense of expanded self-identity, but in the end it's an illusion, perhaps useful, perhaps edifying, but at bottom a beguiling brain state devoid of transcendent import.

Why indeed not dismiss the transpersonal as edifying illusion? Several arguments seem possible. To begin with, some might say argument is unnecessary. *Sola fide,* 'by faith alone,' is the Protestant formula for salvation. One can always believe in the transpersonal on the basis of the authority of some guru, prophet, or sacred text. Apart from the dangers of authoritarianism, this is at odds with an integral ideal that encompasses faith *and* reason, intuition *and* sensation. The view that rests solely on faith and sheer subjectivity lends itself to a fragmented and therefore enfeebled consciousness.

An argument against the illusory nature of transpersonal experience: they are a universal feature of human life. Some say that the universality of an experience is proof enough of its reality; any experience so deep-seated and recurrent must be functionally real and objectively true. Jung argued like this for the reality of archetypes. But Jung went further. He was throughout his career keen on parapsychology, and welcomed the work of J.B. Rhine and the early psychical researchers as supporting his form of transpersonal psychology. 'Parapsychology is important because everywhere it lurks just below the surface,' he said (Main 1997).

There is also the pragmatic criterion for justifying transpersonalism. Experiences that so inspire, elevate, and transform people are 'true' and 'real' because in the long run they benefit the human race. There are, of course, difficulties in the pragmatic criteria of truth, and a poisonous scepticism might still insist that transpersonal experiences might be universal, transformative, and beneficial, but still insubstantial epiphenomena of the brain.

Parapsychology uniquely gives grounds for resisting this deflationary tendency. It warrants belief that we inhabit a universe in which there is a basis for transpersonal experiences. Call it the transcendent psi factor. The psi factor in nature is apparently not constrained by the laws of physics, chemistry, and biology, at least as they are understood today. Besides physical reality, there is an irreducible realm of Something Else: the *Urstoff,* raw material and pervasive background of our mental, psychic, and spiritual life. John Mack faces the challenge to the transpersonal vision as follows:

> We are witnessing a battle for the human soul between two opposing ontologies. In one view, the physical or material world is the ultimate, if not the only, reality ... In the transpersonal view, the physical world and all its laws represent only one of an indeterminable number of possible realities whose qualities we can only begin to apprehend through the evolution of our consciousness. (Walsh & Vaughan 1993.xi)

The most powerful strategic ploy at our disposal in this battle — because it addresses head on the question of the ontology of consciousness — is parapsychology. With the assumption that psi is a fact of nature, we claim an invaluable ally to the transpersonal vision.

To demonstrate the supportive role of psi, look at a few statements from the classic literature of transpersonalism. Consider this from the Katha Upanishad: 'The knowing Self is not born; It does not die. It is not sprung from anything. Birthless, eternal, everlasting, and ancient, It is not killed when the body is killed.' (Nikhilananda 1963.73) One could have a vast range of extraordinary experiences, but none could fully confirm this Upanishadic description of the Self. Parapsychology, however, lends it *some* objective reference. It could ratify the claim that the experiencing Self, by means of ESP and psychokinesis, reaches beyond the normal constraints of time and the ordinary constraints of physical existence. It would be a step toward making the Upanishadic Self intelligible to a culture mired in dogmatic materialism. It provides some support for the ancient Hindu claim that the Self is not destroyed by death. Without something like the notion of psi, the majestic Indian Self might be dismissed as balderdash. The reality of psi adds plausibility that there is something we call the 'higher self' that transcends time and space

We need to place this argument in historical context. In traditional societies, the problem of verifying and authenticating spiritual reality does not come up with the same urgency of today. Rational self-consciousness had yet to fully emerge as an historical force, along with its prodding doubts and searching questions. In today's multi-cultural world and stiffly competitive market of ideas, the need for empirical grounding is felt more widely, and its apparent absence is more likely to be felt as inhibitive. Comparative mythology and the methods of phenomenology are valuable means for establishing the range and quality of the transpersonal vision. But we need psi studies, experimental and spontaneous, to mark off the ontological ground in and around which the transpersonal vision can grow and flourish.

I have only scratched the surface of the various ways psi and transpersonalism support and reflect each other. My main hope in writing this paper is to stimulate thought on the possibilities of creative convergence. Although many parapsychologists refrain from speculating on how psi relates to religion, spirituality, and the transpersonal, many have shown interest. J.B. Rhine, the person noted for developing the modern experimental paradigm, was keen on what he called 'the parapsychology of religion' and wrote that 'religious communication is basically psi communication' (Rhine 1975). The Scientific and Medical Network, in the capable hands of director David Lorimer, covers both psi and the transpersonal, and so does the California Institute of Noetic Sciences, with Marilyn Schlitz at the experimental helm.

I would also single out the publication of Charles Tart's anthology *Body, Mind, Spirit* (Tart 1997), which contains discussions exploring the links between parapsychology and spirituality. One strong theme that emerges from Tart's volume is that parapsychology connects us with a wider world; and that it does so in a real, physically anomalous, and efficacious way that would be impossible if scientific materialism were the whole truth. Connection to a wider world through psi is, in my view, key to the scientific basis of transpersonal psychology. Psi is what gives the *trans* part some real kick. Looking, then, to the future, Rhea White, who writes about 'exceptional human experiences' (EHEs) in Tart's anthology, exemplifies the integral approach when she puts psi and the transpersonal under one umbrella:

> The special quality of many EHEs is their timelessness ... not only in mystical moments when time seems to stop, but in verifiable moments in which people see the future (precognition), the past (retrocognition), and possibly past lives (reincarnation). (White 1997)

## *Conclusion*

Since the nineteenth century the English-speaking world has tried to create a science of spiritual consciousness. The Transcendentalist movement in New England with its oversoul, cosmic consciousness, and spiritualism was a proto-scientific example. The project assumed at least two different forms. One was to isolate experiences that speak to our transcendent potential, cut them loose from their religious and ideological moorings, and get at their most interesting properties. Another was to authenticate these experiences, produce evidence of their transcendent reality. In this paper I argued for an integral approach, a coincidence of opposites, theory married to practice, data gathering to experimental daring. For survival research I recommend a careful blend of inference and intuition. If, moreover, we want to play the science game, I hold that transpersonal psychology without parapsychology is a beautiful castle with weak foundations. Finally, by integral I do not mean compartmental, hierarchic, or absolutistic; rather, with Stanley Krippner (2001) I opt for a postmodern view that is at home breaking boundaries and not getting stuck in rigid thinking, a mobile, self-revising perspective suitable to the adventures of spiritual science.

## References

Almeder, R. 1992. *Death and personal survival.* Maryland: Rowman & Littlefield.

Assagioli, R. 1973. *The act of will.* New York: Viking.

Becker, E. 1973. *The denial of death.* New York: Free Press.

Boniface, E. 1971. *Padre Pio le Crucifié.* Paris: Nouvelles Editions Latines.

Cook, E., B. Greyson, I. Stevenson. 1998. Do any near-death experiences provide evidence for the survival of human personality after death? Relevant features and illustrative case reports. *Journal of Scientific Exploration.* 12.3.

Corbin, H. 1994. *The man of light in Iranian Sufism.* Lebanon, NY: Omega.

Dossey, L. 1993. *Healing words.* Harper San Francisco.

—. 1997a. *Be careful what you pray for ...* Harper San Francisco.

—. 1997b. The return of prayer. *Alternative Therapies.* 3.6.

Eliade, M. 1965. *The two and the one.* New York: Harper Torchbooks.

—. 1970. *Shamanism: archaic techniques of ecstasy.* Princeton University Press.

Ellenberger, H. 1970. *The discovery of the unconscious.* New York: Basic Books.

Evans-Wentz, W.Y. 1967. *Tibetan yoga and secret doctrines.* New York: Oxford University Press.

Flournoy, G. 1911. *Spiritism and psychology.* Harper, New York.

Goodrick-Clarke, Nicholas. 1985. *The occult roots of Nazism.* Wellingborough: Aquarian.

Grosso, M. 1997. *Soulmaking.* Charlottesville: Hampton Roads.

Honorton, C. 1977. Psi and internal attention states. In B. Wolman (ed.) *Handbook of parapsychology,* New York: Van Nostrand.

Humphreys, C. 1966. *The Sutra of Hui Neng.* London: Buddhist Society.

Huxley, A. 1970. *The perennial philosophy.* New York: Harper.

Hyslop, J. 1918. *Life after death: problems of the future life and its nature.* New York: Dutton.

James, W. 1913. *The varieties of religious experience.* New York: Longman.

Johansson, E.A. 1970. *The psychology of Nirvana.* New York: Anchor Books.

Kerenyi, C. 1967. *Eleusis and the Eleusinian mysteries.* Princeton University Press.

Krippner, S. 2001. Psi and postmodernity in the twenty-first century. *International Journal of Parapsychology.*

Main, R. 1997. *Jung on synchronicity and the paranormal.* Princeton University Press.

Moody, R. 1992. Family reunions: visionary encounters with the departed in a modern-day psychomanteum. *Journal of Near-Death Studies,* 83-121.

Monroe, R. 1970. *Journeys out of the body.* New York: Doubleday.

Morse, M. with Paul Perry. 1992. *Transformed by the light.* New York: Ivy Books.

Muhl, A. 1963. *Automatic writing.* New York: Helix.

Myers, F. 1903. *Human personality and its survival of bodily death* (2 vols.) New York: Longman.

Osis, K. 1974. Perspectives on out-of-body research. In W. Roll (ed.) *Research in Parapsychology.* Metuchen, NJ: Scarecrow.

Peterson, R. 1997. *Out of body experiences.* Charlottesville: Hampton Roads.

Rhine, J. B. 1975. The parapsychology of religion: a new branch of inquiry. In *The Centrality of Science and Absolute Values: Proceedings of the Fourth International Conference of the Unity of Science.* New York: The International Cultural Foundation. 585–96.

Richmond, Z. 1938. *Evidence of purpose.* London: G. Bell & Sons.

Ring, K. 1999. *Lessons from the light.* New York: Plenum.

Ring, K. and S. Cooper. 1999. *Mindsight: near-death and out-of-body experiences in the blind.* Palo Alto: William James Center for Consciousness Studies,

Rogo, S. 1983. *Leaving the body.* Englewood Cliffs: Prentice Hall.

Roll, W. 1974. A new look at the survival problem. In John Beloff (ed.) *New directions of parapsychology.* 144–65. Metuchen, NJ: Scarecrow.

Sabom, M. 1998. *Light and death.* Grand Rapids: Zondervan.

Schlitz, M. and W. Braud. 1997. Distant intentionality and healing: assessing the evidence.' In *Alternative Therapies,* Vol.3, No.6, pp. 62–72.

Stevenson, I. 1987. *Children who remember previous lives.* Charlottesville: University Press of Virginia.

—. 1997. *Where reincarnation and biology intersect.* Westport: Praeger.

Tart, C. 1968. A psychophysiological study of out-of-body experiences in a selected subject. *Journal of the American Society of Psychical Research.* 62.

—. 1997. *Body, mind, spirit: exploring the parapsychology of spirituality.* Charlottesville: Hampton Roads.

Unamuno, Miguel de. 1921 (1954). *The tragic sense of life.* New York: Dover.

Walsh, R. and F. Vaughan. 1993. *Paths beyond ego.* New York: Putnam Publishing.

Wilhelm, R. 1962. *The secret of the golden flower.* New York: Harcourt Brace.

White, R. 1997. Exceptional human experiences and the experiential paradigm. In C. Tart 1997, pp.83–100.

# Frontiers in Consciousness and Healing

# Enlightenment and Endarkenment

CHARLES T. TART

*Charles T. Tart, Ph.D., Core Faculty at the Institute of Transpersonal Psychology, Professor Emeritus of Psychology at UC Davis and Senior Research Fellow of the Institute of Noetic Sciences, is internationally known for his research with altered states of consciousness, transpersonal psychology and parapsychology. His books include two that have been called classics —* Altered States of Consciousness *and* Transpersonal Psychologies *— as well as eleven others dealing with states of consciousness, marijuana intoxication and parapsychology. His 1986* Waking Up: Overcoming the Obstacles to Human Potential *synthesised Buddhist and Sufi mindfulness training ideas transmitted by G. I. Gurdjieff with modern psychology, as did* Living the Mindful Life *and his most recent book,* Mind Science: Meditation Training for Practical People (2000), *further exploring the possibilities of awakening. He has been a student of Aikido, Buddhist meditation, Gurdjieff's work and of other psychological and spiritual growth disciplines. His primary goals are to build bridges between the scientific and spiritual communities and to help bring about a refinement and integration of Western and Eastern approaches to personal and social growth.*

I've always believed that science, and psychology in particular, should be comprehensive by taking into account *all* aspects of human consciousness — not just those that happen to be fashionable at the moment. And all through my career in psychology I've noticed how certain things were out of fashion. I did a lot of research in hypnosis in the early part of my career for instance, in which, through the act of speaking with someone for half an hour, I could sometimes totally change their reality. Psychology almost totally ignored this sort of thing. I couldn't understand how such powerful effects could be ignored. So I've explored a variety of unfashionable phenomena. Willis Harman, in his introduction, has mentioned some of them: things like hypnosis and dreams, altered states in general, meditation, the human potential movement, biofeedback, parapsychology. Many of these are almost moving into the mainstream now and that's gratifying. What I'm going to focus on is one that is not represented in the mainstream at all, but which I think is vitally important, one which I'll call, 'enlightenment.'

Now for the moment I'll avoid defining what I mean by enlightenment. I actually can't do it anyway, but we'll pretend I can define it later, and try to share some preliminary understandings about it. I'm not going to explain consciousness either, but if I can expand our concept of what consciousness is, then I'll be happy. We can't explain it of course, but it's great fun to try.

Enlightenment is a major psychological goal of hundreds of millions of people on this planet. But of course they are Easterners, not us, and so we pay no attention to them. Our own cultural limitations make science and psychology almost blind to questions about enlightenment. You won't find enlightenment mentioned at all in introductory psychology texts. I find this lack of interest in or knowledge about enlightenment in psychology ironic, because, in a strange sort of way, I find that modern psychology probably knows more about the obstacles to enlightenment than the spiritual enlightenment traditions do! I've sometimes expressed this by saying that in modern psychology we have a profound knowledge of endarkenment.

I can certainly claim that personally. I don't really know what enlightenment is, but personally and professionally, I've studied endarkenment for more than fifty years now and claim considerable expertise on the topic ... Nevertheless, I'll have the presumption to try to present something about the enlightenment perspective on life and to introduce that.

You might say that from the perspective of the enlightenment traditions, our ordinary consciousness is highly restricted and that we are, in a very real sense, prisoners in a very constricted subset of possibilities. And while we have some very powerful techniques in modern psychology, we use them to decorate our prison cells and make things much more comfortable here, rather than using them to further enlightenment, which is possible. But from the enlightenment perspective, I do believe that modern psychological knowledge could help us move in the direction of enlightenment.

## *Definitions*

We are all well trained as intellectuals here, so we know we have to define our terms to begin with. As a psychologist, I went to the *Encyclopedic Dictionary of Psychology* (Harre and Lamb 1983) to see what it said about enlightenment ... and there was no entry — so that takes care of the regular psychological definition of enlightenment! Then I pulled out my copy of *Webster's New Collegiate Dictionary* and I found 'enlightenment.' *1. The act or means of enlightening, the state of being enlightened.* Well, that's nice but it doesn't tell us anything. *2. Enlightenment* (with a capital 'E') *a philosophic movement of the eighteenth century marked by questioning of traditional doctrines and values, a tendency towards individualism and an emphasis on the idea of universal human progress, the empirical method in science and free use of reason.*

I thought, 'Well, that's not what I plan to talk about, but it's certainly compatible. So that's all right. Although the individualism is a little funny there.' And *3. Enlightenment in Buddhism, a final blessed state marked by the absence of desire or suffering.* I thought about that and that sounds like you're dead! So that's not quite an adequate definition either and besides, the way I understand it, it's not an *absence* of desire, it's an absence of *attachment* to desire, which is quite different.

Now, as you all realize, enlightenment is inherently indefinable. Enlightenment is about a radical change in not only your consciousness but your whole *state of being,* but when we try to define something, our ability to define, to use words, is a *part* of the whole vast spectrum of our totality as human beings. I have never expected the part to be able to define the whole. And so it always puzzles me when people seem to drive themselves mad because they can't define something adequately, as if we then can't deal with the reality of it. I'm not bothered by that. To me, words are a convenient way of *pointing* towards realities, and if we can point carefully and accurately, that's fine.

Now, of course that's difficult. For instance, many times I've told my cat, 'Look over there,' and if my cat pays attention to me at all, he stares at my finger. So words do tend to trap us: instead of looking in the direction the words point, we get caught up in the words themselves. For those of us who want it fancier, I think you could invoke Gödel's Theorem to show that the part can never be fully explained in its own terms. So I'll try to use my words carefully today, but the words I'll use are intended to be *pointers*. If they point to something that you have some experiential understanding of and so lead you to make some useful connections, good. If you get caught in the words, that's dangerous.

## *The experience of Doctor S.*

As we all know, this topic of enlightenment has a great deal of nonsense and psychopathology associated with it as well as sheer plain craziness — but there is nothing unique about that. All areas of life have pathology and craziness mixed in with them. So we won't worry about that. I'm going to try to focus today on the question of 'What is enlightenment?' and I'll try to share the essence of the phenomena here.

The examples I'll give you today are deliberately not drawn from the spiritual traditions. I have enormous respect for the spiritual traditions, but they also each have an investment in a certain conceptual system. So I'm going to try to draw my examples from people who had no *a priori* beliefs about enlightenment, who have less investment in trying to make it sound as if their experience conforms to a certain kind of doctrine.

I'll begin by giving you an example of a spontaneous experience that will illustrate enlightenment in one sense of the word as a special altered state of consciousness. It's extremely important.

The example comes from an anaesthesiologist. At the time this experience happened, he was a rather militant atheist, but most of the time he basically didn't give a damn one way or the other about anything spiritual. He was a young professional, an assistant professor, had a lot of research grants, was rising very rapidly in his career, and was clearly going to be offered tenure. This experience so affected him that instead of going on and getting tenure, he gave it up so he would have more time to explore his own mind. For academics, where tenure equals success and security, this is a big effect!

This is a fairly precise description of the experience. One of the reasons it's precise is that when I first met him, I said, 'You've got to write this up,' because he'd also had some experiences with psychedelics afterwards. I said to him, 'You know, there's a whole literature arguing whether psychedelics can induce *genuine* mystical experiences or not, and by and large it's a classic case of the blind leading the blind. The arguments are by people who have never had a spontaneous mystical experience or a psychedelic experience, yet they are arguing about what's real.' He had experienced both. So he insisted that I work with him and keep pressing him on, 'What *exactly* do you mean by so-and-so?' Hence there's quite a bit of precision here. Doctor S., as I will call him, is not quite ready to come out of the closet but almost.*

> My cosmic consciousness event occurred unexpectedly while I was alone one evening and watching a particularly beautiful sunset. The experience began with some mild tingling in the perineal area between the genitals and anus. The feeling was unusual but was neither particularly pleasant nor unpleasant. After the initial few minutes I either ceased to notice the tingling or did not remember it. I then noticed that the level of light in the room as well as that of the sky outside seemed to be increasing slowly. The light seemed to be coming from everywhere, not only from the waning sun. If fact, the sun itself did not give off a strong glare. The light gave the air a bright thickened quality that slightly obscured perception rather than sharpened it. It soon became extremely bright but the light was not in the least unpleasant. Along with the light came an alteration in mood. I began to feel very good, then better still, then elated. While this was happening, the passage of time seemed to become slower and slower. The brightness, mood elevation, and time slowing all progressed together. [*Here I questioned him and tried to get the correlations.*] It's difficult to estimate the time period over which these changes occurred since the sense of time was itself effected. However, there was a feeling of continuous change rather than a discrete jump or jumps to a new state. Eventually the sense of time passing stopped entirely. It's difficult to describe this feeling but perhaps it would be better to say that there was no time or no sense of time. Only the present moment existed. My elation proceeded to an ecstatic state, the intensity of which I have never even imagined could be possible. The colourless white light around me merged with the reddish light of the sunset to become one all enveloping intense light field. Perception of other things faded.
>
> At this point I merged with the light and everything including

* Allan Smith and I have now published a joint paper on his experience.

> myself became one unified whole. There was no separation between myself and rest of the universe. If fact, to say that there was a universe, a self, or any *thing* would be misleading. It would be an equally correct description to say that there was nothing, as to say that there was everything. To say that subject merged with object might be almost adequate as a description to the entrance to cosmic consciousness, but during cosmic consciousness, there is no subject and object. All words and discursive thinking had stopped and there was no sense of an observer to comment or categorize on what was 'happening.' In fact, there were no discrete events to happen, just a timeless unitary sense of being.

He goes on to say that cosmic consciousness is impossible to describe, partly because describing involves words and the state is one in which there are no words.

> My attempts at description here originated from reflecting on cosmic consciousness soon after it had passed, and while there was still some taste of the event remaining. Perhaps the most significant element of cosmic consciousness was the absolute 'knowingness' that it involves. This knowingness is a deep understanding that occurs without words.
>
> I was certain that the universe was one whole and that it was benign and loving at its ground. The benign nature and ground and being with which I was united was God. However there is little relation between my experience of God as ground of being and the anthropomorphic concept of God from the Bible. That God is separate from the world and has many human characteristics. 'He' demonstrates love, anger and vengeance, makes demands, gives reward, punishes, forgives, etc. God as experienced in cosmic consciousness as the very ground or beingness of the Universe and has no human characteristics in the usual sense of the word. The Universe could no more be separate from God than my body could be separate from its cells. Moreover the only emotion that I would associate with God is love, but it would be more accurate to say that God *is* love, than that God is loving. Again, characterizing God as love in the ground of being is only a metaphor but it's the best I can do to describe an indescribable experience. The knowingness of

> cosmic consciousness permanently convinced me about the true nature of the Universe. However, it did not answer many of the questions that quite rightly seem so important to us in our usual state of consciousness. From the perspective of cosmic consciousness questions like, 'What is the purpose of life?' or 'Is there an afterlife?' are not answered because they are not relevant. That is, during cosmic consciousness ontological questions are fully answered by one's state of being and verbal questions are not the point. Eventually, the cosmic consciousness faded. The time changes, light and mood elevation passed off. When I was able to think again, the sun had set and I estimate that the event must have lasted about twenty minutes.

I would say that this is beyond ordinary consciousness.

## *Methodological assumptions*

Now, let me state the assumptions I'm making in approaching this subject. I would also like to point out that they are assumptions from the perspective of our ordinary state of consciousness, but they are testable from various altered states of consciousness. So they don't necessarily have to remain assumptions even though for those of us who haven't experienced this, they remain so. The fact that these assumptions are testable is quite important to me. For all my interest in spiritual things, which is very deep, I really like science and think it's useful. But I think the approach to enlightenment is totally compatible with science. Let me give you a quote from an early 'psychologist' who was quite interested in the psychology of motivation: Gautama Buddha.

> Do not believe in anything simply because you have heard it. Do not believe in traditions because they have been handed down for many generations. Do not believe in anything because it is spoken and rumoured by many. Do not believe in anything because it is found written in your religious books. Do not believe in anything merely on the authority of your teachers and elders. But after observation and analysis, when you find that anything agrees with reason and is conducive to the good and benefit of one and all, then accept it and live up to it.

I can agree with that and I think this is a perfectly scientific attitude.

Now the fact that these assumptions are testable is very important because enlightenment, as I'm going to present it, is not about blind belief, it's not about how you can't use your mind and must believe something whether it's contradictory or not. There's a lot of blind belief around, of course, in the scientific enterprise as well as in other areas. But these assumptions are compatible with the basic scientific approach. They are not compatible with what sociologists have called 'scientism,' where the current physical findings of science are taken as the absolute answer and must be protected from heresy. I have no concern with being compatible with scientism.

So here are the assumptions:

The first one is that our everyday consciousness is a subset of all the possibilities. Everyday, 'normal' consciousness is what I have technically named *consensus consciousness,* because the way our individual minds work is strongly reflective of what our culture has taught us about what is real and what is important.

The second assumption is like the first, but it brings in a certain value judgment: everyday consciousness is shrunken or contracted or a distorted version of the total possibilities of human consciousness. And this is where I use a term used by Willis Harman, the term consensus *trance,* when I deliberately intend it in a pejorative kind of way. This shrunken version of our possible consciousness, this consensus trance, does indeed imply a certain dullness, ignorance, suffering, lack of will, and so forth.

Now what do I mean by this? Let me give you a parallel with some of the hypnosis experiments that we did routinely in the laboratory many years ago. We could take a person and hypnotize them, and tell them, 'You can't bend your arm, no matter how hard you try, you can't bend it.' For many people, they would then struggle and struggle and they could not bend their arm. If I tell you that you can't bend your arm now, you can just bend it. But in the constricted hypnotic state that we set up deliberately in the laboratory, a person did not have all their capacities available and they could indeed not bend their arm. There was a certain sense in which they accepted the suggested reality at face value instead of remembering a larger reality.

Now that problem of being unable to bend your arm could be solved by the almighty hypnotist giving a suggestion that you could do so, or by coming out of hypnosis — in which case the problem ceased to exist, rather than being 'solved.' A traditional analogy used in the spiritual traditions is that ordinary, consensus consciousness is really like being in a night-time dream. In a certain sense, compared with your waking state, in dreams you have reduced intelligence, you don't have all of your knowledge available, you have reduced volition and so forth. And so we often suffer in a dream trying to do something that in ordinary life we could handle quite easily. There would be nothing to it. Moreover, in a nighttime dream we are generally ignorant of our real condition, namely that we are asleep and dreaming. We think that we are in a world. As with hypnosis, by waking up to ordinary consciousness, the dream problems disappear without having to be 'solved.' The enlightenment traditions make a similar claim: that if we could genuinely wake up, from that perspective we would realize that now we are in a dream-like condition of consensus trance and, as Doctor S's experience illustrated, many things that seemed to be major problems would simply cease to be problems from that other state of being. So those are my assumptions.

## *Suffering and its causes*

Now, let's ask the question: Why do we suffer?

From the enlightenment perspective, quoting that old motivational psychologist Gautama Buddha, he set the answer down as four noble truths. His first noble truth was the reality of suffering. I've never heard anyone quarrel with that and say, 'No, no we never suffer.' So that's a universal truth. Then his second noble truth was an analysis of the causes of suffering, his third was the good news that suffering can be overcome, and his fourth was a set of practices for overcoming suffering.

Now, what did he mean by suffering and its causes? He gave three major causes of suffering. The first of these was *ignorance.* Ignorance in two senses. One, the ordinary sense. If you don't know how to fix a flat tyre and you get a flat tyre on your car, you're going to suffer while you wait for someone else to do it. Whereas if you knew how to repair it and you were in a hurry to get somewhere, you could avoid that suffering. That kind of ignorance is handled through education. We are actually quite good in the West at dealing with that kind of ignorance.

But the Buddha was focusing on a much more profound ignorance, and that's an ignorance of who we really are, or since he was fond of negatives, perhaps who we really are *not,* that we have a transpersonal nature, that there is something about us that is infinitely more vast than the usual ordinary self and we are ignorant of that. Because we are ignorant of that, we give our energy, our volition, our beliefs to things that are much too limited. The two common beliefs to which we give our energy are that our physical body and that our ordinary personality are all there is to us. I particularly like Gurdjieff's term, 'false personality,' to refer to our identification with our ordinary self, because this personality was caused by many things over which we had no control when personality was forming, rather than our having had real choice about it.

So we have a fundamental ignorance which makes us identify with our body and with our false personality. Well, once you do that, certain things fall in naturally. This body is quite vulnerable to injury, to suffering, to death. So clearly, one of my major jobs in life is to protect this body from suffering and death. My false personality is also susceptible to injury. Someone might look and me and frown and *I* would be hurt. I've got to do things to make people approve of me.

As a result of this identification with the body and personality, as a result of this ignorance of our true nature, we then (according to the Buddha) spend our lives between the twin poles of *grasping* and *aversion,* the two other main causes of suffering. On the one hand, anything that protects me in some sense or makes me happy, I want more of it, I need it, I've got hold onto it, I've got to grasp it. On the other hand, anything that threatens my personality or my body, I've got to push it away, I develop aversions to it, and so life is a constant oscillation between these two things: grasping and aversion, within a context of fundamental ignorance.

So from the Buddha's analysis, the dynamics of consensus consciousness are based on ignorance, grasping, and aversion, and they lead to a distorted perception of our own being, of other people, and of the world around us. Now I'm going to slide over the distorted part in a moment because when I talk about this from a more modern psychological perspective, I think that this could become clearer. The Buddhists took an idea which was also available in Hinduism, that we live in illusion. *Samsara* is the Buddhist term for it. This is usually translated as meaning that the world is not real, but that's not the main point. It's not that the world isn't real. It's that our perception of the world is so badly distorted that the *experiential* world we live in is very much an illusion, is very much not the real world.

As a result of living in illusion, we suffer. If we have an illusion about what somebody else wants from us, e.g., we give them the wrong thing, they resent it, and so things go on and on from there. Tibetan Buddhists also have a nice term for ordinary consciousness. They talk about ordinary consciousness as being a *fabricated* state, and fabrication can be looked at in two senses. One, fabrication simply in the sense of manufacturing. We do a lot of work to create our ordinary consciousness even though we are so used to it we don't notice it. But also fabrication in the sense of lying, in the sense of making things up.

## *The virtual reality of experience*

Now, let's look at this same question, 'Why do we suffer?' from a modern psychological perspective. Whatever you think consciousness ultimately is, it's clear that it's intimately involved with the brain and the nervous system. It's as if each of us was given this personal computer at birth and our eyes are glued to the screen so the programmes in that computer are going to have a major effect on what we can see. We know, for instance, that what we see is in a very literal sense very much a result of processing in the nervous system. The fact that we see the colours we see is a function of the way the eye is constructed. The fact that we hear sounds is a function of way the ear and brain are constructed. The fact that, for instance, we see separate people in this room is a function of the nervous system. If you could see the visual field simply as the light patterns that actually reach your eyes, things would be very blurry and colourful. But the brain artificially uses a process called *lateral inhibition* to sharpen visual impressions up. Engineers call it *edge detection.* It makes edges sharper in your perception than they actually are, which is very handy for separating one object from another, instead of having things blur together. So consciousness, as we ordinarily experience it, is very much controlled by the functioning of the brain, and you can't alter those aspects. But we know psychologically that what you perceive is also controlled, among other things, by your desires, your fears, your defence mechanisms, your cultural biases to see certain things readily and not notice other kinds of things. Those things are potentially changeable.

Years ago, in 1975, I came up with a *systems approach* (Tart 1975) to try to understand both ordinary consensus consciousness and various altered states of consciousness. I've now been expanding that to use a wonderful model that's come along to show what ordinary consciousness is like. This is the model of *computer generated virtual reality.* You put on a pair of goggles so the computer controls the images you see. There is a little sensor on your head that tells the computer when you look up or down or turn your head, and the picture is adjusted accordingly. Well, when a picture changes according to what you perceive as your head movements, the brain very quickly says, 'You are looking at reality.' There is a little sensor on your hand that asks, 'Where's the hand? Is it grasping, is it opening up, is it moving up, down, turning over?' You see a computer-generated computer hand that moves as you feel your hand move. The brain has a very simple rule, built into it at a very deep level. *If something moves with you and with your intention, it is you.* That's why you are so upset if someone runs into *your* car when you're driving it. There's a very real sense in which our body image goes between all four fenders when we're driving. I have taken this analogy into my systems approach, as we know how easy it is to get totally caught up in the reality of these computer-generated virtual realities, but it has made me realize that *we already know all about virtual reality. We live in one.*

I call this a *bio-psycho virtual reality,* a biological-psychological virtual reality. Information is coming into our senses, but our neural processes are constructing a reality, a 'realization' of the outcome of the construction process. In fact, the best example of that reality is when you dream at night. When you dream at night you are in a world. For those of us who are rich dreamers, that world has all the rich characteristics of ordinary reality. What we experience in a dream in a formal sense is the *world simulation process,* the bio-psycho virtual reality running the same as it does in our waking state, except that in our waking state, a world is not only being created as in dreaming. A play is not only being performed in an internal theatre, but there is massive sensory input from the outside with which the play, the simulated world, must conform.

Right at this moment, there is a sense in which each one of us lives *inside* this virtual reality, this simulation. But this simulation must take good account of sensory, physical input. If it doesn't, you die. If your virtual reality says there is no cliff there, everything is wonderful, you walk forward, you fall off and die, and don't get to reproduce, so there is definite evolutionary selection that this internal simulation must match the external reality quite well.

But, here's the funny thing: most of us do not spend most of our time and energy dealing simply with the physical world. Most of our time and energy is spent in a social reality, and things are much more arbitrary here and much less obvious.

Let me give you an example. Some years ago, I was giving a talk in the Midwest, and five minutes into my lecture, I happened to look into the audience and I saw a woman who looked just like my mother. Now, my mother, God bless her soul, was quite wonderful, but she did not share my interests and I never talked too much about them, as I know she probably wouldn't approve! Well, intellectually, I knew this couldn't possibly be my mother. She would never fly half way across the country to watch me give a lecture. But it looked an awful lot like her — and she was frowning. And she frowned throughout my lecture! This automatic world simulation part of my mind, this bio-psycho virtual reality, just went into overdrive. 'She's found out, she knows I've been bad.' It took a great deal of will power for me not to look in the woman's direction. Anywhere but there. No matter how much I knew intellectually that it couldn't be my mother, I kept thinking: 'Oh, God, she's found me out!' We live in a social reality where our simulation or reality, our internal representation, is often badly distorted.

This is why the Buddha talked about suffering arising from living in samsara, from living in (my terms) this simulation. We're too good at simulation. The simulation can be so real that — this is what we know from a modern psychological perspective — that we get lots of satisfaction from it. So, when external reality is not making us happy, it's easy to gild the lily, as it were, to create an internal simulation which we immediately mistake for reality that makes it better, that makes it more satisfying.

If this were an Alcoholics Anonymous or Narcotics Anonymous meeting, I would introduce myself by saying, 'Hi. My name is Charley. My drug of choice is *thoughts*. I get drunk on thoughts, I *love* them! They drive my system.' This 'thoughtaholism' a common disease in the academic world, I'm afraid, and very difficult to get rid of. I've tried to remain sober, but it is not easy!

We have the ability to create imaginary representations that seem as real as most perceptions, that produce all sorts of internal satisfactions, and that tune us out from the reality of what is actually going on outside us and also in a very real sense tune us out from a transpersonal reality, the greater reality of who we really are. This is why consciousness is a fabrication in the Tibetan sense, why we live in this bio-psycho-virtual reality, a created reality which is very good and useful in some ways — and very badly distorted in other ways. Unfortunately, many of the ways in which it is badly distorted are 'normal' by contemporary social standards, and everybody else is crazy in the same way, so we reinforce each other.

I won't go into more detail on this. I'd love to but this is fleshed out in my, *Waking Up* (Tart 1986) or *Living the Mindful Life* (Tart 1994) books. And, as I said earlier, we are probably getting a little depressed by now, although I've tried to keep it light, so let's talk about enlightenment, which is my main focus here. We've looked at endarkenment and gotten our baseline.

## *Cosmic consciousness*

I can't really define enlightenment. I'm going to illustrate it and I'm going to make one distinction, or rather set out a continuum with respect to enlightenment.

One the one hand, the term 'enlightenment' is referring to special altered states of consciousness, which are nevertheless transitory; they may have some after-effects, but there's an intense experience which largely fades. On the other hand, there's the use of 'enlightenment' in the sense of a permanent change in the nature of your *being*. To illustrate the altered states with some after-effects, I now want to read you the classic description of cosmic consciousness by the man who coined the term. And you'll see some fascinating parallels with Doctor S.'s experience a century later. The man who coined the term was a nineteenth century physician, Richard Maurice Bucke. This experience came on him quite unexpectedly. He wanted to be objective about it. He was caught up in the scientific fashions of the time so he thought the best way to be objective was to describe it in the third person, as if it had happened to someone else. I wish objectivity were so easily guaranteed just by using third person language. Let me read you his wonderful description.

Bucke says it occurred in the early spring, at the beginning of his 36th year. He was in England at the time. He and two friends had spent the evening reading Wordsworth, Shelley, Keats, Browning and especially Whitman. It's the way we all spend our evenings, of course, not watching the TV but doing that sort of thing. They parted at midnight and he had a long drive in a hansom cab. His mind deeply under the influence of the ideas, images, and emotions called up by the reading and talk of the evening, was calm and peaceful. He was in a state of quiet, almost passive enjoyment.

All at once, without any warning of any kind, he found himself wrapped around, as it were, by a flame-coloured cloud. For an instant he thought of fire, some sudden conflagration in the great city. The next he knew the light was within himself. Directly afterwards came upon him a sense of exaltation, of immense joyousness, accompanied, or immediately followed by an intellectual illumination quite impossible to describe. Into his brain (he believed in the brain, of course, as so many people do now) streamed one momentary lightning flash of the Brahmic splendour which ever since lightened his life. Upon his heart fell one drop of Brahmic bliss leaving thenceforward and always an aftertaste of heaven. Among other things, he saw and knew that the cosmos is not dead matter but a living presence, that the soul of man is immortal, that the universe is so built and ordered that without any peradventure, all things work together for the good of each and all. That the foundation principle of the world is what we call love and that the happiness of everyone is, in the long run, absolutely certain. He claims that he learned more within the few seconds in which the illumination lasted than in previous months or even years of study and that he learned much that no study could have ever taught. The illumination continued not more than a few moments, but its effects proved ineffaceable, it was impossible for him to ever forget what he at that time saw and knew. Neither did he, nor could he ever doubt the truth of what was then presented to his mind.

I must say, incidentally, that a colleague of mine who heard me give a preliminary version of this talk asked, 'Why do give such wonderful accounts that seem so far from us? Why don't you just talk about what us ordinary folks can do?' I've decided to try to be inspirational, though, even if it seems unusual, and this kind of experience is not necessarily beyond what we can do — and points in a direction.

Now, let me try to illustrate the other end of this spectrum of enlightenment experiences where the emphasis is not so much on an altered state of consciousness, a flash that then fades, but on a permanent change of being.

## *John Wren-Lewis*

To illustrate this, again from a source totally devoid of any traditional spiritual background, I want to tell you the experiences of a retired mathematical physicist, a Briton by the name of John Wren-Lewis. His wife, Anne Faraday, wrote some wonderful and highly popular books on dreams some years ago. John was not at all interested in mystical-shmistical weirdo kinds of stuff. My wife Judy and I had the pleasure of having dinner with him and Anne because of our mutual interest in dreams some years before his enlightenment experience. At that time, we noted that John was a wonderful fellow, and very polite to his wife's weird friends, but clearly had no interest whatsoever in this kind of material.

John and Anne were in Thailand, researching material on the Senoi, the tribe that was written up by Kilton Stewart in my *Altered States of Consciousness* (Tart 1969) because they allegedly had this wonderful system of working with dreams in the morning, inducing lucid dreams during the night, and the like. It's a very interesting account — I imagine some of you have read it. It's now clear that this account is largely fictional, not straightforward anthropological reporting (Domhoff 1985, Domhoff 1991). There were never a people who really did all those things. Nevertheless, it's 'true,' because if you believe and try those things, it works. Anyway, they had come out of spending a year in the jungle doing this and were catching a bus. A nice young man helped them with their luggage, got on the bus with them, and offered them some candy, some Cadbury's chocolates, I believe. Anne didn't eat hers. It smelled a little musty but John wanted to be polite and ate his.

The bus went on. John was tired and fell asleep and then he began turning blue and Anne realized that this was not normal! There's a long, complex story of how she barely managed to get him to a hospital in time and, with lots of drugs they managed to keep him from dying. He probably was clinically dead but as you know, in situations like that the effort is on resuscitation, not on seeing if someone has just crossed the line or not. Besides, we know that in near-death experiences the very fact that they're *near* means that your not really, really, really, *really* dead. Anyway, John was apparently given a massive dose of morphine mixed with cocaine in the chocolate, which is commonly used by robbers in Thailand, apparently to knock tourists out so their luggage can be stolen, but they sometimes get the dose wrong and victims die.

John's experiences are going to be very inspiring, but I don't recommend the method. That *near* part is very tricky. Most people who come this near do not tell you about interesting experiences: they get buried.

My wife and I had the pleasure of spending a fortnight with John and Anne in Australia a couple of years ago, so I was able to talk to him at length about what had happened with him. He first discovered that something was different approximately half an hour after he had finally regained consciousness in the hospital. For the first half hour he was too distracted to notice that anything was different. They were running tests on him and asking him about his condition and all that. Finally they decided he was all right and left him alone, but he didn't fall asleep. He began to notice this quite beautiful hospital room he was in, but he realized logically, '*Beautiful* hospital room? Not likely!' Here's his initial description of his discovery of the state of consciousness/being he was in, which has become his permanent state.

> In visual terms everything was highlighted. Though in this case the effect was more than visual, somehow seeming to include the other senses, as with the smell of the toilet, the buzzing of the insects and the touch of the bed sheets. And it was more than merely sensuous. It was like the sheer "isness" of each thing standing out as a kind of greeting.

I'm reading from an early draft of his book called *The 9:15 to Nirvana,* named after the bus schedule that began all this.

'The radiant blackness of being ...'

OK, most people talk about the *light* after a near death experience. John feels something more profound, behind the light, was part of his experience. You'll get the flavour from it as I talk about it and use the phrase, 'darkness.'

> The radiant blackness of being at the back of my head recognizing and saluting itself, rather its no-self, in each other thing, both the objects and events of the outer universe and the thoughts, feelings, sensations and imaginings of John Wren-Lewis' personal inner universe. And 'at the back of my head' is no idle figure of speech. The experience was so palpable that I actually put my hand up to my head to check that my skull was still intact. I suddenly felt for all the world as if the doctors had removed the back of that bony shell, and somehow exposed my brain to infinite darkness of space. The openness at the back of my head felt like an enormous liberation, as if I'd had some kind brain cataract removed, making true perception possible

> for the first time in my life. I knew what William Blake must have really meant by that famous statement about everything being perceived in its true infinite nature when the doors of perception are cleansed.

He thought, 'This must be some kind of drug after-effect, although there should have been time for all the drugs to be flushed out of my system by now. Surely it will go away.'

It's never gone away, except for a few moments in the last ten years when he's gotten very distracted. But his everyday state has now changed, and it's changed his understanding of things. For instance, the question of death.

> Fear and horror of death had gone because I was no longer experiencing my aliveness as particularly mine, a property or possession of the individual psycho-physiological organism called, 'John Wren-Lewis.' This perspective was giving a kind of deep, tranquil satisfaction to the mere fact of existence in every moment, which altogether transcended the shallow and transient pleasures of John's personal progression along the time line. The eternity experience in each moment. [That's the flavour of John's consciousness now.] The eternity experience in each present moment makes the whole issue of possible immortality unimportant, whereas the desire for immortality shows a preoccupation which separate selfhood along the line of time that might very well block the joy and tranquillity of eternity experience.

He feels a constant oneness with all life, with all being. I won't take the time to illustrate that. He also realized that, 'What a change in him, and wasn't this supposed to be the exclusive property of really important religious figures? How in the world had it happened to an ordinary person like him?' *And yet his own direct experience is that there is nothing special about it.* He says,

> Yet, my experience equally didn't carry the slightest hint of my being anything like a very special person or even a fairly special person. On the contrary, my sense of my self as a focusing down of the one infinite consciousness was simultaneously a sense of everyone else, indeed, of everything else as also that.

> Even the fact that other people around me seemed unaware of their 'thatness' didn't seem to make me special in any way, other than perhaps especially lucky.

Another classic characteristic associated with enlightenment is an inherently compassionate approach to life — not a feeling that he *should* be kind, generous and compassionate, but an inherently compassionate approach to life. He began to understand this in a more verbalizable way a couple weeks later when his wife became very ill and there were great complications in trying to get Anne to a hospital in Malaysia. He didn't notice his changed state for a while. He was simply too busy trying to deal with the exigencies of getting his wife into a hospital. And then he notes that,

> Eternity blind consciousness takes for granted that satisfaction comes to individuals only through getting their personal needs and preferences met, from which it seems to follow that the impulse to help others must depend upon their being some kind of feeling identification with them. The very words, 'compassion' and 'sympathy' imply this if taken back to their original common root. From my perspective inside nirvana consciousness, however, the whole situation looks completely different. Eternity satisfaction automatically flows over into caring energy along the line of time, as the direct expression of eternity's love for time's productions. It is no great effort of renunciation for a mystic actually living in nirvana consciousness to put aside individual comforts and preferences to help someone else because personal comforts and preferences are only very secondary sources of satisfaction. Helping others in distress is direct participation in the ultimate satisfaction: eternity's love for the productions of time.

Now John makes it very clear he does not want to be regarded as some kind of saint and that he certainly isn't. He thought these were stereotypes, that certainly don't apply to him. He still enjoys wine and meat, for instance. He doesn't think he is some marvellous person saving the world. He's just automatically compassionate. In the earliest enlightenment traditions I find an almost universal message that in the highest levels of enlightenment, even though they may include other components, compassion is automatic. In fact, if you have a kind of enlightenment that doesn't include compassion, continue working. You're not there yet. You're seriously distorted in some way.

Another stereotype that had to fall by the wayside is one we tend to attribute to all enlightenment and mystical states: that it changes you into a certain kind of person. The 'technical term' that some Americans have humorously and sarcastically coined for this is that you become a 'bliss ninny.' You sit there in some ecstatic state, thinking Ooooooom ... Which is probably nice for you but not of much value for the world. On the contrary, John found that, if anything, his effectiveness and intelligence has been increased.

I'll give you another example of the change in John's state of being from his manuscript.

The day after they got out of the hospital, John needed to get some rest before they caught the 9:15 again the next day. They realized the changes were going to have interesting psychological significance, and they wanted to find a quiet hotel. They made some inquiries and were recommended one but unfortunately, as so many Thai hotels, this was basically a house of prostitution and partying. It wasn't terribly restful, but it led to an interesting experience.

The next morning John came down early, before Anne and his daughter were awake, to try to arrange some breakfast before they went to the bus station. John reports that:

> What greeted me between the foot of the stairs and the entrance to dining room was a huge pool of vomit, presumably evidence of the excess at the previous night's revelry. [This is good teaching technique to read this now, because this is what's going to fix my talk in my mind forever as you think about that huge pool of vomit!] And I was truly astonished to experience its greeting with as much welcome as that of an edelweiss. Astonished, for I have been extremely squeamish ever since I can remember as a result of cosseting in infancy by a neurotically hygiene-conscious mother.
>
> Now, as the Dark confronted me in the pool of vomit, I experienced that ability to enjoy, literally enjoy, contradictory feelings, which I had already recognized as characteristic of mystical consciousness. On the one hand, I saw and smelt particles of semi-digested food mixed with bile fluid and they were quite fascinating sensations, each giving me greetings as if they were wonderful artworks at whose creation I'd been

> personally present. And simultaneously, I experienced my disgust reactions, even to the point of my gorge beginning to rise, as itself a creative act of John's body-mind under the direction of his mother's neurotic fears, which was also a marvel. Moreover, deep underneath it, an integral part of the appreciation was that peace past understanding of complete being. And as I negotiated my way around the pool of divine vomit, I also noted that the new awareness didn't make me in the least careless about getting mess on my shoes. On the contrary, the Dark's perspectivizing of my conditioned anxieties allowed much greater efficiency of coping with the purely practical problem of avoiding contamination than would have been possible with gritted teeth. As I've found again and again in the years since then, the practical business of getting good results along the line of time is in no way hindered by mystic awareness that everything is perfect in the dimension of eternity. Freedom from domination by anxious thoughts for the morrow actually makes for far greater efficiency in doing.

So again I stress that while there are altered states that may temporarily transform one into a bliss ninny, all enlightenment doesn't seem to involve that. If you look at history, some of the greatest mystics were extremely effective people in the practical world.

## *Characteristics of enlightenment*

So let me summarize some of these qualities of enlightenment that I have tried to illustrate here in expanding our perspective. There's a change in one's relation to death. One is no longer afraid of it or perhaps even concerned about it. There is a very deep feeling of openness, of relationship to the whole of life or to everything in the universe. There's a feeling of ultimately knowing all that's worth while knowing, and at the same time feeling like you are no one special at all. This is simply the way everything is. There is an automatic compassion towards every other being, and also a feeling of greater effectiveness and intelligence in approaching life.

Now, it's probably an understatement to say that this kind of transitory state or more permanent change in being is of interest to science and psychology. This is *vitally* interesting. It's personally desirable of course. I would love to experience the universe as John experiences it or as Bucke experienced it. And I also think that moving in this direction is essential if the planet is going to survive. Remember, the primary characteristic of ordinary consensus trance is *separateness,* so when it comes down to a choice between me and you, since we're separate, I'll choose *me.* People may *tell* us that we are all one, but that's a lot of words and when the instincts of this body have to be saved, this personality has to be pleasured, those philosophies go easily by the board. But if we can find ways of helping people to experience more directly something like cosmic consciousness or enlightenment, then a real change can happen.

Of course, I said earlier that I'm talking about dramatic examples here, but there are many more quiet and subtle things that happen as people move in this direction that are important. I'll say just a little about how we, as real human beings, can do something to become a little more enlightened.

## *Moving in the direction of enlightenment*

One thing that I find increasingly necessary to stress to us Westerners is to give up the quick fix idea and realize that the spiritual path starts with basic morality. Someone once remarked to me that, from a Buddhist perspective, it is hard to quiet your mind in meditation if you've been out looting and killing all day long. It's a little more profound than that, but the conviction from these high enlightenment perspectives is that we really are all one, so it simply becomes stupid to hurt anybody else — you're simply hurting yourself, and if that's the way you feel about yourself, how could you possibly open up to any aspects of yourself? So a basic morality is a foundation for this, and that means that we can't skip important developmental tasks in learning how to deal with each other.

Many people are attracted to the idea of enlightenment because they don't get along in the world. Rather than discover what the problem is and cure it, it's easier to say that the world is corrupt and to follow a spiritual path so as to bypass all of that. You can't do that! As Jack Engler, a psychologist and American Buddhist teacher once said so clearly, 'You've got to be *somebody* before you can be *nobody.'* So you start with this moral foundation and then you develop concentration and insight skills.

When you look at our ordinary mind, it's terribly fragmented, it's jumping all over the place — we can't focus on anything for very long. It makes it very hard to understand anything more deeply, especially as we live in this bio-psycho virtual reality that's already strongly removed from actual reality. That ordinary mind jumping about is creating a pseudo reality, a virtual reality all the time that fools us. So, the Buddhist path, for instance, emphasises *concentrative* meditation, where you learn to put the mind on one thing and keep it there. Not by gritting your teeth and trying to kill any thought that comes in, but by learning to keep coming back to one thing.

This gradually strengthens your ability to pay attention. As that ability strengthens, you then apply it to a scientific-like investigation of your own inner nature. 'What am I *really,* that I can see through *direct experience,* not what do I think I ought to be? What am I *actually* experiencing at this moment, before I cover it up in layers of thoughts and feelings?' So you turn from simple concentration to insight into your actual self, and eventually reach deeper and deeper levels of insight.

One of the key things these insights involve, for instance, is a phenomenon they often called *emptiness,* which is a very misleading (albeit common) and nihilistic translation of the Buddhist term, implying 'nothing,' which isn't the case at all. A better word is *impermanence.* We realize the constant changeableness and in fact we learn to identify with the changeable, both in the outside world and in ourselves. So there is a great emphasis in Buddhism on impermanence, on transience, because our ordinary mind has this tendency to over-concretize things, to treat things as if they were eternal. Someone frowned at me and I'm going to be unhappy forever. No, it's just a momentary event!

When you begin to see the impermanence of the ordinary self, you stop giving it so much energy, you stop identifying with it so strongly, and then comes the possibility of gaining glimpses of the deeper self. Perhaps these full cosmic consciousness experiences begin to happen. Also, you will eventually develop the insights that were talked about here: the inherently compassionate nature of reality.

Now Buddhism is very sophisticated here on a tricky point. There is a quality of these enlightenment experiences in which you see that everything is perfect. A child's being run down by a lorry? That's perfect. It's all part of the perfection of everything. The war in Bosnia? It's all perfect. That is a component of the enlightenment experience, to realize there is a perspective from which it's all perfect, but yet, as people get deeper insights, this inherent compassion comes in. You must never use the feeling that it's all perfect as a reason not to *act* in a compassionate way. That's a very bad distortion. So you always strive to be helpful, to be loving, to be compassionate whenever possible, even if, from another perspective, things are perfect.

If you find that a little bit confusing, that's all right. It's not supposed to be understandable on our ordinary level of consciousness, but it's potentially experienceable. Again, I said there were certain assumptions we made in approaching this but these are potentially testable, experienceable as to whether they are true.

What can psychology do to help us become enlightened? How can modern scientific psychology and science in general be of some help? I said earlier that psychology has expert knowledge on endarkenment, without any concept of enlightenment. We know the specifics of how we misidentify, of how we mess things up, how we distort our simulation of the world. I'll give you instances of some of the psychological mechanisms we know that contribute to endarkenment

To do this I looked at the index of an introductory psychology textbook. I have a very long list here, but I'll read you a dozen or so just to give you a feeling that we know a great deal about the flavours of endarkenment. Abuse, acceptance, anger, anxiety, attitude, attribution errors, aversion, beliefs, biases, bystander effects, competition, compliance, compulsion, concepts ... I'm only up to 'C.'

We know a great deal about endarkenment. It's my hope that, as psychology and science in general expand their perspectives, we begin to understand more about these blocks that keep us from realising our transpersonal selves, or not-selves, that keep us from expanding into this larger and very vital perspective. I particularly hope that some day we will have a sophisticated enough understanding of how this is done to be able to give people *specific* help on how to grow, on how to find a spiritual path. At present if you go for advice to someone who is very good at spiritual things, what they'll tell you to do is probably what they did. And yet, I think we know from modern psychology that what is a wonderful path of spiritual growth for one person may be a total waste of time for a second person, and might be an invitation to psychosis for a third. If we knew enough about the individual ways in which enlightenment is prevented to be able to prescribe specifically, as it were, that your type of person, for instance, should never do Sufi dancing because there's a thirty percent psychosis rate, but the satisfaction of Zen sitting is much higher, that would be a wonderful contribution we could make.

Well, I'm going to end at this point. I'm going to end, in a sense, rather suddenly. I haven't really told you what enlightenment is. I've just pointed. I hopefully stretched your mind in a certain direction and now it's up to us. Thank you.

## References

Domhoff, G.W. 1985. *The mystique of dreams: a search for Utopia through Senoi dream theory.* University of California Press, Berkeley, California.

Domhoff, G.W. 1991. Senoi, Kilton Stewart and the mystique of dreams: further thoughts on an allegory about an allegory. *Lucidity.* 10.327–33.

Harre, R. and R. Lamb 1983. *The encyclopedic dictionary of psychology.* Oxford: Blackwell.

Tart, C. 1969. *Altered states of consciousness: a book of readings.* New York: John Wiley & Sons.

—. 1975. *States of consciousness.* New York: Dutton.

—. 1986. *Waking up: overcoming the obstacles to human potential.* Boston: New Science Library.

—. 1994. *Living the mindful life,* Boston: Shambhala.

# Non-Ordinary States of Consciousness: Healing and Heuristic Potential

STANISLAV GROF

*Stanislav Grof M.D. is a psychiatrist with forty years of experience in research of non-ordinary states of consciousness, and is Professor of Psychology at the California Institute of Integral Studies in San Francisco. He is one of the founders and chief theorists of transpersonal psychology and the founding president of the International Transpersonal Association. Among his publications are over one hundred papers in professional journals and the books* Realms of the Human Unconscious; LSD Psychotherapy; The Adventure of Self-Discovery; Beyond the Brain; The Books of the Dead; The Holotropic Mind; *and* The Cosmic Game.

The objective of this article is to summarize my experiences and observations concerning the nature of the human psyche and its healing potential that I have collected during more than thirty-five years of research of non-ordinary states of consciousness (NOSC). These states are characterized by dramatic perceptual changes, intense and often unusual emotions, profound alterations in the thought processes and behaviour, and by a variety of psychosomatic manifestations. Consciousness can be profoundly altered in a wide variety of situations and in different ways; however, not all NOSC have heuristic significance and therapeutic potential. This presentation focuses upon a large and important subgroup of such states that are of great theoretical and practical significance. I have coined for them the name holotropic (literally 'oriented toward wholeness' from the Greek *holos* = whole and *trepein* = moving toward or in the direction of something) (Grof 1992).

## *Holotropic states of consciousness*

In holotropic states, consciousness is changed qualitatively in a very fundamental way, but is not grossly impaired. This distinguishes these changes from trivial deliria accompanying traumas, intoxications by various poisonous substances, infections, or degenerative and circulatory processes in the brain. People suffering from delirious conditions are typically disoriented (not knowing who and where they are and what date it is), show a disturbance of intellectual functions, and subsequent amnesia. All such functions are intact in the holotropic states of consciousness. In addition, the content of holotropic experiences is often spiritual or mystical. It involves sequences of psychological death and rebirth and a broad spectrum of transpersonal phenomena, including feelings of oneness with other people, nature, and the universe, past life experiences, and visions of archetypal beings and mythological landscapes as described by C.G. Jung (1960).

### HOLOTROPIC STATES OF CONSCIOUSNESS AND HUMAN HISTORY

Ancient and aboriginal cultures have spent much time and energy developing powerful mind-altering techniques that can induce holotropic states. They combine in different ways chanting, breathing, drumming, rhythmic dancing, fasting, social and sensory isolation, extreme physical pain, and other elements. These cultures used them in shamanic procedures, healing ceremonies, and rites of passage — powerful rituals enacted at the time of important biological and social transitions, such as circumcision, puberty, marriage, or birth of a child. Many cultures have used psychedelic plants for these purposes. The most famous examples of these are different varieties of hemp, the Mexican cactus peyote and Psilocybin mushrooms, the African shrub eboga, and the Amazonian jungle liana *Banisteriopsis caapi,* the source of *yagé* or *ayahuasca.*

Additional important triggers of holotropic experiences are various forms of systematic spiritual practice involving meditation, concentration, breathing, and movement exercises, that are used in different systems of yoga, Vipassana or Zen Buddhism, Tibetan Vajrayana, Taoism, Christian mysticism, Sufism, or Kabbala. Other techniques were used in the ancient mysteries of death and rebirth, such as the Egyptian temple initiations of Isis and Osiris and the Greek Bacchanalia, rites of Attis and Adonis, and the Eleusinian mysteries. The specifics of the procedures involved in these secret rites have remained for the most part unknown, although it is likely that psychedelic preparations played an important part (Wasson, Hofmann, and Ruck 1978).

Among the modern means of inducing holotropic states of consciousness are psychedelic substances (isolated from plants or synthesised in the laboratory) and powerful experiential forms of psychotherapy such as hypnosis, neo-Reichian approaches, primal therapy, and rebirthing. My wife Christina and I have developed Holotropic Breathwork, a method that can facilitate profound holotropic states by very simple means — conscious breathing, evocative music, and focused bodywork. There also exist very effective laboratory techniques for altering consciousness. One of these is sensory isolation, which involves significant reduction of meaningful sensory stimuli. In its extreme form the individual is deprived of sensory input by submersion in a dark and soundproof tank filled with water of body temperature. Another well-known laboratory method of changing consciousness is biofeedback, where the individual is guided by electronic feedback signals into non-ordinary states of consciousness characterized by preponderance of certain specific frequencies of brainwaves. We could also mention here the techniques of sleep and dream deprivation and lucid dreaming.

It is important to emphasise that episodes of NOSC of varying duration can also occur spontaneously, without any specific identifiable cause, and often against the will of the people involved. Since modern psychiatry does not differentiate between mystical or spiritual states and mental diseases, people experiencing these states are often labelled psychotic, hospitalized, and receive routine suppressive psycho-pharmacological treatment. Christina and I refer to these states as spiritual emergencies or psychospiritual crises. We believe that properly supported and treated, they can result in emotional and psychosomatic healing, positive personality transformation, and consciousness evolution (Grof and Grof 1989, 1990).

Although I have been deeply interested in all the categories of NOSC mentioned above, I have done most of my work in the area of psychedelic therapy, Holotropic Breathwork, and spiritual emergency. This paper is based predominantly on my observations from these three areas in which I have most personal experience. However, the general conclusions I will be drawing apply to all the situations involving holotropic states.

## HOLOTROPIC STATES IN THE HISTORY OF PSYCHIATRY

It is worth mentioning that the history of depth psychology and psychotherapy is deeply connected with the study of NOSC — Franz Mesmer's experiments with 'animal magnetism,' hypnotic sessions with hysterical patients conducted in Paris by Jean Martin Charcot, and the research in hypnosis carried out in Nancy by Hippolyte Bernheim and Ambroise Auguste Liébault. Sigmund Freud's early work was inspired by his work with a client (Miss Anna who experienced spontaneous episodes of non-ordinary states of consciousness). Freud also initially used hypnosis to access his patients' unconscious before he radically changed his strategies. In retrospect, the shifting of emphasis from direct experience to free association, from actual trauma to Oedipal fantasies, and from conscious reliving and emotional abreaction of unconscious material to transference dynamics was unfortunate, and both limited and misdirected Western psychotherapy for the next fifty years (Ross 1989). While verbal therapy can be very useful in providing interpersonal learning and rectifying interaction and communication in human relationships (e.g. couple and family therapy), it is ineffective in dealing with emotional and bioenergetic blockages and macrotraumas, such as the trauma of birth.

As a consequence of this development, psychotherapy in the first half of the last century was practically synonymous with talking — face to face interviews, free associations on the couch, and the behaviourist deconditioning. At the same time NOSC, initially seen as an effective therapeutic tool, became associated with pathology rather than healing. This situation started to change in the 1950's with the advent of psychedelic therapy and new developments in psychology. A group of American psychologists headed by Abraham Maslow, dissatisfied with behaviourism and Freudian psychoanalysis, launched a revolutionary movement — humanistic psychology. Within a very short time, this movement became very popular and provided the context for a broad spectrum of new therapies.

While traditional psychotherapies used primarily verbal means and intellectual analysis, these new, so-called experiential therapies emphasised direct experience and expression of emotions and used various forms of bodywork as an integral part of the process. Probably the most famous representative of these new approaches is Fritz Perls' *Gestalt* therapy (Perls 1976). However, most experiential therapies still rely to a great degree on verbal communication and require that the client stay in the ordinary state of consciousness. The most radical innovations in the therapeutic field were approaches which are so powerful that they profoundly change the state of consciousness, such as psychedelic therapy, Holotropic Breathwork, primal therapy, rebirthing, and others.

The therapeutic use of NOSC is the most recent development in Western psychotherapy. Paradoxically, it is also the oldest form of healing and can be traced back to the dawn of human history. Therapies using holotropic states actually represent a rediscovery and modern reinterpretation of the elements and principles that have been documented by historians and anthropologists studying the sacred mysteries of death and rebirth, rites of passage, and ancient and aboriginal forms of spiritual healing, particularly various shamanic procedures.

Shamanism is the most ancient religion and healing art of humanity, the roots of which reach far back into the Paleolithic era. Among the beautiful images of primeval animals painted and carved on the walls of the great caves in Southern France and northern Spain, such as Lascaux, Font de Gaume, Les Trois Frères, Niaux, Altamira, and others, are figures that undoubtedly represent ancient shamans. In some of the caves, the discoverers also found footprints in circular arrangements suggesting that their inhabitants conducted dances, similar to those still performed by some aboriginal cultures for the induction of NOSC. Shamanism is not only ancient, it is also universal; it can be found in North and South America, in Europe, Africa, Asia, Australia and Polynesia.

The fact that so many different cultures throughout human history have found shamanic techniques useful and relevant suggests that they address the 'primal mind' — a basic and primordial aspect of the human psyche that transcends race, culture, and time. All the cultures with the exception of the Western industrial civilization have held NOSC in great esteem and spent much time and effort to develop various ways of inducing them. They used them to connect with their deities, other dimensions of reality, and with the forces of nature, for healing, for cultivation of extrasensory perception, and for artistic inspiration. For pre-industrial cultures, healing always involves non-ordinary states of consciousness — either for the client, for the healer, or both of them at the same time. In many instances, a large group or even an entire tribe enters a non-ordinary state of consciousness together, as it is, for example, among the !Kung Bushmen in the African Kalahari Desert.

Western psychiatry and psychology does not see NOSC (with the exception of dreams that are not recurrent or frightening) as potential sources of healing or of valuable information about the human psyche, but basically as pathological phenomena. Traditional psychiatry tends to use indiscriminately pathological labels and suppressive medication whenever these states occur spontaneously. Michael Harner (1980), an anthropologist of good academic standing who underwent a shamanic initiation during his field work in the Amazonian jungle and practises shamanism, suggests that Western psychiatry is seriously biased in at least two significant ways. It is *ethnocentric,* which means that it considers its own view of the human psyche and of reality to be the only correct one and superior to all others. It is also *cognicentric* (a more accurate word might be 'pragmacentric'), meaning that it takes into consideration only experiences and observations in the ordinary state of consciousness. Psychiatry's lack of interest in holotropic states and disregard for them has resulted in a culturally insensitive approach and a tendency to pathologize all activities that cannot be understood in its own narrow context. This includes the ritual and spiritual life of ancient and pre-industrial cultures and the entire spiritual history of humanity.

## *Implications of consciousness research for psychiatry*

If we study systematically the experiences and observations associated with NOSC or, more specifically, holotropic states, this leads inevitably to a radical revision of our basic ideas about consciousness and the human psyche and to an entirely new psychiatry, psychology, and psychotherapy. The changes we would have to make in our thinking fall into several large categories:

### THE NATURE OF EMOTIONAL AND PSYCHOSOMATIC DISORDERS

In what is traditionally called psychogenic psychopathology, psychiatry uses an explanatory model limited to biology and biographical traumas in infancy, childhood, and later life. The new understanding has to include additional realms of the psyche as potential sources of emotional problems. These are transbiographical and transpersonal in nature.

### Therapeutic mechanisms and the process of healing

Traditional psychotherapy knows only therapeutic mechanisms operating on the level of biographical material — remembering of forgotten events, lifting of repression, reconstruction of the past from dreams, reliving of traumatic memories, analysis of transference, etc. The work with NOSC reveals many important additional mechanisms of healing and personality transformation operating in realms that lie beyond normally accessible biography.

### Strategy of psychotherapy and self-exploration

The goal in traditional psychotherapies is to reach an intellectual understanding as to how the psyche functions and why symptoms develop and then derive from this understanding a strategy how to 'fix' the patients. A serious problem with this strategy is the amazing lack of agreement among psychologists and psychiatrists about these fundamental issues, resulting in an astonishing number of competing schools of psychotherapy. The work with holotropic states shows us a surprising alternative and a way out of this confusion, which I will discuss later.

### The role of spirituality in human life

Western materialistic science has no place for any form of spirituality and considers it incompatible with the scientific world-view. Modern consciousness research shows that spirituality is a natural and legitimate dimension of the human psyche and of the universal scheme of things. In this context, it is important to distinguish spirituality from religion .

### The nature of reality

The necessary revisions which I have discussed up to this point were related to the theory and practice of psychiatry, psychology, and psychotherapy. However, the work with NOSC brings challenges of a much more fundamental nature. Many of the experiences and observations that occur during this work are so extraordinary that they can not be understood in the context of the Newtonian-Cartesian materialistic paradigm and undermine the most basic metaphysical assumptions of the entire edifice of Western science.

## The dimensions of the human psyche and consciousness

The phenomena observed in modern consciousness research cannot be explained by a model limited to postnatal biography and to the Freudian individual unconscious. The dimensions of the human psyche are infinitely larger than academic psychology would like us to believe. In an effort to account for the experiences and observations from NOSC, I have myself suggested a cartography or model of the psyche that contains, in addition to the usual biographical level, two transbiographical realms: the perinatal domain, related to the trauma of biological birth; and the transpersonal domain, which accounts for such phenomena as experiential identification with other people or with animals, visions of archetypal and mythological beings and realms, ancestral, racial, and karmic experiences, and identification with the Universal Mind or the Void. These are experiences that have been described throughout ages in the religious, mystical, and occult literature. Here I concentrate on the transpersonal domain. For a detailed account of my work on the perinatal see Grof 1985.

## *The transpersonal domain of the psyche*

The second major domain that has to be added to mainstream psychiatry's cartography of the human psyche when we work with NOSC is now known under the name *transpersonal,* meaning literally 'beyond the personal' or 'transcending the personal.' The experiences that originate on this level involve transcendence of the usual boundaries of the individual this or her body and ego) and of the limitations of three-dimensional space and linear time that restrict our perception of the world in the ordinary state of consciousness. The transpersonal experiences are best defined by describing first the everyday experience of ourselves and the world — how we have to experience ourselves and the environment to pass for 'normal' according to the standards of our culture and of Newtonian-Cartesian psychiatry.

In the ordinary or 'normal' state of consciousness, we experience ourselves as Newtonian objects existing within the boundaries of our skin. The American writer and philosopher Alan Watts referred to this experience of oneself as identifying with the 'skin-encapsulated ego' Our perception of the environment is restricted by the physiological limitations of our sensory organs and by physical characteristics of the environment. We cannot see objects we are separated from by a solid wall, ships that are beyond the horizon, or the other side of the moon. If we are in Prague, we cannot hear what our friends are talking about in San Francisco. We cannot feel the softness of the lambskin unless the surface of our body is in direct contact with it. In addition, we can experience vividly and with all our senses only the events that are happening in the present moment. We can recall the past and anticipate future events or fantasize about them; however, these are very different experiences from an immediate and direct experience of the present moment. In transpersonal states of consciousness, however, none of these limitations are absolute; any of them can be transcended.

Transpersonal experiences can be divided into three large categories. The first of these involves primarily transcendence of the usual spatial barriers, or the limitations of the 'skin-encapsulated ego.' Here belong experiences of merging with another person into a state that can be called 'dual unity,' assuming the identity of another person, identifying with the consciousness of an entire group of people (e.g. all mothers of the world, the entire population of India, or all the inmates of concentration camps), or even experiencing an extension of consciousness that seems to encompass all of humanity. Experiences of this kind have been repeatedly described in the spiritual literature of the world.

In a similar way, one can transcend the limits of the specifically human experience and identify with the consciousness of various animals, plants, or even a form of consciousness that seems to be associated with inorganic objects and processes. In the extremes, it is possible to experience consciousness of the entire biosphere, of our planet, or the entire material universe. Incredible and absurd as it might seem to a Westerner committed to Cartesian-Newtonian science, these experiences suggest that everything we can experience in the everyday state of consciousness as an object, has in the non-ordinary states of consciousness a corresponding subjective representation. It is as if everything in the universe has its objective and subjective aspect, the way it is described in the great spiritual philosophies of the East (e.g. in Hinduism all that exists is seen as a manifestation of Brahma, or in Taoism as a transformation of the Tao).

The second category of transpersonal experiences is characterized primarily by overcoming of temporal rather than spatial boundaries, by transcendence of linear time. We have already talked about the possibility of vivid reliving of important memories from infancy rind of the trauma of birth. This historical regression can continue farther and involve authentic fetal and embryonal memories from different periods of intrauterine life. It is not even unusual to experience, on the level of cellular consciousness, full identification with the sperm and the ovum at the time of conception. But the historical regression *does* not stop here and it is possible to have experiences from the lives of one's human or animal ancestors, or even those that seem to be coming from the racial and collective unconscious as described by C.G. Jung. Quite frequently, the experiences that seem to be happening in other cultures and historical periods are associated with a sense of personal remembering; people then talk about reliving of memories from past lives, from previous incarnations.

In the transpersonal experiences described so far, the content reflects various phenomena existing in space-time. They involve elements of the everyday familiar reality — other people, animals, plants, materials, and events from the past. What is surprising here is not the content of these experiences, but the fact that we can witness or fully identify with something that is not ordinarily accessible to our experience. We know that there are pregnant whales in the world, but we should not be able to have an authentic experience of being one. The fact that there once was the French Revolution is readily acceptable, but we should not be able to have a vivid experience of being there and lying wounded on the barricades of Paris. We know that there are many things happening in the world in places where we are not present, but it is usually considered impossible to experience something that is happening in remote locations (without the mediation of the television and a satellite). We may also be surprised to find consciousness associated with lower animals, plants, and with inorganic nature.

However, the third category of transpersonal experiences is even stranger; here consciousness seems to extend into realms and dimensions that the Western industrial culture does not consider to be 'real.' Here belong numerous visions of archetypal beings and mythological landscapes, encounters or even identification with deities and demons of various cultures, and communication with discarnate beings, spirit guides, suprahuman entities, extraterrestrials, and inhabitants of parallel universes. Additional examples in this category are visions and intuitive understanding of universal symbols, such as the cross, the Nile cross or ankh, the swastika, the pentacle, the six-pointed star, or the yin-yang sign.

In its farther reaches, individual consciousness can identify with cosmic consciousness or the Universal Mind known under many different names: Brahman, Buddha, the Cosmic Christ, Keter, Allah, the Tao, the Great Spirit, and many others. The ultimate of all experiences appears to be identification with the Supracosmic and Metacosmic Void, the mysterious and primordial emptiness and nothingness that is conscious of itself and is the ultimate cradle of all existence. It has no concrete content, yet it contains all there is in a germinal and potential form.

Transpersonal experiences have many strange characteristics that shatter the most fundamental metaphysical assumptions of the Newtonian-Cartesian paradigm and of the materialistic world view. Researchers who have studied and/or personally experienced these fascinating phenomena realize that the attempts of mainstream science to dismiss them as irrelevant products of human fantasy and imagination or as hallucinations — erratic products of pathological processes in the brain — are naïve and inadequate. Any unbiased study of the transpersonal domain of the psyche has to come to the conclusion that the observations represent a critical challenge not only for psychiatry and psychology, but for the entire philosophy of Western science.

Although transpersonal experiences occur in the process of deep individual self-exploration, it is not possible to interpret them simply as intrapsychic phenomena in the conventional sense. On the one hand, they appear on the same experiential continuum as the biographical and perinatal experiences and are thus coming from within the individual psyche. On the other hand, they seem to be tapping directly, without the mediation of the senses, into sources of information that are clearly far beyond the conventional reach of the individual. Somewhere on the perinatal level of the psyche, a strange flip seems to occur and what was up to that point deep intrapsychic probing becomes experiencing of the universe at large through extrasensory means. Some people have compared this to an 'experiential Moebius strip,' since it is impossible any more to say what is inside *and* what is outside.

These observations indicate that we can obtain information about the universe in two radically different ways: *besides* the conventional possibility of learning through sensory perception and analysis and synthesis of the data, we can also find out about various aspects of the world by direct identification with them in a non-ordinary state of consciousness. Each of us thus appears to be a microcosm containing in a holographic way the information about the macrocosm. In the mystical traditions, this was expressed by such phrases as: 'as above so below' or 'as without, so within.'

The reports of subjects who have experienced episodes of embryonal existence, the moment of conception, and elements of cellular, tissue, and organ consciousness abound in medically accurate insights into the anatomical, physiological, and biochemical aspects of the processes involved. Similarly, ancestral, racial and collective memories and past incarnation experiences provide quite frequently very specific details about architecture, costumes, weapons, art forms, social structure, and religious and ritual practices of the culture and historical period involved, or even concrete historical events.

People who experienced phylogenetic experiences or identification with existing life forms not only found them unusually authentic and convincing, but often acquired in the process extraordinary insights concerning animal psychology, ethology, specific habits, or unusual reproductive cycles. In some instances, this was accompanied by archaic muscular innervations not characteristic for humans, or even such complex behaviours as enactment of a courtship dance.

The philosophical challenge associated with the already described observations, as formidable as it is all by itself, is further augmented by the fact that the transpersonal experiences correctly reflecting the material world often appear on the same continuum as, and intimately interwoven with, others that contain elements which the Western industrial world does not consider to be real. Here belong, for example, experiences involving deities and demons from various cultures, mythological realms such as heavens and paradises, and legendary or fairy-tale sequences.

For example, one can have an experience of Shiva's heaven, of the paradise of the Aztec raingod Tlaloc, of the Sumerian underworld, or of one of the Buddhist hot hells. It is also possible to communicate with Jesus, have a shattering encounter with the Hindu goddess Kali, or identify with the dancing Shiva. Even these episodes can impart accurate new information about religious symbolism and mythical motifs that were previously unknown to the person involved. Observations of this kind confirm C.G. Jung's idea that beside the Freudian individual unconscious we can also gain access to the collective unconscious that contains the cultural heritage of all humanity.

It is not an easy task to convey in a few sentences conclusions from daily observations in the course of over thirty-five years of research of non-ordinary states of consciousness and make this statement believable. It is not realistic to expect that a few sentences would be able to override the deeply culturally ingrained world-view in those of the readers who are not familiar with the transpersonal dimension and who cannot relate what I say to their personal experience. Although I myself had many experiences of non-ordinary states of consciousness and the opportunity to observe closely a number of other people, it took me years to absorb fully the impact of this cognitive shock.

Due to space considerations, I cannot present detailed case histories that could help to illustrate the nature of transpersonal experiences and the insights which they make available. I have to refer those readers who would like to explore this area further to my book *The Adventure of Self-Discovery* (Grof 1978) where I discuss in detail the various types of transpersonal experiences and give many illustrative examples of situations where they provided unusual new information about different aspects of the universe. The same book also describes the method of Holotropic Breathwork which opens the access to the perinatal and transpersonal realms for anybody who is interested in personal verification of the above observations. Comparable information about psychedelic sessions can be found in my book *LSD Psychotherapy* that has been published in a new edition (Grof 1994).

The existence and nature of transpersonal experiences violates some of the most basic assumptions of mechanistic science. They imply such seemingly absurd notions as relativity and arbitrary nature of all physical boundaries, non-local connections. In the universe, communication through unknown means and channels, memory without a material substrate, non-linearity of time, or consciousness associated with all living organisms, and even inorganic matter. Many transpersonal experiences involve events from the microcosm and the macrocosm, realms that cannot normally be reached by unaided human senses, or from historical periods that precede the origin of the solar system, formation of planet earth, appearance of living organisms, development of the nervous system, and emergence of *Homo sapiens.*

The research of non-ordinary states thus reveals an amazing paradox concerning the nature of human beings. It clearly shows that, in a mysterious and yet unexplained way, each of us contains the information about the entire universe and all of existence, has potential experiential access to all of its parts, and in a sense is the whole cosmic network, as much as he or she is just an infinitesimal part of it, a separate and insignificant biological entity. The new cartography reflects this fact and portrays the individual human psyche as being essentially commensurate with the entire cosmos and the totality of existence. As absurd and implausible as this idea might seem to a traditionally trained scientist and to our commonsense, it can be relatively easily reconciled with new revolutionary developments in various scientific disciplines usually referred to as the new or emerging paradigm.

I firmly believe that the expanded cartography which I have outlined above is of critical importance for any serious approach to such phenomena as shamanism, rites of passage, mysticism, religion, mythology, parapsychology, near-death experiences, and psychedelic states. This new model of the psyche is not just a matter of academic interest. As I will try to show in the remaining pages of this article, it has deep and revolutionary implications for the understanding of emotional and psychosomatic disorders, including psychoses, and offers new and revolutionary therapeutic possibilities.

## *The nature of emotional and psychosomatic disorders.*

Traditional psychiatry uses the medical model and the disease concept not only for disorders of a clearly organic nature, but also for emotional and psychosomatic disorders for which no biological cause has been found. Psychiatrists use quite loosely the term 'mental' or 'emotional disease' and try to assign various disorders to specific diagnostic categories comparable to those of general medicine. Generally, the time of the onset of symptoms is seen as the beginning of the 'disease' and the intensity of the symptoms is used as the measure of the seriousness of the pathological process. Alleviation of the symptoms is considered 'clinical improvement' and their intensification is seen as 'worsening of the clinical condition.'

The observations from the study of NOSC suggest that thinking in terms of disease, diagnosis, and allopathic therapy is not appropriate for most psychiatric problems that are not clearly organic in nature, including some of the conditions currently labelled as psychoses. To exist in a material form, to have experienced the embryological development, birth, infancy and childhood has left traumatic imprints in all of us, although we certainly differ as to their intensity, extensity, and also availability of this traumatic material for conscious experience. Every person is carrying a variety of more or less latent emotional and bioenergetic blockages which interfere with full physiological and psychological functioning.

The manifestation of emotional and psychosomatic symptoms is the beginning of a healing process through which the organism is trying to free itself from traumatic imprints and simplify its functioning. The only way this can happen is by emergence of the traumatic material into consciousness and its full experience and emotional and motor expression. If the trauma that is being processed is of major proportions, such as a difficult birth that lasted many hours and seriously threatened biological survival, the emotions and behavioural expressions can be extremely dramatic. Under these circumstances, it might seem more plausible that it is a result of some exotic pathology than to recognize that it is a potentially beneficial development. However, when properly understood and supported, this process can be conducive to healing, spiritual opening, personality transformation, and consciousness evolution. The emergence of symptoms thus represents not only a problem, but also a therapeutic opportunity; this insight is the basis of most experiential psychotherapies. Symptoms manifest in the area where the defence system is at its weakest, making it possible for the healing process to begin. According to my experience, this is true not only in relation to neuroses and psychosomatic disorders, but also to certain conditions traditionally considered psychotic (psychospiritual crises or 'spiritual emergencies'). It is interesting to mention in this context that the Chinese pictogram for 'crisis' is composed of two others, one meaning 'danger' and the other 'opportunity.' The idea that the symptoms are not manifestations of the disease, but are expressions of a healing process and should be supported is also found in a therapeutic system called homeopathy.

In traditional psychotherapy, emotional and psychosomatic symptoms that are not organic in nature, but psychogenic in origin, are seen as resulting from postnatal biographical traumas, especially those that occurred in infancy and childhood. Therapeutic work using NOSC reveals that they actually have a multidimensional structure with additional roots on the perinatal and transpersonal levels. Thus, for example, somebody suffering from psychogenic asthma can discover that the underlying biographical material consists of memories of suffocation during a near-drowning accident in childhood and an episode of diphtheria in infancy. On a deeper level, the same problem is also connected with choking in the birth canal and its deepest root can be a past life experience of being strangled or hanged. To resolve this symptom, it is necessary to allow oneself to experience all the layers of problems associated with it. New insights concerning this multilevel dynamic structure of the major forms of emotional and psychosomatic disorders were described in detail elsewhere (Grof 1985).

## The role of spirituality in human life

Traditional psychology and psychiatry are dominated by materialistic philosophy and have no recognition of spirituality in any form. From the point of view of Western science, the material world represents the only reality and any form of spiritual belief is seen as reflecting lack of education, primitive superstition, magical thinking, or regression to infantile patterns of functioning. Direct experiences of spiritual realities are then relegated to the world of gross psychopathology. Western psychiatry makes no distinction between a mystical experience and a psychotic experience and sees both as manifestations of mental disease. In its rejection of religion, it does not differentiate primitive folk beliefs or fundamentalists' literal interpretations of scriptures from sophisticated mystical traditions and Eastern spiritual philosophies based on centuries of systematic introspective exploration of the psyche. It pathologizes spirituality of any kind and together with it the entire spiritual history of humanity.

The observations from the study of NOSC confirm an important insight of C.G. Jung. According to him, the experiences originating in deeper levels of the psyche tin my own terminology perinatal and transpersonal experiences) have a certain quality that he called (after Rudolph Otto) *numinosity.* They are associated with the feeling that one is encountering a dimension which is sacred, holy, and radically different from everyday life, and which belongs to a superior order of reality. The term *numinous* is relatively neutral and thus preferable to others, such as religious, mystical, magical, holy, or sacred, which have often been used incorrectly and are easily misleading.

To prevent confusion and misunderstandings that in the past have compromised many similar discussions, it is critical to make a clear distinction between spirituality and religion. Spirituality is based on direct experiences of other realities. It does not necessarily require a special place, or a special person mediating contact with the divine, although mystics can certainly benefit from spiritual guidance and a community of fellow seekers. Spirituality thus involves a special relationship between the individual and the cosmos and is in its essence a personal and private affair. At the cradle of all great religions are visionary (perinatal and/or transpersonal) experiences of their founders, prophets, saints, and even ordinary followers. All major spiritual scriptures — the Vedas, the Buddhist Pall Canon, the Bible, the

Koran, the Book of Mormon, and many others — are based on revelations in holotropic states of consciousness.

By comparison, the basis of organized religion is institutionalized group activity that takes place in a designated location (temple, church), and involves a system of appointed mediators. Ideally, religions should provide for its members access to and support for direct spiritual experiences. However, it often happens that a religion completely loses the connection with its spiritual source and becomes a secular institution exploiting the human spiritual needs without satisfying them. Instead, it creates a hierarchical system focusing on the pursuit of power, control, politics, money, and other possessions. Under these circumstances, religious hierarchy tends to actively discourage and suppress direct spiritual experiences in its members, because they foster independence and cannot be effectively controlled. When this happens, genuine spiritual life continues only in the mystical branches and monastic orders.

From the scientific point of view, the main question here is the ontological status of transpersonal experiences. While mainstream psychiatry and psychology see them as indications of pathology, transpersonal psychology considers them important phenomena *sui generis* that have great heuristic and therapeutic value and deserve to be seriously studied. While much of what is found in mainstream religions and their theologies is certainly in serious conflict with science, this is not true in regard to spirituality based on direct transpersonal experiences. The findings of modern consciousness research show actually remarkable convergence with many revolutionary developments in Western science referred to as the emerging paradigm. As Ken Wilber (1982) has noted, there cannot possibly be a conflict between genuine science and authentic religion. If there seems to be a conflict, we are very likely dealing with 'bogus science' and 'bogus religion,' where either side has a serious misunderstanding of the other's position and very likely represents a false or fake version of its own discipline.

## *The nature of reality*

As we have seen, the observations from the research of NOSC represent a serious challenge to contemporary psychiatry and psychology and require a drastic revision of our thinking in these fields. However, many of them are of such a fundamental nature that they transcend the narrow frame of these disciplines and challenge the most basic philosophical assumptions of Western science and its Newtonian-Cartesian paradigm. They seriously undermine the belief that our consciousness is an accidental product of the neuro-physiological processes in our brains and strongly suggest that it is a primary attribute of all existence. In this context, I cannot offer a comprehensive discussion of this important subject. I have already done it in my book *Beyond the Brain: Birth, Death, and Transcendence in Psychology* (Grof 1985) and can thus refer interested readers to this publication.

When confronted with the challenging observations from modern consciousness research, we have only two choices. The first one is to reject the new observations simply because they are incompatible with the traditional scientific belief system. This involves an arrogant assumption that we already know what the universe is like and can tell with certainty what is possible and what is not possible. With this kind of approach, there cannot be any surprises, but there is also very little real progress. In this context, everybody who brings critically challenging data is accused of being a bad scientist, a fraud, or a mentally deranged person.

This is an approach that characterizes pseudoscience or scientistic fundamentalism and has very little to do with genuine science. There exist many historical examples of such an approach: people who refused to look into Galileo Galilei's telescope, because they 'knew' there could not be craters on the moon; those who fought against the atomic theory of chemistry and defended the concept of non-existing substance phlogiston; those who called Einstein a psychotic when he proposed his special theory of relativity, and many others.

The second reaction to challenging new observations is characteristic of true science. It is excitement about and intense interest in such anomalies combined with healthy critical scepticism. Major scientific progress has always occurred when the leading paradigm has seriously failed to account for some significant findings and was seriously questioned. In the history of science, paradigms come, dominate the field for some time, and then are replaced by new ones. If instead of rejecting and ridiculing the new observations, we would consider them an exciting opportunity and conduct our own study to test them, we might very likely find that the reports were accurate.

It is hard to imagine that Western academic science will continue indefinitely to censor all the extraordinary evidence that has in the past been accumulated in the study of various forms of holotropic states, as well as ignore the influx of new data. Sooner or later it will have to face this challenge and accept all the far-reaching theoretical and practical consequences. When that happens, we will realize that the nature of human beings is very different from what is being taught at Western universities and what the industrial civilization believes it to be. It will also become clear to us that materialistic science has an incomplete and inadequate image of reality and that its ideas about the nature of consciousness and the relationship between consciousness and matter (particularly the brain) have to be radically revised. It is my firm belief that we are rapidly approaching a point when transpersonal psychology and the work with non-ordinary states of consciousness will become integral parts of a new scientific paradigm of the future.

## *References*

Alexander, F. 1931. Buddhist training as artificial catatonia. *Psychoanalytical Review.* 18:129.

Campbell, J. 1956. *The hero with a thousand faces.* New York: Meridian Books.

Grof, C. and S. Grof. 1990. *The stormy search for the self.* Los Angeles: J.P. Tarcher.

Grof, S. 1975. *Realms of the human unconscious.* New York: Viking.

—. 1985 *Beyond the brain.* Albany: State University of New York Press.

—. 1988 *The adventure of self-discovery.* Albany: State University of New York Press.

—. 1992. *The holotropic mind.* Harper San Francisco.

Grof, S. and C. Grof (eds.) 1989. *Spiritual emergencies.* Los Angeles: J.P. Tarcher.

Harner, M. 1980. *The way of the shaman.* New York: Harper & Row.

Jung, C.G. 1960. *The archetypes and the collective unconscious.* In: *Collected works,* Vol. 9.1. Princeton University Press.

Perls, F. 1976. *The gestalt approach and eye-witness to therapy.* New York: Bantam.

Ring, K. 1984. *Heading toward Omega.* New York: William Morrow.

Sabom, M. 1982. *Recollections of death.* New York: Simon & Schuster.

Talbot, M. 1991. *The holographic universe.* Harper San Francisco.

Wasson, G., A. Hofmann, and C.A.P. Ruck. 1978. *The road to Eleusis: unveiling the secret of the mysteries.* New York: Harcourt, Brace & Jovanovitch.

Wilber, K. 1982. *A sociable god.* New York: McGraw-Hill.

# Beyond Space and Time: The Unbounded Psyche

ANDREW POWELL

*Dr Andrew Powell, F.R.C.Psych., qualified in medicine from Cambridge. After postgraduate studies in general medicine and psychiatry, he specialized in psychotherapy at the Maudsley Hospital, London. Trainings in group and individual psychoanalytic therapies were later followed by psychodrama, which opened the way to psycho-spiritual approaches, including past life regression, soul retrieval and spirit release. He worked and taught at St George's Hospital, London as consultant and senior lecturer until 1989, when he moved to the Warneford Hospital, Oxford, where he held a consultant and honorary senior lecturer post until 2000. He has a deep interest in the influence of spiritual dynamics on physical and psychological wellbeing and in the study of eastern approaches to consciousness. He has served as a member of council of the Scientific and Medical Network from 1993 to 2000, chairs the Spirituality and Psychiatry Special Interest Group in the Royal College of Psychiatrists and is an Associate of the College of Healing.*

A good many years back, I was taking part in a group meditation, which began with a guided fantasy. We were asked to imagine ourselves walking in a field in the countryside on a summer day, with birds singing, bees humming and the smell of grass and flowers. Then we were instructed to look around until we saw something of special interest, to go towards it and let the experience take us where it will. This is where it took me:

> I am standing before a majestic and mysterious tree. It has the appearance of a sequoia or giant redwood and soars up into the sky. As soon as I come close to the trunk I begin ascending

> rapidly, as if I am going up in a fast lift. I shoot past the top of the tree and suddenly find myself scrambling up a rocky outcrop. At once I know exactly what is going on. This is Arizona, the year is eighteen forty-eight, my name is Tom McCann and I am being hunted down by a raiding party of Apache Indians. I heave myself up onto the flat top of the rock. I can hear the Indian braves a short way below and I know they will get to me in a couple of minutes and have my scalp. I pull out of my pocket a worn leather wallet and gaze for the last time with sadness and longing on the picture of my wife and two young daughters. Then I take out my gun, put the muzzle to my head and pull the trigger. There is no sound and no impact. I simply find myself floating peacefully up and away from the body lying on the top of the rock.

At just this moment the person leading the group exercise said it was now time we came back to our bodies. I burst out laughing, for the remark could not have been more apt! The memory of that experience is etched as sharply in my mind now as the day it happened. It was my first taste of what popularly are called past lives.

Consciously, I had known nothing about this period of American history but while preparing this paper, I looked up a few facts. Eighteen forty eight is the year the war ended between the USA and Mexico with the USA seizing control of what are now the states of New Mexico and Arizona. American Indians were given the right to vote but most remained at war with the white man for another twenty years. I also found that the name of the sequoia tree comes from a Cherokee Indian, Sequoya, who pioneered the first written language for North American Indians. Yet at this same time the Cherokee were being driven west of the Mississippi by the federal troops of the US army, a shameful chapter of history known as the 'trail of tears' during which more than four thousand Cherokee died of starvation and disease.

Sceptics consider past lives to be nothing but instances of cryptomnesia, the historical facts having been once known and then stored away in the unconscious until they happen to surface in vivid phantasies. I would concur but with the proviso that the 'facts' emerge not from the personal unconscious but from the collective unconscious as described by Carl Jung. In my case, the guided fantasy had set in motion what Jung called 'active imagination' (Chodorow 1997). The alchemical tree, an archetype of transformation, had transported me to the realm of the archetypes of death and rebirth in which a stream of images welled up in the psyche over which I had no control

Jung wrote: '... the Collective Unconscious is anything but an encapsulated personal system: it is sheer objectivity, as wide as the world and open to the entire world. *There I am the object of every subject, in complete reversal of my ordinary consciousness, where I am always the subject that has an object*' (Jung 1954.22). This fits perfectly with what is found in past lives; the drama takes a course that the ego has no power to change, for things are as they are and the entire script is set out from start to finish. There is no sense of one doing the thinking. Rather, 'it thinks me,' through to the end, when death supervenes and consciousness invariably separates from the body.

The archetypes of the collective unconscious can never be apprehended directly. They are the primordial potentia, which give structure and meaning to consciousness through the formation of symbols and images. Symbols and images fall within space-time but the archetypal realm itself does not, for it functions as though time and space as we know them do not exist. Yet we certainly experience archetypal images in an entirely personal way since they are constellated according to the psychic reality of the individual. An example would be the poignant theme of loss in the past life fragment I have just given. The scene affected me deeply, for I too had a 'trail of tears' to contend with in my life at that time.

The breakthrough of archetypal material has a profound and often disturbing impact. Take Jung's account of the events, which occurred in 1916 immediately prior to his writing the Gnostic text 'Seven Sermons to the Dead' under the mysterious inspiration of Basilides of Alexandria. Jung records: 'There was an ominous atmosphere around me. I had the strange feeling the air was filled with ghostly entities.'

He goes on to relate how his children also saw and felt these entities:

> Then the doorbell began ringing frantically ... it was a bright summer day ... there was no one in sight ... I not only heard it but saw it moving ... then I knew that something had to happen. The whole house was filled as if there were a crowd present, crammed full of spirits. They were packed deep right up to the door, and the air was so thick it was scarcely possible to breathe. As for myself, I was all a-quiver with the question, 'For

> God's sake, what in the world is this?' Then they cried out in chorus, 'We have come back from Jerusalem where we found not what we sought.' Then it began to flow out of me and in the course of three evenings the whole thing was written. As soon as I took up the pen, the whole ghostly assemblage evaporated. The room quieted and the atmosphere cleared. The haunting was over. (Jung 1961.215)

Accessing the collective unconscious also gives rise to uncanny coincidences to which Jung gave the term 'synchronicity,' when two or more causally unrelated events turn out to have the same or similar meaning. Jung describes three kinds synchronistic phenomena (Main 1997). The first is when a psychic event and an apparently unrelated physical event occur in the same place and at the same time. Jung tells of a patient who had just been recounting a dream of a scarab beetle when a scarabaeid beetle tried to fly in through the window of the consulting room (1952.439). Such strange coincidences are not rare, though we tend to brush them aside. Here is one I remember well from my own life:

> I was feeling both apprehensive and excited because it was the start of my first day as a hospital consultant. I searched the building looking for my room but when I did find it, the door was locked. I tracked down the professor's secretary who took the Yale key off a large ring, gave it to me and I put it in my jacket pocket. It was a big moment for me, for I was now about to take possession of my room. I went back down the corridor and pulled the key out of my pocket. To my astonishment, the shank of the key had bent on itself through ninety degrees. I could not enter my sanctum until I had clamped the key in a doorframe and straightened it out with brute force.

The episode of the key can be interpreted symbolically as reflecting my heightened anxiety on my first day as a young consultant that I would not be able to live up to what was expected of me. We no longer have the benefit of rites of phallic initiation to prepare us for manhood, as did our tribal forefathers. But the classical laws of physics cannot account for the bent key I stood staring at in amazement, the more so since Uri Geller was not yet a household name.

The large body of evidence for psychokinesis that has accumulated since is still ignored by most scientists, who prefer the comfort of the familiar. Jung showed astonishing prescience when in 1954 he wrote:

> Despite the materialist tendency to understand the psyche as a mere reflection or imprint of physical and chemical processes, there is not a single proof of this hypothesis ... There is thus no ground at all for regarding the psyche as something secondary or as an epiphenomenon ...

and also:

> Sooner or later nuclear physics and the psychology of the unconscious will draw closer together as both of them, independently of one another and from opposite directions, push forward into transcendental territory, the one with the concept of the atom, the other with that of the archetype. (Jung 1954.58).

Jung's second variety of synchronicity deals with non-local phenomena. Here is an example from clinical practice:

> I had been supervizing a trainee psychiatrist with her first psychotherapy patient, a young woman named Gillian. Gillian longed for closeness but was deeply mistrustful of intimacy. The therapy went well and after a few months, Gillian decided to track down her mother, whom she had never known. She followed up various leads only to discover that her mother had died a year or two earlier. This was a bitter blow but she took it well.
>
> A couple of weeks later, my trainee attended for supervision. She seemed flustered and somewhat embarrassed. She said, 'I want to tell you something, you'll probably think its stupid of me.' She went on to say that on the previous Sunday, which she had been spending at home with her family, she had suddenly experienced a terrible sadness. It came on inexplicably at three in the afternoon and she could not shake it off. Then at about six o'clock the feeling vanished as quickly as it had come.
>
> On Monday, she saw her patient Gillian who told her that since the last session, she had found out that her mother had been buried in a London cemetery and that on Sunday she had gone there to try to find her. For hours she had searched

> in vain but at three pm. she found the grave. She spent the next three hours there, crying for the mother she had never known.

According to Newtonian physics, this exact coincidence of emotions at a distance can only be due to chance. Yet we know that when two people who share an empathic rapport are separated and electromagnetically shielded from each other, an evoked electrical potential stimulated in the brain of one by a flashing light is instantaneously mirrored in the brain of the second subject by a transferred potential. This correlation of brain waves is independent of the distance between subjects. Nor can it be accounted for on the basis of information passing from one subject to the other through physical space because it occurs simultaneously (Grinberg-Zylberbaum *et al.* 1992).

This takes us to Quantum Theory and the famous EPR thought experiment of 1935. Albert Einstein argued that two electrons, which first interacted and were then separated in space, would, in theory at least, still be related even if light years apart by virtue of the common wave form they had once shared. Einstein thought this must be patently untrue but in due course he was proved to be wrong. In nineteen seventy two, John Clauser experimentally showed that reversing the spin of one particle instantly reversed the spin of the other and then in 1982 Alain Aspect demonstrated that this synchronicity, which transcends the speed of light, holds true even when the electrons are widely separated in space.

There is a lively debate going on about how non-local correlations can take place with large structures like brains but there is strong empirical evidence that psi occurs, as shown in a host of Ganzfeld experiments (Radin 1997). In one such experiment, the subject is required to describe a target picture or location which has been selected, and which may be in a remote place, hundreds of miles away. Honorton (1989) has extensively researched this phenomenon and the findings of his meta-analysis of the research evidence are compelling. Even more extraordinary is the work of Helmut Schmidt demonstrating that subjects show precognition of the target *before* the target itself has been selected (Schmidt 1986). *The conventional rules of not only space but also time are violated.*

Jung would have applauded these findings. He was intrigued by instances of synchronicity in which a psychic event relates to a physical event that takes place in the future. Nor are they so uncommon. I vividly recall one instance, which happened to me twenty years ago:

> My wife and I were due to drive down from the North of Scotland. During the small hours of the night before the journey, my wife had a fearful dream. In it, we were overtaking on a country road when suddenly a car came speeding head on towards us. She could see clearly that it was a green Austin A40. She awoke just before the impact. My wife was not given to superstition but so powerful was the dream that she was very reluctant to travel. I promised her I would drive extra carefully and assured her I would keep a close look out for any green Austins that might be around! Half way across Sutherland, on an empty country road, I was held back by an ancient tractor. As I swung out to overtake, I remembered the dream and pulled back. The next instant a green Austin, the first car for many miles, hurtled round the bend and past us.

Jung did not, to my knowledge, describe a fourth category of synchronicity, when a psychic event occurs with the corresponding physical event in the remote past. Here is an account of what one of my patients, Alice, experienced a few months back:

Briefly, this forty-three-year-old lady came with a ten-year history of sarcoidosis, which was causing her to go blind. She was now increasingly reliant on her husband, John. Theirs was a loving marriage and she said of him with a smile, *'He was a good catch!'* All her life Alice had been a resourceful person. Now her loss of sight was challenging her to try to make sense of her misfortune. Recently she had heard about past life regression and wanted to see if it could provide any clue.

The sarcoid had begun with blinding headaches and in the session we went back to that time when she lay exhausted and crying, holding her head in her hands in a darkened room.

> I ask Alice to find words for the terrible pain in her head. If her headache could speak what would it say? She cries out, 'Let me alone. Let me be free.' I suggest she gives in to that longing and see where it takes her. Her face relaxes and she lies with her eyes closed and a smile on her lips. She finds herself transported to an idyllic, warm ocean, swimming lazily in the

calm water. I ask her to look around. She can see the sandy shore line some way off and beyond that, dense vegetation covering the lower slopes of distant mountains. Next, I ask her to look down at her body. She says with astonishment, 'I'm like a fish' and can feel herself leaping exultantly out of the water. Then she exclaims 'No, I'm not a fish, I'm a dolphin!' Her expression is one of intense pleasure. After a pause, I ask if there are any other dolphins nearby. It seems this young dolphin had disobeyed her parents; such was her longing for adventure, and has swum off on her own. But she has no fear, for she is in her element.

I then ask her to go forward in time to the next important thing that happens. It is now late in the day. She finds herself lying on the sand, unable to move. (Alice's body makes ineffectual jerking movements on the couch). She does not know what is happening to her. I ask her to check her body and she finds a large hole in her side. Now tears begin to trickle down her cheeks. There is no pain but her strength is ebbing away. She looks up and can see the prow of a boat a few feet away. Standing on it and staring at her is a fisherman with a painted face and body, holding a spear in his hand. Then the boat slides away. As darkness falls, she grows calm. Suddenly, to her surprise, she finds herself rising up into the sky and looking down, without emotion or regret, at the lifeless body of the dolphin on the beach.

Does she need to face this fisherman who had killed her with his spear? At first she is reluctant, saying 'It wasn't his fault. He never killed another dolphin.' Then she agrees that it could be important. So she waits there for a while until his turn comes to die and he crosses over. Now she can see him coming closer.

At this point in the session, Alice starts retching, cries out, 'I'm going to be sick' and has to rush to the lavatory. When she comes back she says she has been sick, with diarrhoea. We continue where we left off. Involuntarily, she finds herself going forward and embracing the fisherman. I ask her to take a good look and see if she recognizes him. She cries out in amazement, 'Of course, it's my husband John' and begins laughing and crying at the same time. 'He caught me and now I've caught him. We are together and this time he is here to take care of me!'

> The account of Alice's past life as a dolphin has to be taken for what it is, psychic reality, along with its karmic meaning, which made such patently good sense to my patient. On the other hand, scientific enquiry into reincarnation has depended on meticulous fieldwork. Professor Ian Stevenson has intensively studied not only historical evidence but also cases of children claiming to remember past lives who bear physical birthmarks which correspond to the site of physical trauma in the past life, usually the injury which brought that life to an end (Stevenson 1966, 1997).

Sceptics hold the view that over ninety per cent of information revealed in past lives can be readily accounted for by fantasy but there remains a stubborn minority where the facts defy such explanations. There is the phenomenon of xenoglossia, speaking a language unknown to the subject, which Stevenson (1984) again has researched as well as a number of well documented case studies (Ducasse 1960, Tarazi 1997) which contain obscure but verifiable historical detail. One objection raised concerns the many times when the lives of the same handful of famous historical personages have been recounted and we have to question whether an account of a past life can be said to belong to any one individual alone. It may be that we are dealing with shared access to the archetypal contents of a transcendent realm through some kind of sympathetic resonance.

When working transpersonally, a plane of existence is regularly reported between lives corresponding to the spirit world in Theosophy and the *Bardo* in Tibetan Buddhism (Newton 1994, Woolger 1999). It frequently holds the key to powerful therapeutic insights (Powell 1998), as when my patient Alice recognized the fisherman to be her husband John. But sometimes we find a limbo in which the spirit wanders confused or lost. Here is such a case:

Barbara, the patient, had been visiting a well-known museum and wanted to go upstairs to look at the paintings on the first floor. There was a big central staircase with stairwells on both sides. Halfway up, she started feeling dizzy, was flooded with anxiety and could not proceed. Since that time, open spaces and heights triggered severe panic attacks.

> I ask Barbara to close her eyes and imagine herself back at the bottom of the staircase. She becomes visibly tense. Then I ask

> her to focus on the sensation of fear and go with the feeling to the very first time it happened, wherever that might take her.
>
> To her surprise, Barbara then reports that she seems to be standing at the bottom of a stone pyramid with big steps leading upwards and a sheer drop on each side. What is she wearing? Rough leather sandals and a long cotton skirt. I ask her what she is doing there. She says she is going to be sacrificed. By whom? The chief priest. Where? She can see him, waiting for her at the top of the pyramid. What is he going to do? He is going to cut her throat.
>
> How come she has been chosen for the sacrifice? This takes her back to the scene in the village the night before. There had been a meeting and the elders pointed to her and said 'It might as well be her.' She had no relatives to protect her and so she was dragged away. I ask her to go back further, to her childhood in that lifetime. The name she answers to is Miria. She recalls a life of hardship and drudgery. She is a solitary child by nature who likes best playing alone in the forest. She grows up and is expected to marry according to the tribal custom but she is fiercely independent and scares away her suitors. This is why she had no status in the village and no husband to protect her.
>
> Now she is standing at the foot of the pyramid and knows what she has to do. As if in a trance she climbs slowly upwards. The height makes her dizzy. At the top she is lifted onto on a stone slab. The priest raises his ceremonial sword. What next? Suddenly she is free. It is over. She feels no pain or fear. She is moving away and has no further interest in the body lying on the stone slab.

In past life work, the subject may be flooded with emotion or remain detached, for defence mechanisms feature in past lives also. In this case, as Miria mounted the steps of the pyramid, she was protected from the overwhelming terror of her execution by going into a dissociative state. But as Freud declared, sooner or later the repressed must return, as it did in this case for my patient Barbara, with the breakthrough of severe anxiety as she climbed the museum stairs.

At the transpersonal level, what Barbara experienced can be understood in a number of ways. It could simply be the emergence of phantasy constellating the archetypal theme of ritual sacrifice. But then, if every event in space-time sets up an everlasting vibration in the collective unconscious, akin to what Rupert Sheldrake has called morphic resonance (Sheldrake 1999), could Barbara have tuned in to Miria's death through some kind of sympathetic identification? Alternatively, Barbara may really have been visiting a life she herself once lived, leaving her psyche with a wound that her body, though not her conscious mind, recalled. Last but not least, had we uncovered the source of a spirit attachment, which was afflicting my patient?

> We return to the moment of death and again Miria floats away from her body. But she remains suspended in a shadowy, featureless world, without any sensation of space or time. I ask her to look around and tell me if she can see anyone. At first there is nothing. Then Miria looks down and sees a five-year old girl playing alone in the fields behind some houses. As she comes closer, she sees that it is Barbara as Barbara was in the childhood of this present life. Miria feels attracted to the little girl and so she merges with her, staying with her from that time on and enjoying the companionship, for there seems to be nowhere else to go.

In view of this account, I concluded that Miria's fate had been to remain an earthbound spirit. The history is typical (Baldwin 1992) with a traumatic ending to life, the failure to move on to the light after leaving the body, a resulting limbo state and then the attraction to a sympathetic soul, for Barbara too had been a solitary child. There had been no symptomatic disturbance until the day, many years later, when museum steps had triggered the breakthrough of Miria's unresolved terror and had rooted Barbara to the spot.

> Once this was explained to Miria, she readily agreed to leave, for she had no wish to inflict her fears on Barbara. I encouraged Miria to look upwards. After a while she reported that she could see a point of light way above her. She found herself moving rapidly towards it and then was gone.

In psychodynamic therapy, terms such as projection and introjection serve us well as explanatory metaphors. But our modern psychology has its roots in deep soil, for shamans have been dealing with soul loss and soul retrieval for thousands of years. Such methods, when used, are no less effective today.

Sally is in her mid-fifties. Despite successfully raising a family, she has suffered from treatment-resistant depression for twenty years, tormented by feelings of guilt and unworthiness. Her problems began during early childhood, which was blighted with insecurity. The coup de grace came when she was seven and fell into the hands of a fundamentalist schoolteacher, Miss Edwards, who terrified the child with threats of hell and damnation. Sally had recurring visions of flames licking around her bed and the red face of the devil would appear at night and in her dreams.

In adulthood, Sally seemed to overcome these fears, but following major surgery, which left her body scarred, she once again succumbed to these hallucinations and lived from day to day in a state of sheer panic. I was asked by Sally's psychiatrist to see her for a therapeutic consultation.

> I encourage Sally to visualize her soul. She locates it inside her chest but it is a feeble thing, not much more than a glimmer of light. Then I ask her to look carefully to see if there are any strands or cords running out from it into the darkness. She finds a cord, so I urge her to follow it and see where it leads. After a moment she looks up and says she can see Miss Edwards, looking very old but as fierce as ever, holding the end of the cord tightly in her hand.
>
> I then have a frank discussion with Miss Edwards, speaking through the agency of Sally. Miss Edwards insists that what she did what was right, the child had to be controlled and if she instilled fear in her, it was for her own good. I point out that instead of helping, it has led to a lifetime of misery and torment. Is this what Miss Edwards as a Christian really intended? She falters for the first time and I press home my advantage. She herself is nearing the end of her life and will soon be facing her Maker. How will he judge her? Then Miss Edwards becomes fearful. She hadn't intended harm. She hopes God will have pity on her. I put it to her that she can start making amends right now by letting go of Sally's soul and giving it back to her. Miss Edwards agrees and lets go of the cord. I ask Sally to draw it back into herself, after which we spend time giving healing to her soul. Afterwards, to Sally's immense relief, she finds the red devil has lost his power over her, the fear has gone and she can move on to the next phase of her therapy, mourning for her lost childhood.

The clinical examples I have been giving all point to one thing. When we move beyond the constraints of sense perception and the bounds of physical space-time, we enter a domain in which *all time is now and all space is here.* I want to enlarge on this concept, for it reinstates the sixth sense, which three hundred years of western science discounted and even scorned.

Newton's laws of motion and gravitation, together with René Descartes' dualism of mind and body, gave rise to a science of material realism that profoundly shaped how we think about the nature of reality. We conceive of an enduring physical universe out there, a stage on which we live our lives and make our exit. The physical realm is held to be the primary one and consciousness is seen as a miraculous by-product of evolutionary biology. Anyone holding the view that we are eternal souls in physical bodies has been obliged to hypothesise another parallel but non-physical world in which the soul resides. This has led to all kinds of problems, such as where heaven is situated and why no energy transfer has ever been shown to take place between the two worlds. On the other hand, the science of material realism has advanced apace, its world firmly bounded by the five senses and all that it contains.

Just when it begins to look like game, set and match to material realism, physicists discover quantum theory, which tells a different story. The wave-particle experiment breaks with three hundred years of certainty. *Depending on the way the experimenter sets up the light experiment, particles become waves and waves particles.* We find we have two realities with equal validity. If two, why not twenty? If three dimensions, why not four? Some mathematicians assure us there are at least twenty-six dimensions, all but four of them curled up into a space smaller than a millionth of an inch. That is, of course, looked at from the point of view of our space-time. From within that multi-dimensional world, our whole physical universe might look like a mere drawing on a piece of paper!

Electrons are no longer thought of as particles spinning around the nucleus of the atom like a miniature solar system. Instead, the electron is smeared throughout all of space as a probability wave, which only collapses into its space-time location when a conscious observer makes a measurement. Nor can the velocity and position of the electron be known at the same time, for this is a world of uncertainties. There is only a statistical probability that the electron will appear where you expect it to be. It may just materialize hundreds, thousands or even millions of miles away and when it does so, it takes zero time to get there.

Both space and time are bypassed. Such fundamental non-locality reveals the breath taking interconnectedness of the cosmos. Here is what three eminent physicists have to say. First, Henry Stapp: 'The fundamental process of nature lies outside space-time but generates events that can be located in space-time' (Goswami 1993.61). Second, David Bohm: 'Ultimately, the entire universe (with all its particles, including those constituting human beings, their laboratories, observing instruments, etc.) has to be understood as a single undivided whole, in which analysis into separately and independently existent parts has no fundamental status' (Bohm 1980.174). Last, from Amit Goswami: 'The universe exists as formless potentia in myriad possible branches in the transcendent domain and becomes manifest only when observed by conscious beings.' (Goswami 1993.141)

The new cosmology sweeps away the old dualism of mind and matter. Goswami names it monistic idealism after Plato, remarking that 'between observations, the electron exists as a possibility form, like a Platonic archetype, in the transcendent domain of potentia' (Goswami 1993.59). Indeed, all of quantum reality is unbounded potentia until consciousness collapses the wave function, *when mind and matter arise simultaneously.* Together, they form a tangled hierarchy, like two sides of one coin, a complementarity called by Mark Woodhouse 'energy monism' (Woodhouse 1996*). Each individual consciousness is now identified with its own bodily existence in space-time, from which singular vantage point it goes on to play its own part in contributing to further innumerable collapses of the wave.*

We have to conclude that the old-style Newtonian universe is an illusion, for there is no such thing as an external world 'out there' that exists apart from consciousness. Everything is mind. We are not part of the universe, we *are* the universe. More extraordinary still, it is we as conscious observers that bring the world of the five senses into being. Along with all creatures of consciousness, we are co-creators of the physical universe.

According to Goswami, the brain-mind, being two sides of one coin, is unsurpassed in combining both Newtonian and quantum properties. By means of its classical Newtonian function, it brilliantly performs as a measuring instrument, obeys the law of cause and effect and provides us with memories, a personal history and a stable identity. It can do this because the wave function collapses in line with the maximum probability according to all the countless collapses that have previously taken place. Our physical world has structural stability because the probability wave has been generated by millions of individual consciousnesses pooled together over time. Consequently, you can expect to find your home still standing where you left it when you went off to work this morning. But also, since the wave contains everything in potentia, there is no limit to what is possible. A mind of great power can collapse the wave uniquely, apparently miraculously, on one notable occasion turning water into wine.

The brain-mind's quantum function is one of endless renewal, drawing on a transcendent realm in which everything that has already happened, is happening now and someday will happen, co-exists. The opaque window of space-time obscures from us what ultimately comprises this realm, yet mankind intuitively divines it in the archetype of the *Imago Dei* (Powell 1993). The part we play in the cosmic drama is no small one, for in our collective creation of the physical universe, we provide a stage for the self-realization of God, just as the Christian Gnostics always asserted.

In the case histories I have given so far, specific therapeutic interventions were called for but Nature in her wisdom provides a powerful tool for self-help in the form of dreams. Here is an account of one such dream brought to me recently:

The patient in question had survived an early childhood of great hardship, having been rescued from the streets aged four by Bob, a neighbour who took the boy in. From that time Bob was father in all but name. Everything he had, he shared with the boy and the boy loved him like no other.

The boy grew into a man and made good. He married, had a family and moved south where he did well professionally. But he often went back to see Bob, now ageing and alone but fiercely independent. Then the time came when Bob grew so frail, his neighbours had to come in and start washing and caring for him. Bob couldn't bear it. One day he got himself upstairs to the spare bedroom, lay on the bed with cap on head as ever, took tablets and died.

My patient was devastated at the news. He kept dreaming Bob was still alive and then, every time on waking, the shock of his death would hit him all over again. He fell into a severe depression.

He then told me that just a few days before coming to see me something had happened which had knocked him for six. He had dreamed again of Bob but this was different.

> In the dream, he knew for the first time that Bob was dead. Yet there was Bob, sitting across from him, large as life, cap on head, just the way he always sat. My patient asked him outright, 'Bob, are you dead?' Bob answered him as direct as ever, 'Yes!' His next question was, 'Is there life after death?' Another emphatic 'Yes,' came right back. Then he challenged Bob head on. 'Prove it to me!' Bob pulled out a book that looked like a bible with some detailed drawings in it and sure enough, the proof was all there.

Then he awoke. All day he could intensely feel Bob's presence. He found his emotions welling up and although in one way it hurt more than ever, he could say to me in that first meeting 'I know I'm getting better.'

Thus far, I have drawn on a number of case studies and a modicum of theory to highlight the clinical perspective. When it comes to the intriguing question of whether our individual identities as we know them continue forever in the discarnate realm, it is worth noting that our Newtonian habit of mind leads us to look at things in a dichotomous way. For instance, a great many people believe that there is no individual consciousness after death. Since the collapse of the wave is probabilistic, a stable body of opinion forms which heuristically is most likely to reinforce itself with further collapses of such a wave. On the other hand a great many people hold the opposite view, that individual identity survives death and they too are reinforcing their own probabilistic collapse of the wave. Humankind then tries to resolve these differences by turning the whole thing into a dialectic in which the opposing views compete for the truth.

There is another way to look at this, not with the *'either-or'* but the *'both-and'* solution that lies at the heart of the wave-particle experiment I mentioned earlier.

Within the quantum realm, everything that has been, is now and ever shall be, exists as one coterminous whole. When viewed from the standpoint of self, its contents assume the form of archetypal personifications, which sustain our belief in the continuity, and survival of individual identity in spirit. Buddhists, on the other hand, see such desire for continuity of selfhood as a sign of attachment to ego standing in the way of enlightenment. With the realization of nirvana, subject and object merge, giving rise to the awareness of total connectedness sometimes called at-onement, a paradoxical state of emptiness and fullness in which all the trappings of individual identity dissolve away.

It follows that we must give equal weight to both kinds of experience. Indeed, reports of the near-death experience suggest there are many mansions to be visited according to our need. By all accounts, those who need angels will see them, those who yearn for family and friends are welcomed by them, while others who know where they are going head straight for the Divine source.

Dreams are the royal road to the unconscious, as Freud famously remarked. By way of ending, here is a lucid dream, which took the dreamer self-aware into the enchanted realm and then showed him why he could not stay.

> In the dream, I found myself back at my old school. I decided to go up to the roof so I launched myself into the air and floated gently upwards. Now I was at treetop level and looked down at the woods all around the school. It was crystal clear, like a still autumn day, the sun shining and with the leaves red and gold. I descended some way and floated along, following a path through the woods. Everything was inexpressibly beautiful, more vivid even than in waking life. I somehow knew that I had created this experience and that I could make happen whatever I wanted to happen. It was sheer beauty and perfection. I felt joy, like when you hear beautiful music. At the same time I had a profound realization, which brought a kind of sadness. I saw that because I could make it all happen without any effort, like being God, I wouldn't be meeting any situations, or other real people, that would really challenge me. There would never be anything to learn and I would always be alone. I found myself longing for that other 'real' world again. Then I awoke.

However intriguing and captivating we find the primary nature of consciousness, we are equally indebted to the physical universe, for without it there would be no such thing as experience. The same apple that tempted Eve could not then have fallen at Newton's feet and both science and religion would have been the poorer. Our task is to bring the instrument of human consciousness to bear on the quantum wave with the greatest care, for whether we do it in love or hate literally determines whether we create a heaven or hell. We can surely rely on finding our individual identity where and when it is most needed, within the bounds of space and time. Beyond that, in the quantum realm, there is a more important truth to be discovered, that we are one. If humankind should ever learn that what belongs to one belongs to all, heaven on earth will be assured.

## *References*

Baldwin, William. 1992. *Spirit releasement therapy.* New York: Headline.

Bohm, David. 1980. *Wholeness and the implicate order.* London: Routledge.

Chodorow, J. 1997. *Jung on active imagination.* London: Routledge.

Ducasse, C. J. 1960. How the case of the search for Bridey Murphy stands today. *Journal of the American Society of Psychical Research.* 54.3–22.

Goswami, Amit. 1993. *The self-aware universe.* New York: Putnam.

Grinberg-Zylberbaum, J., M. Delaflor, M.E. Sanchez Arellano, M.A. Guevara, M. Perez. 1992. Human communication and the electrophysiological activity of the brain. *Subtle Energies.* 3:3.26–43.

Honorton, C., D.C. Ferrari. 1989. Future telling: a meta-analysis of forced-choice precognition experiments, 1935–1987. *Journal of Parapsychology.* 53.281–308.

Jung, C.G. 1952. Synchronicity: an acausal connecting principle. *The structure and dynamics of the psyche.* In: *Collected works,* Vol. 8. Princeton University Press.

—. 1954. *Archetypes and the collective unconscious.* In: *Collected works,* Vol. 9.1. Princeton University Press.

—. 1961. *Memories, dreams, reflections.* New York: Random House.

Main, Roderick. 1997. *Jung on synchronicity and the paranormal.* London: Routledge.

Newton, Michael. 1994. *Journey of souls.* St Paul: Llewellyn.

Powell, Andrew. 1993. The psychophysical matrix and group analysis. *Group Analysis,* 26:4.449–68.

—. 1998. Soul consciousness and human suffering. *Journal of Alternative and Complementary Medicine,* 4:1.101–8.

Radin, Dean. 1997. *The conscious universe.* Harper Edge.

Schmidt, H., R. Morris, L. Rudolph. 1986. Channelling evidence for a PK effect to independent observers. *Journal of Parapsychology,* 50.1–16.

Sheldrake, Rupert. 1999. *New science of life — the hypothesis of morphic resonance.* Rochester, VT: Park Street Press.

Stevenson, Ian. 1966. *Twenty cases suggestive of reincarnation.* Charlottesville: University Press of Virginia.

—. 1984. *Unlearned language: new studies in xenoglossia.* Charlottesville: University Press of Virginia.

—. 1997. *Reincarnation and biology.* Westport: Praeger.

Tarazi, L. 1997. *Under the Inquisition: an experience relived.* Charlottesville: Hampton Roads.

Woodhouse, Mark. 1996. *Paradigm wars.* Berkeley: Frog Ltd.

Woolger, Roger. 1999. *Other lives, other selves.* New York: Bantam.

# The Implications of Alternative and Complementary Medicine for Science

MARILYN SCHLITZ AND WILLIS HARMAN

*Marilyn Schlitz, Ph.D., is Director of Research at the Institute of Noetic Sciences. Trained in anthropology and parapsychology, she has published numerous articles on consciousness-related issues, including cross-cultural healing, psi research and sociolinguistics. Prior to joining the staff at IONS, she held the Thomas Welton Stanford Chair in Psychical Research in the Department of Psychology at Stanford University.*

Prior to the modern period in which we now live, health care was characterized by a pluralism of choices. Indeed, during the eighteenth and nineteenth centuries, various types of alternative and complementary medicines co-existed with the fledging, allopathic, science-based medicine throughout Europe and North America. The 1910 report on North American medical schools by Abraham Flexner (1910), commissioned by the Carnegie Foundation, changed this situation by supporting the growing movement that used a dogmatic definition of science to judge medical options. Alternative approaches such as homoeopathy, midwifery, and chiropractic were essentially forced out of the official medical system (Starr 1982).

Today, alternative and complementary medicines are experiencing a revitalization. New developments include a growing professionalization, creation of several professional journals, establishment of the Office of Alternative Medicine at the National Institutes of Health, reimbursement of selected alternative treatments by some insurance providers, a proliferation of books and conferences concerning research and clinical practice, and survey data suggesting that Americans are spending billions of dollars per year on alternative treatment options (Eisenberg, *et al.* 1993).

Despite these advances, alternative and complementary medical practices remain marginalized relative to the dominant bio-medical model. One important factor in this situation is the form of science that has shaped modern medicine; a form that has evolved with a certain passion and world-view about the nature of reality. Indeed, modern Western science fundamentally entails three important metaphysical assumptions that limit its ability to integrate alternative medicines.

These are:

a. *Realism* (ontological — leads to epistemological conclusion). There is a real material world independent of mind which is, in essence, physically measurable (positivism). We are embedded in that world, follow its laws, and have evolved from an ancient origin. Mind or consciousness evolved within that world; the world pre-existed before its appearance, and continues to exist and persist independent of consciousness.
b. *Objectivism* (epistemological and ontological). A form of materialist realism which says that the world is knowable and persists as a domain of objects un-affected by perceiving subjects. That real world therefore can be studied as object. That is, it is accessible to sense perception and can be consensually observed and validated.
c. *Reductionism* (epistemological). Knowledge is attained by a process of analysing, explaining, or validating data in terms of the constituent parts of objects and/or the laws which determine their behaviour. The real world is described by the laws of physics, which are believed to apply everywhere. The essence of the scientific endeavour is to provide explanations for complex phenomena in terms of the characteristics of, and interactions among, their component parts.

These assumptions, and the methods they require, currently dominate biomedical science. The present situation in American medicine involves a deepening understanding of such factors as the role of DNA in determining the nature of the organism, an expanding reliance on advanced and expensive technology, and a growing faith in the power of modern biomedical theory. To some extent these metaphysical premises have been re-evaluated through an understanding of the relativistic views of science recently explicated by works in the history, sociology, and philosophy of science (Lakatos & Musgrave 1970;

Kuhn 1970; Latour 1987). More central to our concern here, however, are the new findings in the areas of alternative and complementary medicine that have profound implications for science and its application in the biological and medical domains. In particular, many alternative epistemologies involve a worldview in which human experience — including thoughts, feelings, and intentions — is believed to interact in causal ways with subtle forms of 'energies,' 'forces,' or 'spirits' to create a healing response. Such beliefs currently have no place in the Western scientific paradigm.

A fundamental difficulty appears to be that Western science continues to be caught in a basic dualistic trap — that of considering the subject doing the mapping as separate from the map. Getting a more accurate map (based more on modern physics, more 'holistic,' more 'systems') does not seem to solve this problem. Rather, it may be useful to reflect on the possibility that thoughts are not merely a reflection on reality, but are also a movement of that reality itself. The mapmaker, the self, the thinking and knowing subject, may actually be a product and a participant of what it seeks to know and represent (Wilbur 1995, 1996). The critical epistemological issue is whether we humans have basically *one* way of contacting reality (namely, through the physical senses) or *multiple* (the others including intuition, somatic feelings, and direct apprehension) (Harman & De Quincey 1994).

The importance of the issue shows up in a central ontological question: is consciousness caused (by physiological processes in the brain, which in turn are consequences of a long evolutionary process) or is it *causal* (in the sense that consciousness is not only a causal factor in present phenomena, but also a causal factor throughout the entire evolutionary process)? Western scientific method urges towards the former choice, whereas some of the phenomena of alternative and complementary medicines (e.g., placebo effects, psychosomatic trauma and healing, intentionality) suggest the latter choice.

There is in the medical world much faith that explanations of some of the claimed results in alternative and complementary medicine (as well as debunking of some other claimed results) will be forthcoming from this strengthening biomedical science. At the same time, much of complementary and alternative medicine does not fit even with accepted new views of science, such as quantum mechanics and complexity theories. It seems to be true that, taken together, these diagnostic, therapeutic, and health-promoting practices pose a fundamental challenge to the metaphysical foundations of Western science — based on assumptions of materialism, objectivism, reductionism, and physical determinism. We wish to explore the extent and implications of that challenge.

## *Incompatibilities between alternative medicine and science*

There are areas of alternative and complementary medicine where we not only lack scientific models that would help explain the 'mechanisms' of healing, but the models that do arise from the various complementary medical systems (e.g. subtle energies, mind-body-spirit holism, intentionality) do not seem compatible with the Western scientific worldview. Examples include homeopathy; acupuncture, qigong, and traditional Chinese medicine; Ayurvedic (Indian) medicine; Tibetan medicine; and various practices utilized by Fourth World peoples. Even herbal therapies, nutritional supplements, aromatherapy, meditation and biofeedback, guided imagery, body work, etc. may be of questionable compatibility to the extent that they involve holistic models which include causal consciousness.

### Subtle Energies

Many alternative healing practitioners associate healing with what are commonly referred to as 'subtle energies,' or 'fields.' This concept may include electromagnetic and other energy fields throughout, and in the space surrounding the body, but it may also involve factors which are, at least so far, non-physically measurable (Schlitz 1997). The admitted ambiguity allows a co-convening of those who believe all phenomena will eventually be understood in terms of energy fields which fit within the known models of science, together with those who find psychological and spiritual phenomena to involve aspects of reality not representable in terms of measurable fields.

There are many cultural instances of such 'subtle fields.' In the Eastern cultures, we find such concepts as *prana, ch'i,* or *ki,* concepts that find no easy place in our scientific lexicon. Traditional Chinese medicine (TCM), for example, is a comprehensive professional discipline, based on a complete system of thought. Within this epistemology, the human body is seen as a reflection of the natural world — a whole within a larger whole. Energy and fluids in the body are spoken of as flowing like channels and rivers. A medical diagnosis describes the body in terms of the elements — wind, heat, cold, dryness, dampness–concepts that have no place in current Western diagnostic categories.

The complementary terms *yin* and *yang* are used by the TCM practitioner to describe the various opposing physical conditions of the body. *Yin* refers to the tissue of the organ, while *yang* refers to its activity. TCM also introduces a major component of the body, *ch'i,* that Western medicine does not acknowledge. This 'vital life energy' flows through the body following pathways called meridians, which move along the surface of the body, and through the internal organs. According to this view, organs can be accessed for treatment through their specific meridians, and illness can occur when there is a blockage of *ch'i* in these channels. TCM incorporates a wide range of methods of treatment, including herbal medicine, acupuncture, dietary therapy, and massage. These have all become more or less acceptable in Western medicine; however, the conceptual model including the central *ch'i* concept is by no means compatible with the assumptions of Western science. While the medical model makes use of the body's energy using electroencephalography, electrocardiography, and electromyography for diagnostic purposes, it has yet to incorporate 'subtle energies' for the purpose of healing (Micozzi 1996).

For another example of subtle energies within the framework of alternative medicine, we turn to homeopathy, which was founded in the late eighteenth century by German physician Samuel Hahnemann (Jonas and Jacobs 1996). It remains reasonably acceptable in continental Europe, where in one sense it is more or less integrated with conventional medicine. Within the current scientific medical paradigm, however, the underlying principles comprise a challenge to conventional medicine's concepts of illness and healing. These basic underlying principles are:

a. Like cures like; the same substance that in large doses creates symptoms like those of the disease, in minute dosage can be used to cure it.
b. Dilution increases potency; potency is greatest after dilution has reduced the amount below chemical detection.
c. Illness is specific to the individual; an illness generally defined will be treated in homeopathy only after finding the symptom pattern unique to the patient.

Like TCM, homeopathy is a complete self-contained alternative system of medicine that reportedly can have a therapeutic effect on almost any disease or health condition. On the other hand, the implied formal causality in homeopathy does not fit the efficient causality of Western science.

### Intentionality

The role of the mind and intentionality represents one of the key features of most alternative medical systems and is an important challenge to Western scientific epistemology (Schlitz 1995). Broadly defined, intentionality involves the projection of awareness, with purpose and efficacy, toward some object or outcome. It includes ways in which a person's mind is able to interact with his or her own body, such as in self-healing; ways in which people's intentions can influence others through direct or indirect communication, such as in placebo and 'nocebo' effects; and more difficult to reconcile with our current scientific worldview, ways in which intentions may influence others through some 'non local' means.

While psychological approaches that assume intentionality, including imagery techniques, have been used by alternative practitioners for centuries in order to help mobilize the healing process, such concepts as psychosomatic illness, stress disorders, placebo effect, dissociation, and mind/body medicine, have met with considerable resistance. This is due, in large part, to the fact that consciousness as a causal factor is excluded from the scientific worldview. Today, guided imagery is widely used for relief of chronic pain and other symptoms, and for accelerating healing and minimizing discomfort from injuries and illness symptoms (Achterberg 1985, Achterberg & Lawlis 1984, Benson 1975, Dacher 1993, Dienstfrey 1991, Lock & Colligen 1986). Imagery has been used to bring about healing from serious illness; spontaneous patient imagery has been used to better understand the meaning of symptoms or to access inner resources. Intentionality is not only implicit in all of this; a connection between imagery and real physiological effects is assumed.

As of now, we have no clear understanding of how this healing effect works within the context of our bio-medical models. The influence of a healers' or patients' intentions (including expectations) on the physical state of the patient puzzles or disturbs some medical professionals, and is a troubling artifact for many researchers. But it can also be viewed as an untapped resource in healing. Although the typical view of placebos is that they should be controlled or eliminated, the phenomenon may in fact turn out to be a powerful agent in linking intention, belief, expectations, and bodily responses (Dienstfrey 1997). The challenge of delineating all significant variables is considerable and may be one reason that so little has been done to integrate placebos into clinical practice. More research could be done to analyze nonspecific factors including rapport, anticipation, and hope, in a way that begins to clarify their roles in healing. At the same time, we must develop reliable holistic methods and approaches that allow us to understand the healing relationship in other than reductionistic terms.

More difficult conceptually are the claims made by healers that they can use intentionality to access some form of 'transpersonal' consciousness — consciousness that seemingly originates from a 'higher source,' passes through one person, the healer, to another, the patient — at a distance. The idea of transpersonal or 'non-local' healing has widespread support in many cultures. Further, it is widely believed that people can obtain information about the world around them without any direct sensory contact. So we find, for example, that in the Spanish folk medicine of *curanderismo,* or in the *obeah* practices of the southern Caribbean, or among the Kaluli peoples of the Papua New Guinea rainforest, healers believe that they are able to physically affect other people at a distance through some kind of direct mental or spiritual interaction. What's more, they say they can heal this way without other people necessarily knowing about the effort–presumably eliminating any direct placebo effect. According to the Western scientific paradigm, such phenomena are impossible; nevertheless, increasing data support the claims (Benor 1993, Braud & Schlitz 1989, Schlitz & Braud 1997, Schlitz 1996, Solfvin 1984). But there is currently no explaining such results with accepted scientific concepts.

### Intuitive diagnosis

With regard to medical diagnosis, many alternative practitioners and physicians utilize their consciousness in a fashion that is not understood by Western science. Frequently this is described as a hunch or intuition that the practitioner had no reason to assume would be helpful but which turned out to be exactly what needed to be done. The physician Oliver Wendell Holmes described the intuitive process by saying that 'all of us have a double who is wiser and better than we are and who puts thoughts into our heads and words into our mouths' (Inglis 1989). Despite this, most Western-trained physicians have been taught to rely on objective tools of science for diagnostic insights, excluding their own subjectivity except in some very marginalized way.

The most startling evidence of remote diagnosis is in the form of anecdotal data. Perhaps two of the best known cases are Edgar Cayce and Caroline Myss. Cayce (1877–1945) discovered this apparent ability accidentally. Hundreds of times, in an altered state of consciousness and given by hypnotic suggestion the name and location of an ailing person at some remote location, he would come up with a detailed diagnosis, apparently accurate in the vast majority of cases (Sugrue 1984). The work of Myss is similar except that she remained in a state of conscious awareness. By telephone call from her partner, C. Norman Shealy, a Harvard-trained neurosurgeon and researcher, she would be given a patient's name and date of birth. According to Dr Shealy's data (1988), her diagnoses were '93 percent accurate.' In spite of such anecdotal data on successes, however, little research has been done on the role of intuition in diagnosis. As Daniel Benor (1993) writes: 'Intuitive diagnosis has received less attention than healing. This neglected modality has much to offer modern medicine.' Fulfilling this potential, however, will require some radical alterations in the basic assumptions of modern scientific medicine.

## *Possible alternative ontological assumptions*

At a fundamental level, these alternative approaches imply pictures of reality that are not in accord with the Western scientific worldview. They pose both an epistemological and an ontological challenge. It might seem more reasonable to take up the challenges one by one — the possibilities of subtle energies, the role of the mind in healing, the puzzle of intentionality, the mystery of remote diagnosis, etc. Science has often progressed by focusing on the simplest and most tractable case first, and later proceeding to the more complex.

However there is an alternative strategy that also has a precedent in the history of science. Consider the origin of the evolutionary hypothesis. In the mid-nineteenth century there was much to be learned from studying separately the great variety of micro-organisms, plants, and animals with which the planet is populated. But Charles Darwin boldly turned his attention to the synthesising question: How can we understand *all of these together?* The result was the concept of evolution, around which practically all of biology is now organized.

There would seem to be an analogous situation in the multifaceted challenge posed by alternative and complementary medicine. We appear to need some sort of conceptual framework within which to understand a broad range of phenomena and experiences. As noted by medical historian, Marc Micozzi (1996): 'When homeopathy or acupuncture is observed to result in a physiologic or clinical response that cannot be explained by the biomedical model, it is not the role of the scientist to deny this reality, but rather to modify our explanatory models to account for it. In the end, there is only one reality.' What sorts of conceptual frameworks and organizing metaphors could be used to help us understand the many facets and dimensions of Western medicine and complementary medicine *all considered together?*

A step toward resolving this long-standing impasse may be the recognition that it is, in a sense, a historical accident that physics was taken to be the root science. That led naturally enough to such ideas as seeking objectivity through separating observer and observed; taking reality to be essentially that which can be physically measured; and seeking explanations of the whole in terms of understanding the parts.

But what if the study of living systems had been taken to be the root science, rather than physics (Harman & Sahtoris 1999)? Had this been the case, science would undoubtedly have taken a more holistic turn. It would have recognized that wholes are self-evidently more than the sum of their parts, and would have adopted an epistemology more congenial to living organisms. It might well have adopted a different ontological stance in viewing reality.

Such an alternative ontological stance was proposed, following Arthur Koestler (1969) by American philosopher Ken Wilber (1995, 1996), that of considering reality as composed of 'holons,' each of which is a whole and simultaneously a part of some other whole — 'holons within holons.' (For example, atom-molecule-organelle-cell-tissue-organ-organism-society-biosphere.) Holons at the same time display agency, the capacity to maintain their own wholeness, even as they are also parts of other wholes. A holon can break up into other holons. But every holon also has the tendency to come together with others, resulting in the emergence of creative and novel holons (as in evolution). The drive to self-transcendence appears to be built into the very fabric of the universe. The self-transcending drive produces life out of matter, and may be the basis of consciousness.

Holons relate 'holarchically.' (This term seems advisable because 'hierarchy' has a bad name, mainly because people confuse natural hierarchy [inescapable] with dominator hierarchy [pathological].) Thus cell-holons are parts of organ-holons, which in turn are parts of organism-holons, which are parts of community-holons. For any particular holon, *functions and purposes* come from levels higher in the holarchy; *capabilities* depend upon lower levels.

In the holarchic picture of reality, the scientist-holon seeking to understand consciousness is in an intermediate position. Looking downward in the holarchy (or to the same level, in the social sciences), and exploring in a scientific spirit of inquiry, it is obvious that the appropriate epistemology is a participative one. Looking upward in the holarchy, it is apparent that the appropriate epistemology involves a holistic view in which the parts are understood through the whole. This epistemology will recognize the importance of subjective and cultural meanings in all human experience, including some religious or interpersonal experiences — that seem particularly rich in meaning even though they may be ineffable. In a holistic view, such meaningful experiences will not be explained away by reducing them to combinations of simpler experiences or to physiological or biochemical events. Rather, in a holistic approach, the meanings of experiences may be understood by discovering their interconnections with other meaningful experiences.

If this ontological stance is accepted, a good many seemingly opposing views in Western thought become reconciled. From the level of the human-holon, the scientist looks mainly downward in the holarchy; the mystic looks mainly upward. Science and religion are potentially two complementary and entirely congenial views; each needs the other for more completeness. In Western philosophy there have been three main ontological positions: the materialist-realist, the dualist, and the idealist. Again, the materialist looks downward, the idealist upward, and the dualist tries to reconcile fragments of the two — all represent but partial glimpses of the holarchic whole.

This new ontological stance takes some living with to fully appreciate how successfully it helps resolve many of the time-honoured puzzles of Western philosophy — the mind-body problem, for example, and free will versus determinism. Since everything is part of the one holarchy, if consciousness or purpose is found anywhere (such as at the level of the scientist-holon), it is by that fact characteristic of the whole. It can neither be ruled out at the level of the micro-organism, nor the level of the Earth, or Gaia. Nor need we be nonplussed by evidence of alternative and complementary medicine about experiences that don't fit with a materialist, reductionist ontology.

## *Implications for scientific epistemological assumptions*

As within the presently dominant concept of medical science, the epistemology implied by this ontological stance, and to some extent defensible even without it (James 1912), will insist on *open inquiry* and *public (intersubjective) validation* of knowledge; at the same time, it will recognize that these goals may, at any given time, be met only incompletely. Taking into account how both individual and collective perceptions are affected by unconsciously held beliefs and expectations, the limitations of intersubjective agreement are apparent.

This epistemology will be 'radically empirical' in the sense urged by William James (1912) in that it will be *phenomenological* or experiential in a broad sense. In other words, it will include subjective experience as primary data, rather than being essentially limited to physical-sense data. Further, it will address the totality of human experience — no reported phenomena will be written off because they 'violate known scientific laws.' Thus, consciousness will not be conceptualized as a 'thing' to be studied by an observer who is somehow apart from it; research on consciousness involves the interaction of the observer and the observed, or more accurately, the *experience* of observing.

This adequate epistemology will be, above all else, humble. It will recognize that science deals with *models and metaphors representing certain aspects of experienced reality,* and that any model or metaphor may be permissible if it is useful in helping to order knowledge, even though it may seem to conflict with another model which is also useful. (The classic example is the history of wave and particle models in physics.) This includes, specifically, the metaphor of consciousness. Perhaps this sounds strange?

Indeed, it is a peculiarity of modern science that it allows some kinds of metaphors and disallows others. For example, it is perfectly acceptable to use metaphors that derive directly from our experience of the physical world (such as 'fundamental particles,' acoustic waves), as well as metaphors representing what can be measured only in terms of its effects (such as gravitational, electromagnetic, or quantum fields). It has further become acceptable in science to use more holistic and non-quantifiable metaphors such as organism, personality, ecological community, Gaia, universe. It is, however, taboo to use non-sensory 'metaphors of mind' — metaphors that tap into images and experiences familiar from our own inner awareness. We are not allowed to say (according to the dominant scientific paradigm) that some aspects of our experience of reality are reminiscent of our experience of our own minds — to observe, for example, that some aspects of animal behaviour appear as though they were tapping into some supra-individual nonphysical mind, or as though there were in instinctual behaviour and in evolution something like our experience in our own minds of *purpose.*

The expanded epistemology we seek will recognize *the partial nature of all scientific concepts of causality* (Harman 1994, Harman & Clark 1994). (For example, the 'upward causation' of physiomotor action resulting from a brain state does not necessarily invalidate the 'downward causation' implied in the subjective feeling of volition.) In other words, it will implicitly question the assumption that a nomothetic science — one characterized by inviolable 'scientific laws' — can in the end adequately deal with causality. In some ultimate sense, there really is no causality — only the Whole evolving.

It will also recognize that prediction and control are not the only criteria by which to judge knowledge as scientific. As the French poet Antoine Saint-Exupéry put it, 'Truth is not that which is demonstrable. Truth is that which is ineluctable.' Here we find that the unquestioned authority of the objective and detached observer is challenged. In particular, the double-blind controlled experiment, considered the gold standard of clinical research, is thrown deeply into question if the consciousness of the experimenter or the clinician is causal (Wiseman & Schlitz 1996). An engaged epistemology will involve recognition of the inescapable role of *the personal characteristics of the observer,* including the processes and contents of the unconscious mind. The corollary follows, that to be a competent investigator, the researcher must be *willing to risk being profoundly changed* through the process of exploration. Because of this potential transformation of observers, an epistemology which is acceptable now to the scientific community, may in time have to be replaced by another, more satisfactory new criteria, for which it has laid the intellectual and experiential foundations.

## *Broader implications*

Research on perception, hypnosis, dissociation, repression, selective attention, mental imagery, sleep and dreams, memory and memory retrieval, all suggests that the influence of the unconscious on how we experience ourselves and our environment may be far greater than is typically taken into account. Science itself has never been thoroughly re-assessed in the light of this recently discovered pervasive influence of the unconscious mind of the scientist or the healing practitioner. The contents and processes of the unconscious individually and collectively influence perceptions, 'rational thinking,' openness to challenging evidence, ability to contemplate alternative conceptual frameworks and metaphors, scientific interests and disinterests, scientific judgment — all to an indeterminate extent. What is implied is that we must accept the presence of unconscious processes and contents, not as a minor perturbation, but as a potentially major factor in the construction of any society's particular form of science. Again, we may have to reevaluate the role of the experimenter effect in outcome studies, as well as our firm reliance on double-blind control studies, and other assumptions about objectivity, materialism, and reductionism.

The implications of research in these areas go even further. They suggest holistic interconnection at levels yet to be fully recognized by Western medical science. The ontological stance of the universe as holarchy appears to have great promise as the basis for an extended science in which consciousness-related phenomena are no longer anomalies, but keys to a deeper understanding; a science of medicine that transcends and includes the science we have. The most important thing is not to accept a particular answer, but to open the dialogue about the metaphysical foundations of Western science and their relationship to understanding mind-body-spirit health and healing.

## Conclusion

Science and society exist in a dialectical relationship. The findings of science have a profound effect on society; none of us have any doubts about that. But science is also a product of society, very much shaped by the cultural milieu within which it developed. Western science and medical science have the forms they do because science developed within a culture placing unusual value on the ability to predict and control.

What assumptions underlie the attempt to marry alternative and complementary medicine to the US allopathic, science-based medicine? On the one hand, these approaches encourage openness to whatever has seemed to work in the past; diversity of approaches for a diversity of persons; empowerment of the individual to choose their own medical options, and hence be more highly motivated in their own health care. One the other hand, if alternative medicine in the United States and elsewhere is to be fitted into the fee for services, power of the professional, managed care, and scientific assumption structure, it is likely to be subtly shaped by that structure so that its effectiveness may not be the same as in its original cultural context.

Besides the choice to ignore or adapt to the existing structure, there is a third choice — whole-system change (Harman 1988). We need to look at the forces that might make this plausible. How might society move toward a really integral system of healing?

## References

Achterberg, J. 1985. *Imagery and healing: Shamanism and modern medicine.* Boston: New Science Library.

Achterberg, J. and F. Lawlis. 1984. *Imagery and Disease.* Champaign, Ill.: Institute for Personality and Ability Testing.

Benor, D.J. 1993. *Healing research.* (4 vols.) Munich: Helix.

Benson, H. 1975. *The relaxation response.* New York: Morrow.

Braud, W.G., and M.J. Schlitz. 1989. A methodology for the objective study of transpersonal imagery. *Journal of Scientific Exploration* 3:1.43–63.

Dacher, E. 1993. *Psychoneuro-immunology: the new mind/body healing program.* New York: Paragon House.

Dienstfrey, H. 1991. *Where the mind meets the body.* New York: Norton.

—. 1997. Will current mind/body research lead to a mind/body medicine? *Journal of Mind/Body Medicine.*

Eisenberg, D.M., R.C. Kessler, C. Foster, R.E. Norlock, D.R. Calkins, T.L. Delbanco. 1993. Unconventional medicine in the United States — prevalence, costs, and patterns of use. *New England Journal of Medicine* 328.246–52.

Flexner, A. 1910. *Medical education in the United States and Canada. Bulletin No. 4.* New York: The Carnegie Foundation for the Advancement of Teaching.

Harman, W. 1988. *Global mind change: the promise of the last years of the twentieth century.* Sausalito: Institute of Noetic Sciences.

—. 1994. The scientific exploration of consciousness: towards an adequate epistemology. *Journal of Consciousness Studies.* 1:1.140–48.

Harman, W. and J. Clark (eds.) 1994 *New metaphysical foundations of modern science.* Sausalito: Institute of Noetic Sciences.

Harman, W., and C. de Quincey. 1994. *The scientific exploration of consciousness: toward an adequate epistemology.* Sausalito: Institute of Noetic Sciences.

Harman, W. and E. Sahtoris. 1999. *Biology revisioned.* Berkeley: North Atlantic Press, and Sausalito: Institute of Noetic Sciences.

Inglis, B. 1989. *The unknown guest: the mystery of intuition.* Sevenoaks: Hodder & Stoughton.

James, W. 1912. *Essays in radical empiricism.* New York: Longman, Green.

Jonas, W., and J. Jacobs. 1996. *Healing with homeopathy: the natural way to promote recovery and restore health.* New York: Warner.

Koestler, A. and J.R. Smythies (eds.) 1969 *Beyond reductionism: the new perspectives in the life sciences. The Alpbach symposium.* London: Hutchinson.

Kuhn, T. 1970 (2 ed.) *The structure of scientific revolutions.* University of Chicago Press.

Lakatos, I., A. Musgrave (eds.) 1970. *Criticism and the growth of knowledge.* Cambridge University Press.

Latour, B. 1987. *Science in action.* Cambridge, Mass.: Harvard University Press.

Locke, S. and D. Colligen. 1986. *The healer within.* New York: Dutton.

Micozzi, M. 1996. Characteristics of complementary and alternative medicine. In: M. Micozzi (ed.) *Fundamentals of complementary and alternative medicine.* New York: Churchill Livingstone.

Schlitz, M.J. 1995. Intentionality in healing: mapping the integration of body, mind, and spirit. *Alternative Therapies* 1:5.102–119.

—. 1996. Intentionality and intuition and their clinical implications: a challenge for science and medicine. *Advances: Journal of Mind-Body Health* 12:2.58–66.

—. 1997. Subtle energies and consciousness: An overview of research. In: K. Shaner (ed.) *Where eastern philosophy and western sciences meet: the Smithsonian lectures.* New York: Random House.

Schlitz, M.J., and W.G. Braud. 1997. Distant intentionality and its potential relevance to healing research: assessing the evidence. *Alternative Therapies* 3:6.

Shealy, C.N., and C. Myss. 1988. *The creation of health: merging traditional medicine with intuitive diagnosis.* Walpole, NH: Stillpoint.

Solfvin, J. 1984. Mental healing. In: S. Krippner (ed.) *Advances in parapsychological research.* Jefferson, NC: McFarland.

Starr, P. 1982. *The social transformation of American medicine.* New York: Basic Books.

Sugrue, T. 1984. *There is a river.* Association for Research and Enlightenment Press.

Wilber, K. 1995. *Sex, ecology, spirituality: the spirit of evolution.* Boston: Shambhala.

—. 1996. *A brief history of everything.* Boston: Shambhala.

Wiseman, R. and M.J. Schlitz. 1996. Experimenter effects and the remote detection of staring. *Annual Proceedings of the Parapsychological Convention,* San Diego.

# The Presence of Other Worlds in Psychotherapy and Healing

ROGER J. WOOLGER

*Roger J. Woolger, Ph.D., is a British-born Jungian analyst, past-lives therapist and creator of Integral Regression Therapy. Roger is internationally known as a pioneer in the area of transpersonal psychology. He holds degrees from Oxford and London Universities and the C.G. Jung Institute in Zurich, Switzerland. He lives in suburban Maryland and teaches throughout North America, Europe and South America. His book on past life therapy,* Other Lives, Other Selves, *has been translated into many languages.*

> *Under its first impetus philosophical thought is simply metaphysics because it is a going beyond ... It has been said that this begins in wonder. An initial amazement marks the opening of a new dimension of transcendence. By a movement of defocusing the world becomes disarticulated and is shown in relief.*
>
> *Pierre Thevenaz,* What is Phenomenology? *(162f)*

> *The visible world was made to correspond to the world invisible and there is nothing in this world but is a symbol of something in that other world.*
>
> *Al Ghazzali*

My chief purpose here is to argue for the presence of multiple worlds, spiritual and visionary, that interact with and inter-penetrate this one. And in taking a multi-dimensional view of reality, I emphatically reject the one-dimensional materialist view of reality supported by conventional scientific thinking in which mental events are regarded as the energetic products of brain circuitry and biochemistry. All such scientific, energetic, materialistic views of mind are at root reductionistic, and are unconsciously caught in the literalism of their own metaphors. So in the spirit of the conference, my intention is to go beyond the brain and materialism and re-affirm the spiritual viewpoint common to sacred tradition.

## *Consciousness as energy field or atomic particle*

> *If you are embarrassed by the word 'spirit' think of spirit as the subtlest form of matter ...*
>
> *Sri Aurobindo (Green 1977.63)*

> *If matter has come into being or if flesh has come into being because of the spirit, it is a wonder.*
> *But if spirit has come into being because of matter or flesh it is a wonder of wonders.*
>
> *The Gospel of Thomas (29)*

A major question that always troubled me about the materialist view of mind is: how can consciousness be *in* the brain and how can spirit be *a part of* the natural world when neither seem to be fully material entities governed by time and space? It has always seemed to me analogous to asking: is there actually music *in* my CD? Or: is there actually electromagnetic energy *inside* a magnet? Yet such analogies can be very misleading, if not extremely seductive. For the physicist will say that the music is emitted by the CD (when properly played) as *sound waves* and that the electromagnetism surrounding and penetrating the magnet is *an energy field.* This lets the brain physiologist say that the brain can be seen, by a similar analogy, as having an energy field that transmits thought waves. Then he feels fully warranted in looking for the neural or biochemical pathways along which the energy of thought runs.

By a series of seeming logical (though strictly speaking *analogical*) moves the materialist has neatly located the mind *in nature,* as the philosopher C.D. Broad put it. In support of this are the obvious facts that there is no music if I smash my CD and its player; there is no magnetism without the magnet and there is no thinking if I am run over by a bus. Physical entities of one form or another are clearly necessary conditions for wave patterns, for magnetism, for subtle energy fields and for thought to occur.

But is this the whole picture? Surely my *experience of music* is something different from a sound wave and *to take thought* is not the same as activating a neural circuit?

The philosopher Heidegger has said that science is based on an explanatory scheme designed to convert whatever is studied into something in space, located over there and subsisting separately from that which is over against us. It makes no difference whether the thing in question is a chair, a man, an atom, a sense datum, or a body. It is still in some sense *there.* And when it is out there it has things in it and it is 'in' space. This, says Heidegger (Avens 1982.165), is how we imagine objects.*

To the extent then, that science has made of mind or consciousness an *object* of investigation — not a subject, please note — it has produced much that is stimulating and provocative in the last century. The epiphenomenal view of mind, which treats consciousness as an energy frequency or field surrounding and penetrating the brain and nervous system has occupied some of the finest of scientific minds. One has only to think, for example of Elmer Green's extraordinary work of nearly thirty years at the Menninger Foundation in Kansas where he records vibrational changes in what he calls the biofield. He has successfully measured the fields of several practising yogis, healers and shamans (Green 1977).

In the traditional Hindu teachings these fields are called the sthula or energy sheaths or the subtle bodies. There are subtle hierarchies of them ascending like vibrational octaves. Barbara Brennan's book *Hands of Light* (1988) give us clairvoyant images of these subtle bodies or fields to help us understand how they relate to Wilhelm Reich's concepts of energy flows and blocks in the body. Another western version of this yogic doctrine is David Tansley's theory and practice of what he called *Radionics* (1972). In Tansley as in Brennan you will find descriptions of a hierarchy of subtle bodies called the etheric, emotional, mental and spiritual that surround the physical body. (Interestingly Tansley attributed the source of his model to Alice Bailey's theosophical commentary on the Yoga Sutras of Patanjali (1927), the *locus classicus* of Hindu teaching.)

In the fields of hypnotherapy and birth regression both David Cheek (Rossi & Cheek 1994) and Graham Farrant (Satprem 1982)

* Avens' radical critique of parapsychology sees it as fundamentally hamstrung by a dualism that excludes the soul. His work deserves to be read by all researchers in the field.

have independently introduced the notion of *cellular consciousness,* claiming that memory is actually stored 'in the cells' — surely a metaphor once again, but one that is gaining much popularity. (To what extent they were influenced by Sri Aurobindo's teachings recorded in Satprem's 1982 book *The Mind of the Cells,* I cannot say). Recently in the journal of the Scientific and Medical Network *(Network* 1997. April 63) there has been reference to Professor Sarkar's concept of the *microvita,* minuscule elements of energy which he describes as the ultimate source of life. One might call these models 'atomistic' as contrasted with 'field' metaphors of the location of consciousness.

More broadly, psychotherapists who work with regression, psychodrama, rebirthing and other deep experiential therapies have for many years been talking loosely of body consciousness. Recently Dr Larry Dossey proposed the term 'non-local mind' to challenge the prevalent brain based theory of the location of consciousness. In my own practice when exploring mysterious pains I have found it valuable to use the term 'etheric memory or consciousness' following the subtle body theory. This allows me to talk of an etheric memory of trauma embedded 'in' the foot or 'around' the shoulders.

To return to field theories, most people are familiar with the Russian work on the Kirlian Aura popularized in the anthologies of Stanley Krippner and John White (Krippner & Rubin 1973, White & Krippner 1977, White 1979). More recently, building on Kirlian concepts, the idea of bioplasm, a 'fifth state of matter' has been proposed by Viktor Inyushin. Inyushin (White & Krippner 1977.115) maintains that as well as solids, liquids, gases and plasma there is a fifth state of matter, the bioplasm, which is held in the biofield as follows:

> A living organism can be described as a 'biological field' or a 'biofield,' a 'field' being a region consisting of lines of force which affect each other. The biofield has a clear spacial formation and is separated and shaped by several physical fields, electrostatic, electromagnetic, acoustic, hydrodynamic and quite possibly others inadequately explored.

Clearly for Inyushin the biofield or the subtle energy field made up of bioplasm is a more refined derivative of existing physical energy fields in the body. What we have here is materialist philosophy presented in the form of an energy monism. All events, psychic as well as physical are explicable as one form or another of energy, each and every event deriving from greater or smaller energetic fields that comprise all aspects of reality.

These fairly representative materialist theories of the subtle energy body or energy field in various ways locate energy and spirit not just *around* the body but also at particular places *in* the body: *in* the brain, *in* the meridians, even *in* the cells — as with 'cellular consciousness.' Even in esoteric doctrines spirit or subtle energies are said to be somehow *in* the etheric field or *in* the chakras. Thus Barbara Brennan's clairvoyant images of auras locate energy bodies in the space around the physical body; and dowsers like Sig Lonegren teaches how to measure the extension of the various subtle bodies as bubbles surrounding the physical body in varying degrees.

So even when we talk about '*subtle* bodies' we are still thinking of them as subtly material, extended in space, confirming Heidegger's claim that all science imagines whatever objects or entities it studies as located 'out there, over against us, located in space.' Not surprisingly the word 'subtle' translates in German as *feinstofflisches,* which means literally like fine stuff or fine matter. And because this use of simple metaphors usually goes unchallenged — few scientists seem to have studied phenomenology — our theorists are forever unconsciously overconcretizing their concepts and falling prey to a rather barren reductionism where everything becomes either some kind of energy, vibration or field.

No matter how committed we are to holism, to slaying the dragon of Cartesianism and to open dialogue, I can't help thinking that such pervasive reductionism betrays an unconscious desire to keep spirit firmly *within* the material dimension, where the left brain or rational consciousness can feel secure in understanding and controlling it. By wanting to see spirit or consciousness as objects or energies 'out there' in space, located 'in' a cerebrum, a cell or a chakra we cling to a one dimensional monism and fall into temptations of scientism. Such, I fear, is the impetus behind much otherwise highly original 'scientific' research into consciousness and energy going on today. It seems to me mostly a defence against the 'wonder' of crossing over into higher dimensions, against 'going beyond' in the true spirit of metaphysics.

## *Matter as an emanation of spirit*

> *A good artist lets his intuition*
> *lead him wherever it wants*
> *A good scientist has freed himself of concepts*
> *and keeps his mind open to what is.*
>
> *Lao-Tzu,* Tao Te King *(trans. Mitchell 1989.16)*

> *Consciousness creates reality.*
>
> *Amit Goswami,* The Self-Aware Universe

To my mind a major culprit behind our enthralment to the philosophy of materialism is the tiny little word 'in.' From my somewhat laboured examples it may now be clear how pervasively this innocent little word deceptively conceals a spatial metaphor that betrays its true allegiance to the materialist dogma. The unexamined use of the word 'in' sadly restricts much neurological research and has taken on the status of a scientific myth about mind, energy and spirit, a myth in the Jungian sense of 'something which is believed everywhere and by everyone.'

For when we are talking about spirit as energy or energy as consciousness, even though we fully believe that these phenomena belong to a subtle or non-physical realm we tend to imagine them 'in' the brain or flowing 'through' our energy fields unaware that these are metaphors and not literal, which is to say, empirical truths. It may be clearer when we say something like 'I know it in my heart' or 'I feel it in my gut.' For even though our energy fields seem to have reactions that *correspond* to those parts of the body we still seem to realize that the emotions are not literally stored 'in' these places like glucose or protoplasm. Consider for example, the charming saying: 'You will never find your heart in a temple unless you find the temple in your heart.' It would be hard to mistake this for anything other than a metaphor. We don't go to a cardiologist to find the temple in our heart or to an archaeologist to find our heart in a temple! Yet as soon as we start to talk of memories 'stored in the brain' our metaphorical consciousness suddenly vanishes.

The Indian mystic and poet Kabir (1977.4), anticipated our dilemma in an ironic poem:

> You know that the seed is inside the horse-chestnut tree;
> and inside the seed are the blossoms of the tree,
> and the chestnuts and the shade.
> So inside the human body there is the seed
> and inside the seed there is the human body again ...
>
> Thinkers, listen, tell me what you know of that is not inside the soul?
> Take a pitcher of water and set it down on the water —
> now it has water inside and water outside.
> We mustn't give it a name,
> lest silly people start talking again about the body and the soul ...

Sri Aurobindo (Ghose 1951) puts it similarly: 'all of the body is in the mind, but not all the mind is in the body.' He also said, paraphrasing Madame Blavatsky:

> If you are embarrassed by the word 'spirit' think of spirit as the subtlest form of matter. But, if you are not embarrassed by the word spirit, you can think of matter as the densest form of spirit.

The materialist viewpoint requires a movement upwards, so that spirit is seen as a higher refinement or vibration of matter, yet somehow secondary, a kind of evolutionary by-product. From the spiritual viewpoint, by contrast, matter is the lower emanation or denser manifestation of spirit, whose concreteness and solidity is ultimately an illusion (Maya). As celebrated physicist David Bohm has maintained (Weber 1986.45f): 'matter is frozen light.'

If we contrast these two radically opposed world views we could say that *the ontology of the materialist takes matter as that which is ultimately real* and has therefore to find the origins of consciousness 'within' matter. Mind is then seen as some evolved or *higher* vibrational phenomenon (the epiphenomenal view of mind) whose 'transcendent' aspects need to be explained, reductively, as manifestations of biological energy of some kind.

On the other hand *a spiritual ontology sees consciousness as ultimately real* (Neoplatonism, Buddhism, Advaita Vedanta) and regards matter as a *lower* or denser manifestation of spirit or consciousness, a 'condensation' of spirit into physical form, an incarnation downwards. (It is no wonder that the scientifically minded psychical researchers of Madame Blavatsky's day were so challenged by all the alleged *materializations* of spirits.)

It is easy to appreciate, with our knowledge of radio waves, lasers, atomic particles, microbiology, Kirlian phenomena etc, the seductive appeal of the energetic model proposed by the materialists. It feeds our inflation that as scientists we have finally arrived at the Great Picture of things, that implacable illusion that we have crossed the last frontiers of understanding. Thus it is more comforting to be able to explain what we don't understand in terms of what we do. Nevertheless, biological metaphors like 'bioplasm' or 'cellular consciousness' are at root reductive to the materialist paradigm; to ignore this is to be entranced by our choice of language and our partiality to certain fashionable metaphors. Thus science gets caught in a conceptual prison of its own making.

For from my own and clients' experiences of spiritual and otherworldly encounters it is a travesty to claim that phenomena of spirit can be *reduced* to biological components, be they bioplasm, microvita or even etheric energy. *But this is not to say that spirit cannot manifest in forms that can be perceived in this way by visionary or clairvoyant consciousness.* Almost all biological and materialist metaphors end up mistaking the container for what contains it — as with Kabir's pitcher in the water.

No matter how ingenious the theories of physics and biology, as long as such disciplines fail to find ways to acknowledge those higher dimensions that are not of time and space and which transcend and subsume the physical realm, physical science will never fully embrace and become fruitfully united with *meta*-physics. Without this step all the enterprises of science, no matter how grand or sublime, will remain one dimensional and reductive. What is sought, in the words of Henry Corbin, is 'a cosmology of such a kind that the most astounding information of modern science regarding the physical universe remains inferior to it.'

It is my contention, supported by the metaphysical teachings of sacred tradition, that *the spiritual dimension is other than and of a higher order than the energy fields through which spirit manifests in the physical world.* Moreover, there exists an intermediary crossover universe where spirit manifests *through* the material world and where *mutatis mutandis* we in our spiritual or subtle bodies can move from the material and pass beyond into the spiritual. It is this subtle intermediary world, this halfway place, that is often experienced in the form of psychic fields, or as paranormal forces or supernatural beings, as clairvoyant and subtle perceptions, as ecstatic vision and mystical transport.

Investigation of these realms shows clearly that all such phenomena, though often discounted as 'mere' imagination in fact come from a higher, not a lower source, ontologically speaking, even if their contents may sometimes be of a spiritually inferior or 'demonic' quality. The late Sir George Trevelyan was adamant about the need to reinstate imagination and visionary capacity to its rightful role as the spiritual function that can perceive these 'higher' realms. In writing about the work of the psychic W. Tudor Pole who saw past lifetimes, Sir George wrote as follows:

> To him [Tudor Pole] these recollections are emphatically not the product of imagination; that word has been debased into meaning the weaving of fantasies. In its true sense it implies an entry by pictorial thinking into a higher 'frequency,' a world of reality and being beyonds the limitations of the five senses. This is the first step in research and the exploration into the spiritual realms which interpenetrate our physical world of life and being ...
>
> [Such] memories are an example of something developing today in human thinking. *In our age we are getting a new understanding of the truth that the spiritual realms absolutely interpenetrate the physical.* [Emphasis mine] Indeed the world of material forms is seen as an image or reflection of the spiritual which creates it. The realms of spirit are not far distant, but lie within the sense world and are to be grasped there by our intuitive thinking. (Pole & Lehmann 1983. Introduction)

## *What is imagination?*

> *Oh the mind, mind has mountains; cliffs of fall*
> *Frightful, sheer, no-man-fathomed. Hold them cheap*
> *May who ne'er hung there.*
>
> *Gerard Manley Hopkins*

After nearly two decades as a psychotherapist conducting clients through many kinds of so-called 'regression' experience — to lost childhood scenes, to birth traumas, to impressions of other lifetimes, to realms beyond death and to extraordinary visionary spaces — I found myself questioning many of my basic assumptions about what imagination, imagery and even archetypes are. Though I was trained in the Jungian tradition, which values imagination as the language of the soul, it no longer seemed to me that what we encountered were just images, even archetypal images, and it no longer helped to explain them as occurring in some kind of altered state of consciousness. So many of the visions are so vivid and have such a profound transformative effect on the experiencer that I began to question whether in fact with such language I had subtly succumbed to an even more pernicious form of reductionism — *psychological reductionism.* Was I falling into the trap of believing the ignorant critical slur about all these experiences, that they are 'just imagination' or worse, 'just archetypes'?

People have indeed said over the years 'Your clients are making it all up because it's fashionable to have past lives and out of body experiences.' The trouble with this objection is that it begs a very big question: just what *is* imagination? Now, everybody knows what it's like to imagine but that alone doesn't explain where our images come from or how they are produced or reproduced. One has only to study one's dreams for a few months to be staggered by the amazing variety and range of imagery they throw out. The psyche seems to have an inexhaustible pool of strange and exotic images, most of which would be almost impossible to account for.

Academic psychology, as it now exists, is hard put to define imagination. It is not even a subject of study in standard text books of psychology. If you pick up a basic text for a Psychology 101 course in any American college and look in the index, you will not find the word 'imagination.' You might find the words 'image' or 'imagery.' To study imagination at university level you have to go to a literature department where it comes under the rubric of 'literary theory' — Coleridge, Wordsworth, and so on. Literary theorists, however, are very careful to say that they are not writing psychology. Possibly the only place where you'll find a serious study of imagination is in the psychiatry department of a medical school, where delusions, hallucinations and exotic fantasies are all studied closely as symptoms of mental pathology. Hardly a charitable view of the imagination!

Nevertheless it is the psychiatrists who are closer than anyone to having a respectable and even respectful theory of imagination. Early pioneers of psychoanalysis, especially Sigmund Freud and C.G. Jung, were among the first to study the imagination seriously, dubbing it 'the unconscious mind' following certain German philosophers. Thanks to their researches and perseverance, the idea of the unconscious mind even came to be seen by the American philosopher and psychologist William James, as 'the greatest discovery of the twentieth century.' It is a pity he didn't say the same about the imagination, because unfortunately, it still remains a put-down to say of some unusual experience: 'It's *just* your imagination.' Imagination has, sad to say, sunk to being regarded as one of the most inferior and trivial aspects of the mind. We are a long way from William Blake's 'Holy Imagination.'

In fact, the masters of the imagination who preceded the psychoanalysts were actually the great poets and visionaries. Dante made his imaginal descent into the visionary realms of Hell and then on upwards through Purgatory into the *Paradiso.* Shakespeare's profound exploration of the human heart in his tragedies and comedies has led critic Harold Bloom to class him along with the great mystical visionaries of Sufism. William Blake struggled with his own inner universe of visionary principalities and powers to produce extraordinary enduring literature. Goethe dramatized the perennial fight between good and evil in his great visionary work, *Faust.* Freud and Jung were actually the chief heirs to the visionary courage of these great prior explorers of the creative imagination. In the consulting room the imagination revealed to them its enormous power when manifest in the world of dreams and waking visions. Their work testifies to an undying respect for the huge healing and imaginative power of the soul.

The real problem in understanding the imagination lies in our habit of ignoring the great visionary traditions and instead giving far too much power to the narrow prejudices of academic psychology — a discipline whose almost fundamentalist insistence on being 'scientific' entirely excludes the multi-dimensional reaches of the soul. As James Hillman once said of such academicism: 'the language of psychology is an insult to the soul.' Here again the left brain (the rational side) seems to be trying to co-opt the right brain (the creative side) and totally deny that the latter has a way of knowing that is entirely unique unto itself.

## The shamanic parallel

> *Journeys bring power and love*
> *back into you. If you can't go somewhere,*
> *move in the passageways of the self.*
> *They are like shafts of light,*
> *always changing and you change*
> *when you explore them.*
>
> *Jalal ad-Din Rumi*

In my personal experience as a psychotherapist I did not always find it easy to trust the imaginative faculty in either myself or my clients. Yet I found that the more I sought to interpret my client's experiences by putting them back into a rational or even symbolic framework (Freudian or even Jungian) the more my interpretations were actually preventing them from opening to much deeper experiences. Increasingly I found that I had to let go of my own (left brain) need to interpret. Interpretation, which I now see as yet another kind of reductive activity, prevents us both as healers and clients from fully harnessing those spiritual dimensions mediated by the imagination or from allowing spiritual dimensions to enter fully into our work. It prevents us experiencing that sense of wonder or 'going beyond' that is the essence of genuine metaphysics according to the philosopher Pierre Thevenaz.

Somewhat reluctantly I had come to realize that when I followed my clients into the 'worlds' they experienced in 'imagination' or 'memory' I had been participating in a kind of shamanic journeying. I had unknowingly entered into their subtle worlds and travelled with them, not realizing at first that this is exactly what shamans do: they journey. For what difference is there in the end between 'regression' and 'journeying' or between 'psychic splitting' and 'soul loss'? It is simply a matter of one's language of choice — psychoanalysis or shamanism. Equally, it makes no difference whether one uses a couch, a pendulum or a rattle; if the technique successfully induces a trance state it will enable a person to 'move in the passageways of the self,' as Rumi puts it so beautifully.

Increasingly, therefore, I have come t believe that the more, as psychotherapists, we can leave aside our rational, or 'left brain' attitude of mind — practising Coleridge's 'willing suspension of disbelief' — and can embrace the visionary or 'right brain' perspective of reality, the more we will encounter that subtle awareness that Henry Corbin, the great scholar of Sufism, called *the spiritual imagination.* Once we have begun to cultivate this very powerful species of awareness we will be able to journey between realities, to encounter other worlds beyond the physical world where we have subtle access to the universal source of healing which is Spirit.

Once I began to realize this my work led me to study a variety of esoteric sources, especially those of the Tibetan Books of the Dead, the Upanishads, the Iranian mystics discovered by Henry Corbin, Plato and the Neoplatonist mysticism of Plotinus as well as more modern visionaries like Shakespeare, William Blake and Emmanuel Swedenborg. Among all these traditions and seers it is a commonplace that there are higher or subtle senses that can be deliberately awakened through the practice of certain rigorous spiritual disciplines. These disciplines frequently involve a kind of 'learning how to die' in order to be reborn in a visionary sense into these higher worlds. In fact it becomes clear that the essential feature in all the so-called Mystery traditions of the ancient world had to do with overcoming the fear of literal death to discover that the soul is immortal and can always travel into higher realities when properly instructed.

What has formerly been taught secretly in Gnostic and Neoplatonic schools is today being rediscovered in clinics, hospitals and therapy practices as what might be called *the spiritual phenomenology of dying.* When for example individuals undergoing a regression session to a so-called 'other life' remember what it is like to die in that past life they also commonly report exactly what it is like to pass into a higher or 'other' realm — what would be called a *Bardo* in Tibetan Buddhism. In this other realm these individuals commonly find they have visionary senses, access to higher intelligence and the ability to meet with otherworldly 'beings of light,' that may appear as ancestors, or even divine beings.

Precisely similar experiences have in recent years been collected in the many spontaneous reports of near death experiences now on record, material made famous by the writings of Raymond Moody and Kenneth Ring. All these reports and experiences closely parallel the many accounts we have of shamanic journeys in deep trance to higher and lower spirit worlds where the shaman, travelling in his subtle or luminous body, which has detached from the physical body, meets with and negotiates with spiritual powers in the interests of protection or healing. Reviewing these striking parallels has led German anthropologist Holger Kahlweit (1992) to say that 'as far as I'm concerned, an out of body experience is identical with a near-death experience.'

## *Visionary worlds: the* Mundus Imaginalis *of Henry Corbin*

> *My soul, there is a country far beyond the stars.*
>
> *Henry Vaughan*

> *We are not dealing here with irreality. The mundus imaginalis is a world of autonomous forms and images ... It is a perfectly real world preserving all the richness and diversity of the sensible world but in a spiritual state.*
>
> *Henry Corbin (1966)*

When we enter the visionary world, we are not restricted by material time and space in any way. Images move extremely fast; we can go in and out of other realities and dimensions instantly. To do this in a constructive and not random way it is best to practise some form of concentration, some form of meditation. This is why Jung developed his technique of *active imagination* which enables a spontaneous encounter with the image or spirit forms he called archetypes and which originate in this transpersonal psychic reality he preferred to call the collective unconscious.

In fact when we move through multiple realities and 'journey in the passageways of the self' we are entering into the very essence of prayer no differently than when shamans journey to higher and lower worlds. Indeed, to work with a highly charged archetypal image and to practise following and holding such images firmly in awareness is none other than the secret gateway from the material world of sensory reality into the multi-dimensional imaginal worlds of spirit and pure being. Such practice is also the key to healing.

The multi-dimensional world or visionary world of spiritual forms was known to the Arab and Persian Sufis as the *alam al-mithal.* In Henry Corbin's indispensable studies of Sohrawardi, Avicenna and Ibn Arabi (1972) this term is rendered into Latin as the *mundus archetypus* or *mundus imaginalis.* Archetype, in the Sufi sense, means a spiritual form and the world that these pure forms inhabit is in Corbin's words 'a perfectly real world preserving all the richness and diversity of the sensible world but in a spiritual state.' In his works Corbin also makes a very important distinction between what is *imaginary* — fantasies that we fabricate with our rational waking minds — and what is *imaginal* — that which derives from the *mundus imaginalis* or the higher reality of spiritual Imagination.

The *mundus imaginalis* is known by many names in esoteric and spiritual traditions. It is called in Plato (*Symposium* 202), the Intermediary World, the *metaxy.* In Tibetan Buddhism, the sum total of these worlds, known individually as *Bardos,* or 'in-betweens' are called the *Sambhogakaya* which means the Body of Bliss (we will return later to this cosmology). The *Bardos* include states after and between lives as well as prior to being born; they are *in between* physical reality and pure spirit. In the Western world, this intermediary world is sometimes referred to as the invisible world, the unseen world, the spirit world, or the middle kingdom.

This realm is also the world of subtle bodies, the higher location of which has important implications for the problem of how we locate the subtle energy fields we discussed earlier. For as Corbin also remarks in regard to the *mundus imaginalis:*

> this is the world of 'subtle bodies' of which it is indispensable to have some notion in order to understand that there is a link between pure spirit and material body. (Corbin 1972.9)

> this world in the subtle state which includes many degrees, and which is impenetrable by the sensory organs, is the *real* place of all psycho-spiritual events (visions, charismas, thaumaturgical actions breaching the laws of space and time), which are considered simply as imaginary — that is, as unreal — so long as one remains in the rational dilemma which is restricted to a choice between the two terms of banal dualism, 'matter' and 'spirit,' corresponding to that other one: 'history' or 'myth.' (Corbin 1977.79)

Indispensable too is the awareness that with the subtle body we each have the subtle faculty or organ that enables us to move in the *mundus imaginalis.* This faculty is the creative imagination which, as Corbin emphasizes, is the imaginal power by which spirit acts.

All in all, Corbin's work greatly amplifies and clarifies the nature and dynamics of the visionary journeys or mystical pathways such as Dante's descent to the lower world of the *Inferno* then to the upper world of *Paradiso.* Muhammad made his *mi'raj* or Night Journey in a comparable visionary state. From this perspective there is absolutely no question that when individuals go through a near death experience, they are journeying in the shamanic sense, going temporarily out of body, and encountering a higher reality. (For a good survey of the literature of such journeys see Zaleski 1988.) We are talking about real spiritual *places,* albeit subtle or imaginal places, but in no way simply products of fantasy, which more properly belong to *lower* imagination, that of the ego. When St Paul was taken up into the 'seventh heaven' he undoubtedly went through an ecstatic out of body experience during which he visited a certain clime of the *mundus imaginalis.*

## *Sohrawardi's vision: going beyond Mount Qaf*

*And the rock he touched was the socket of all men's eyes*
*And he touched the spring of vision.*
*Vernon Watkins,* Taliesin and the Spring of Vision

*A man that looks on glass,*
*On it may stay his eye*
*Or if he pleaseth through it pass*
*And then the heavens espy.* *George Herbert,* The Elixir

In an exposition by Corbin (1972.2–6) of *The Crimson Angel,* one of the great Sufi narratives by the mystic Sohrawardi, we are shown how it is possible to move into this world where time and space are purely relative states. According to the story a captive has just escaped the watchful eyes of his jailers. In other words, he has escaped out of the physical world in much the same way described in the famous poem of St John of the Cross, 'I went abroad when all the house was still' (Kavanagh & Rodriguez 1979). (Often these experiences happen to people at night when they wake up suddenly but find they are not in their bodies.)

This captive is the stranger, the outsider in us all, who longs to return home. In *The Crimson Angel* the captive has escaped and finds himself in the desert in the presence of a being who has all the graces of adolescence. This being calls himself the eldest child of the creator, and he says, 'I come from beyond Mount Qaf. This is where you were at the beginning and this is where you will return once you are free of your shackles.' (Corbin 1972.3)

Sohrawardi tells us that Mount Qaf, the cosmic mountain, is:

> summit after summit and valley after valley built up of celestial spheres each enveloping one another. Where then is the road that leads out of it, what is the distance? And the young man says, 'However far you may journey, you will always come back to the point of departure.' Just as the needle of the compass swings back to the magnetic point. Does this simply mean that you must leave yourself to come back to yourself? Not quite, because in the meantime, a very important event will have changed everything. The *self* one finds yonder, beyond Mount Qaf, is a higher self, the self experienced as a 'Thou.' Like Khezir [or Khadir, the mysterious prophet or messenger of Islam], the eternal wanderer, the traveller, has ultimately to bathe in the Spring of Life. [Corbin's summary]

The text goes on to say:

> He who has discovered the meaning of true reality has arrived at the spring. When he emerges from the spring he is endowed with a gift that likens him to the balsam, of which a drop distilled in the hollow of one's hand, held up against the Sun, trans-passes to the back of the hand. If you are Khadir, you, too, can pass beyond Mount Qaf without difficulty. (Corbin 1972.3)

The region beyond Mount Qaf starts at the convex centre of the ninth Sphere of Spheres which is the edge of known reality in Islamic cosmology. This is the sphere that envelopes the cosmos as a whole. This means that to enter spiritual reality, *to go beyond Mount Qaf* is to leave the supreme sphere which defines all types of orientation possible in our world. Once this border has been crossed, says Corbin, the question of 'where,' which is to say, our location in space becomes meaningless. At least in terms of the meaning it has when we talk about leaving the 'where.' As Corbin (1972.3) puts it:

> Leaving the 'where' is equivalent to leaving the outer or natural appearances that cloak the hidden inner realities, just as the almond is concealed in its shell. For the stranger, the Gnostic, this step represents a return home or at least striving in this direction.

> Yet strange as it may seem, once the journey is completed, the reality which is hither to have been an inner and hidden one, turns out to envelope, surround or contain that which was, at first, outer and invisible. As a result of internalization one has moved out of external reality. Henceforth spiritual reality envelopes, surrounds, contains so-called material reality.

Others have crossed that border, that threshold between the physical and spiritual and gone 'inside' so that the inner body has become the total universe. 'The whirling skies, the many-layered earth, the seventy thousand veils, we found in the body,' sang a great Turkish mystic Yunnus Emre. This is also one of the great themes of Indian and Tibetan Tantrism and is reflected in the doctrines of the Mystical Body of Christ and Kabbala's Cosmic Man, *Adam Kadmon.*

## *The three bodies or worlds of the Buddha*

> *Centre of all centres, core of cores*
> *almond self-enclosed and growing sweet —*
> *all this universe, to the furthest stars*
> *and beyond them, is your flesh, your fruit.*
> *Rainer Maria Rilke* Buddha in Glory *(Mitchell 1989.131)*

To summarize some of these difficult and often paradoxical ideas I want to leave the reader a diagram that may help explicate the metaphors behind the actual metaphysics of the three worlds that Corbin and many other traditions allude to. The diagram uses three overlapping circles to symbolize the three interpenetrating realities of classical Mahayana Buddhist cosmology, the three bodies (*kayas)* of the cosmic Buddha. At lowest level of manifestation there is the physical or sensible world, the *Nirmanakaya.* Above that, and interfacing with it from the metaphysical perspective is the subtle intermediary world of the *Sambhogakaya* and finally there is the highest of worlds, the *Dharmakaya* the formless, world of pure spirit or higher angelic intelligences from which all other worlds emanate. (The Three Worlds symbolized by the *Kayas* ('bodies of the Buddha') are well discussed in Lauf 1977.)

In descending order the worlds are each conceived symbolically as 'bodies' or *kayas,* that is to say as manifestations of pure consciousness, which is the root meaning of *Buddha.*

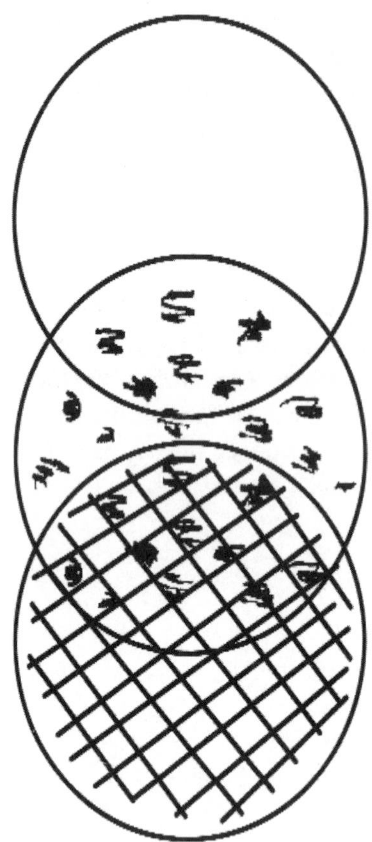

***Dharmakaya***
*Sunyata, pure light of the Void* (Tibetan)
*Ground luminosity* (Sogyal)
*Archangelic intelligences* (Sufi)
*Advaita, the non-dual* (Vedanta)
*Godhead* (Eckhart)
*Al Haqq* (Sufi)
*Xvarnah* (Mazdaism)

***Sambhogakaya***
*Alam al-mithal* (Sufi)
*Mundus imaginalis/archetypus*
*Metaxy: intermediary realm* (Plato)
*Bardo or 'the in between'* (Tibetan)
*Alaya vijnana* (yoga)
*Subtle realm, subtle bodies, daimonic or spirit realm*
*Dreamtime* (Australian aborigine)
*Anima mundi* (Hermetic)
*Collective unconscious* (Jung)
*The Nagual* (Toltec/Yaqui)

***Nirmanakaya***
*Physical, sensory reality*
*Samsara* (Hindu/Buddhist)
*The Tonal* (Toltec/Yaqui)

*The Three Bodies or Worlds of the Cosmic Buddha*

*1. The Dharmakaya,* is what the old Evans-Wentz translation of *The Tibetan Book of the Dead* characterizes as 'the pure light of the void,' *sunyata.* As *dharma,* it is highest Truth cognate with the mysterious and unknowable *tao* of Taoism. In the Sufi and Neoplatonic cosmologies of Sohrawardi, Plotinus and Proclus, it is where the angelic intelligences reside. This is the supreme 'abode' or rather the source of pure luminosity or 'ground luminosity' as it has been translated by Sogyal Rinpoche (1992 Chap.16). It is a state where one can not even speak of having visions of the Light, because if it is reached one *is* the vision; there is no longer a distinction between subject and object. It is a state beyond all distinctions, what in Vedanta is called *advaita* or non-dual.

2. *The Sambhogakaya* emanates from the *Dharmakaya;* and is the visionary world of multiple universes and subtle forms discussed at length above under the name given to it by Henry Corbin, the *mundus imaginalis.* It lies, as it were midway between the physical world and the ultimate and formless reality which is pure light. Here are to be found all possibilities of being in their subtle bodies or archetypal forms; but also the remnants of earlier worlds called the *daimones* by the Greek Platonists and the shades of the dead by Homer; these realms include the ancestors of all traditions. Recently, Patrick Harpur (1995) has proposed renaming this entire realm 'daimonic reality,' and has emphasized how it interpenetrates the physical world in the form of faeries, ghosts and paranormal phenomena.

This middle realm is where the Tibetan *Bardo* experiences of after death encounters with ancestors and with the wrathful and benign deities occur and where visions of previous lives arise. It is also where cosmic cities, the abodes of the gods and endless visionary heavens and hells coexist in non-spatial relationship to each other (of which more below). This is where the entire the memory of mankind and human experience exists in a state of psychic suspension in what is called the *alaya-vijnana,* or 'store consciousness,' which forms the *akasha* or universal etheric field (Zimmer 1951.526, compare Sogyal 1992.111). In Hermetic teachings this universal capacity to bear all traces of memory and all subtle forms, be they angelic or demonic, is called the *anima mundi* or world soul. This level of reality is known in western traditions as the spirit world or the astral world.

3. *The Nirmanakaya,* symbolized by the lowest circle, is the transitory material world of time and space subject to birth, decay and death. It is the sensory world, the world of physics and biology, built of cells and particles and light waves. From the multi-dimensional perspective of sacred tradition it is a manifestation, an incarnation or a 'downloading,' as it were, of the higher worlds. In Hindu and Buddhist teaching it is called *samsara,* world of becoming, and is seen as essentially illusory, a play of evanescent conditions made up of Shakespeare's 'stuff of dreams.' 'Thus should we think of this fleeting world,' said the Buddha in like vein in his *Diamond Sutra:*

> A star at dawn, a bubble in a stream
> A flash of lightning in a summer cloud
> A flickering lamp, a phantom and a dream.

## *Moving in visionary time and space*

*One day the sun admitted:*
*I'm just a shadow*
*I wish I could show you*
*The infinite incandescence*
*That has cast my brilliant image*
*I wish I could show you*
*When you are lonely or in darkness*
*The astonishing light*
*Of your own being.*

*Hafiz (1997)*

Mystics and poets from all the major traditions have described how the three worlds interface. The Sufi Al Ghazzali said, 'The visible world was made to correspond to the world invisible, and there is nothing in this world, but is a symbol of something in that world.' Jung (1951.226) wrote: 'Think carnally and you will remain flesh, think symbolically and you will become spirit.'

The subtle world is frequently seen to be a mirror of the physical world whose physical forms are seen as dim by comparison. Like Alice, we may need to pass through the looking glass. 'A man that looks on glass on it may stay his eye, or if he pleaseth, through it, pass, and then the heaven espy,' said George Herbert.

But perhaps the hardest thing to comprehend from a purely materialist perspective is the very nature of psychic space in the *mundus imaginalis* and how it is that beings in their spiritual forms or subtle bodies are able to move within and between the many visionary intermediary worlds. For in the subtle world we do indeed find distinct representations of psychic or spiritual location in space. Polarized within this cosmos there are 'higher' and 'lower' worlds, 'heavens' and 'hells,' or 'angelic' and 'demonic' realms. How is it then that shamans and visionaries like Dante are able to travel in and between these other worlds?

An important clue was given to us by the great visionary voyager Emmanuel Swedenborg (1900). From his own experience as 'one who walked with God' he wrote:

> Although all things in heaven appear in place and space as they do in the world, still the angels have no notion or idea

> of place and space. [In fact] all progressions or movements in the spiritual world are effected by changes in the state of the interiors ... hence those who are near each other are in a similar state and those who are far apart are those whose state is dissimilar. Spaces in heaven or the spiritual realm are nothing but external states corresponding to internal ones.

Those souls that have reached a certain stage of inner growth will be drawn to other souls of like kind. There is in the spirit world a kind of polarization of forms both evolutionary and devolutionary. In regression and shamanic journeys among the ancestral denizens of the intermediary world it is common to meet clusters of souls, or families, that belong together; and that are working on a similar spiritual level. Those too who remember out of body experiences from a near-death will report going through layers or planes where different assemblies of beings are to be found.

In my book on past lives I recount the story of a young women who remembered dying as a Roman centurion who had served among the horrors of the Coliseum (Woolger 1987). In the *Bardo* realms after death the centurion in his subtle body goes to a lower plane where he sees thousands of souls of Christians who have been martyred, who are in a state of deep confusion and who are angry at Christ for not rescuing them. Yet the centurion had converted to Christianity and had died a peaceful death. As a result he found himself rising beyond the confused souls into a higher plane where there was glory and light and praise. The soul of the centurion had apparently moved into the angelic realms.

The imagery that most consistently recurs in descriptions of higher worlds is that of light. We are thus told that the light emanating from of the highest of worlds, the Dharmakaya, is constantly present at all levels of reality. But because this universal radiance is beyond form it is neither within nor without *and* it is both within and without; in fact it is everywhere and nowhere, as indicated by the koan-like Platonic saying that: 'God is a sphere whose centre is everywhere and whose circumference is nowhere.' (For an exhaustive discussion of this elusive quotation see Borges 1964.) Such paradoxical metaphors of dualist mysticism inevitably crack the moulds of binary logic and the imagination of time and space is beggared beyond words. In the presence of such supreme knowledge 'all nature quaketh, all clerics be fools and all saints and angels be blind,' says the anonymous author of *The Cloud of Unknowing.* The Psalmist David was similarly in awe to the wondersome dimensions of Divine Mind, the utterly limitless power of Spirit when he sang:

> How measureless your mind is, Lord:
> it contains inconceivable worlds
> and is vaster than space, than time.
> If ever I tried to fathom it,
> I would be like a child counting
> The grains of sand on a beach.
>
> Psalm 139 (trans. Mitchell)

All the teachings concur that whenever we journey in what Rumi calls 'the passageways of the self' which are like 'shafts of light' this light is none other than the 'pure light of the void' which interpenetrates and upholds everything eternally. Dante (*Paradiso* 33), in his vision of Paradise saw this divine light as *'l'amor che muove il sole e gli altri stelle'* — 'the love that moves the sun and all the other stars.' Generally it is only great visionaries and saints that can both see and tolerate the stupendous brilliance of this light. Rumi underscores that 'the bodies of holy men and women have the ability to endure the unconditional light that can tear mountain ranges to pieces.' And not only this, the greatest of masters also *embody* that light by means of the purified vessel of their subtle body — so aptly called the *luminous* body in many traditions. 'The light of Joseph's face, when he passed by a house,' Rumi (1991) tells us, 'would filter through the lattice and make a radiance on the wall. People would notice and say, "Joseph must be taking a walk".'

Faced with this light and such illumined beings, most of us are more like the disciples of Jesus as described in the Gnostic *Pistis Sophia* (1984), dazzled by so much brilliance:

> And that light-power came down over Jesus and surrounded him entirely, while he was seated removed from his disciples, and he had shone most exceedingly, and there was no measure for the light which was on him.
>
> And the disciples had not seen Jesus because of the great light in which he was, or which was about him; for their eyes were darkened because of the great light in which he was. But

> they saw only the light, which shone forth many light rays ... in one great immeasurable glory of light. It stretched from under the earth right up to heaven — and when the disciples saw that light, they fell into great fear and agitation.
>
> It came to pass them that when that light-power had come down over Jesus that it gradually surrounded him entirely. Then Jesus ascended or soared into the height, shining most exceedingly in an immeasurable light. And the disciples gazed after him and none of them spake; but they all kept in deep silence.

## *Conclusion: 'the stuff of dreams'*

Such then is the potential for illumination and transfiguration when all three worlds manifest in one being or one place; 'wherever the Footprint is found, that handful of dust holds the oneness of worlds' according to the inspired Sufi Ghalib. For in fact 'the kingdom of the Father is spread upon the earth but men do not see it' (*Gospel of Thomas* 113). Only by the 'cleansing the doors of perception' (Blake) and thereby opening to the visionary senses that inhere within the subtle body can we begin to awaken to our divine consciousness, to the light that is within. Then, and only then, will the multi-dimensional nature of things and their ultimate oneness become manifest. This was how Shelley saw it:

> The One remains, the many change and pass;
> Heaven's light forever shines, Earth's shadows fly
> Life, like a dome of many coloured glass,
> Stains the white radiance of eternity ...
> Flowers, ruins, statues, music, words, are weak
> The glory they transfuse with fitting truth to speak.
>
> *Adonais*

But perhaps one of the greatest visionaries of all times, with his last and deliberately Hermetic work, should have the last word.* So, in conclusion, Prospero's magisterial evocation of the *mundus imaginalis* in Shakespeare's *Tempest* (4.1), a speech which so wistfully echoes the words of the Buddha quoted earlier:

* For Shakespeare's Hermeticism, see Yates, 1975, Dawkins 2000, Huxley 1968.

Our revels now are ended. These our actors,
As I foretold you, were all spirits and
Are melted into air, into thin air:
The baseless fabric of this vision,
The cloud-capp'd towers, the gorgeous palaces,
The solemn temples, the great globe itself,
Yea, all which it inherit, shall dissolve
And like this insubstantial pageant faded,
Leave not a rack behind. We are such stuff
As dreams are made on, and our little life
Is rounded with a sleep.

## *References*


Avens, Roberts. 1982. *Imaginal body: Para-Jungian reflections on soul, imagination and death.* Washington: University Press of America.

Bailey, Alice. 1927. *The light of the soul: the yoga sutras of Patanjali.* New York: Lucis Trust.

Borges, Jorge Luis. 1964. The fearful sphere of Pascal. In *Labyrinths.* San Francisco: New Directions.

Brennan, Barbara. 1988. *Hands of light: a guide to healing through the human energy field.* New York: Bantam.

Corbin, Henry. 1960. *Avicenna and the visionary recital.* Partheon: Bollingen.

—. 1966. The visionary dream in Islamic spirituality. In Grunebaum and Caillais (eds.) *The dreams in human society,* Berkeley: University of California Press.

—. 1969. *Creative imagination in the Sufism of Ibn Arabi.* Princeton: Bollingen.

—. 1972. *Mundus Imaginalis* or the imaginary and the imaginal. Translated Ruth Horine. *Spring.* Zurich.

—. 1977. *Spiritual body and celestial earth.* Princeton: Bollingen.

—. 1995. *Mundus Imaginalis* or the imaginary and the imaginal. A more complete translation in *Swedenborg and esoteric Islam.* Translated Leonard Fox. West Chester, Penn.: Swedenborg Foundation.

Dawkins, Peter. 2000. *Shakespeare's wisdom in* The Tempest. London: I.C. Media.

Ghose, Aurobindo. 1951. *The synthesis of Yoga.* New York.

*Gospel of Thomas, The.* 1976. Trans. A. Guillaumont *et al.* Leiden: Brill.

Green, Elmer and Alyce. 1977. *Beyond biofeedback.* Ft. Wayne, Indiana: Knoll.

Hafiz. 1996. *I heard God laughing.* Translated Daniel Ladinsky. Walnut Creek, California: Sufism Reoriented.

Harpur, Patrick. 1995. *Daimonic reality, understanding otherworld encounters.* London: Arkana.

Heidegger, Martin. 1967. *What is a thing?* Chicago.

Huxley, Aldous. 1968. Shakespeare and Maya. In Julian Huxley (ed.) *Aldous Huxley: a memorial volume.* London.

Jung, C.G. 1951. *Symbols of transformation.* Princeton: Bollingen.
*Kabir Book, The.* 1977. Translated by Robert Bly. Boston: Beacon Press.
Kahlweit, Holger. 1992. *Dreamtime and inner space.* Boulder: Shambhala.
Kavanagh and Rodriguez (ed.) 1979. *St John of the Cross. Collected works.* Washington: ICS Publications.
Krippner, Stanley, and Daniel Rubin. 1973. *Galaxies of light.* New York: Interface.
Lauf, Detlef Ingo. 1977. *Secret doctrines of the Tibetan books of the dead.* Boulder: Shambhala.
Mitchell, Stephen. 1989. *The enlightened heart.* New York: Harper.
*Pistis Sophia.* 1984. Trans. G.R.S. Mead. New York: Garber. (Original edition 1896.)
Pole, W. Tudor, and Rosamond Lehmann. 1983. *A Man Seen Afar.* Saffron Walden: C.W. Daniel.
Rinpoche, Sogyal. 1992. *The Tibetan book of living and dying.* New York: Harper.
Rossi, Ernest L. and David Cheek. 1994. *Mind-body therapy.* New York: Norton.
Rumi, Jalal Udin. 1988. *These branching moments.* Versions by Coleman Barks. Copper Beech.
—. 1991. *Feeling the shoulder of the lion.* Trans. Coleman Barks. Vermont: Threshold.
Satprem. 1982. *The mind of the cells.* New York.
Swedenborg, Emmanuel. 1900. *Heaven and its wonders and hell.* New York: Swedenborg Foundation.
Tansley, David. 1972. *Radionics and the subtle anatomy of man.* Saffron Walden: Health Science.
Thevenaz, Pierre. 1962. *What is phenomenology?* Chicago.
Weber, Renée (ed.) 1986. *Dialogues with scientists and sages.* London: Routledge.
White, John. 1979. *Kundalini, evolution and enlightenment.* New York: Doubleday.
White, John, and Stanley Krippner. 1977. *Future science.* New York: Doubleday.
Woolger, Roger J. 1987. *Other lives, other selves.* New York: Doubleday.
Yates, Frances A. 1975. *Shakespeare's last plays.* London: Routledge.
Zaleski, Carol G. 1988. *Otherworld Journeys.* New York: OUP.
Zimmer, Heinrich. 1951. *Philosophies of India.* Princeton: Bollingen.

# Wider Perspectives on Consciousness

# Consciousness and Energy Monism

MARK WOODHOUSE

*Professor Mark B. Woodhouse, Ph.D., is Associate Professor of Philosophy at Georgia State University, where he teaches courses in Metaphysics, Eastern Thought, and the New Paradigm literature. He is the author of* A Preface to Philosophy *and* Paradigm Wars. *He is also Director of the Aesculapian Institute and is a practising healer.*

Over the past decade, I have developed (most extensively in *Paradigm Wars*) what seems to me a viable theory of consciousness that moves beyond the shortcomings of materialism, dualism, and idealism. Not without some hesitations about the reductionism such a label seems to imply, I call this theory Energy Monism. My exploration of Energy Monism has profited substantially from review and critique by various members of the Scientific and Medical Network. In this article, I shall first describe its fundamental tenets; second, develop the argument(s) for it; third, apply the position to four controversial topics (OBEs, clairvoyant healing, identity over time, and psychoneuro-immunology); and, finally, respond to some important criticisms.

## *Statement of the theory*

Energy Monism is a version of the perennial philosophy with links to process philosophy, theosophical thought, Advaita Vedanta, panpsychism, Spinoza, Amit Goswami, Christian de Quincey, and Ken Wilber. Readers attracted to these thinkers and schools of thought will be naturally sympathetic, even if not fully committed to, Energy Monism. It contains a few semi-original insights, but most aspects have been discussed by others. Its attractiveness, I suggest, stems primarily from its conceptual coherence and ability to integrate both scientific and spiritually oriented phenomena. Its central features are as follows.

All things emerge from and are sustained by a common source, which may be labelled in various ways, e.g., Tao, Nirguna Brahman, Godhead, Unified Field, One-Without-a-Second, and so on.

Source is neither just consciousness nor just energy, but transcends and includes the very distinction between them. We might label this a 'transcendental monism' with both conscious and energetic aspects. In so far as we speak of the stuff of reality, it is energy-consciousness.

All events and objects not only are one in their base ontology (while seeming separate and distinct on other levels of experience), but also have both energetic and conscious aspects. Stated boldly, there is consciousness (awareness, intelligence) in everything from atoms to angels just as there is energy in everything from quarks to thought-forms. One may or may not incorporate angels in one's cosmology, for example. However, if one did, such beings, from the perspective of Energy Monism, would not be exclusively spiritual (nonphysical) entities, but also would have energetic aspects that may include such things as movement, colour, and the ability to intercede in human affairs. Thus, in an expanded naturalistic paradigm, it would be possible to capture the image of an angel on film; it is a matter either of our expanding our technology to appropriate frequency domains, or of angels (assuming they exist) temporarily adjusting their energetic aspects to allow such an imprint.

Reality is structured according to seven (or more) levels of being or as many as twelve dimensions in the case of Superstring theories. The number of levels or dimensions is not especially important for our purposes here. The core idea is that Energy Monism conceptualizes reality multi-dimensionally and that quite different kinds of object or processes may seem to prevail from within the perspective of each dimension.

All levels or dimensions are not merely interconnected, but 'intersuffusing' in a hierarchical asymmetry; each level penetrates its lower-level neighbours, but is not reducible to them. The ontological priority of this Great Spectrum of Being runs from top to bottom; however, all levels including dense materiality, are 'real.' It is only when we assume that physical existence is the only reality that our cosmology is mistaken.

All objects and events are both wholes and parts — 'holons' in the language of Arthur Koestler and Ken Wilber (1996). As wholes, for example, humans are integrated, semi-autonomous systems with identities that persist, yet change, over time; each human, as a whole, subsumes his or her 'parts.' Yet each of us is a part of physical, biological, socio-cultural, and ultimately cosmological systems. No thing is or could be exclusively whole or part, since all things are both.

Change is implemented by, though not reducible to, the language of wave forms, frequencies, phase entanglements, entrainment, harmonic series, etc. Each level of the Great Spectrum of Being has its distinctive vibrational dynamics, as well as its own laws and perspectives of consciousness; levels are in part defined by the perspectives (knowledge filters) shared by its participants.

Common sense reality (gross matter, life, and mind) occupies the lower three levels. All 'beyond-the-brain' phenomena (survival of physical death, mystical experience, angelic encounters, etc.) fit comfortably in this framework. Such experiences are sometimes described as 'dimensional bleedthroughs.' The differences between levels are differences of degree, not principle. Such, then, is the larger background of Energy Monism.

## *Foundations of metaphysical dualism(s)*

All dualisms of mind and body (or spirit and matter) assume the truth of the following core argument, even if they are not consciously based upon it:

1. For what appear as two things to be numerically one and the same, they must have qualitatively identical properties.
2. Mental states and brain states (or mind and body, etc.) do not have identical essential properties.
3. Therefore, mind and brain are not numerically the same, and some form of dualism is true.

The argument is deductively valid. The first premise is a variation of Leibniz's law, which is both *a priori* true and not generally debated. For example, if Bill Clinton is identical with the President of the United States in 1999, then everything true of Bill Clinton in 1999 would have to be true of the present President and vice versa. Support for the second premise comes from various quarters that dualists are *not* in agreement over. However, I will list the various possibilities:

— Certain states of consciousness are non-spatial, whereas all states the brain have spatial location. Depression in itself, for example, is not experienced at any particular place in the body, although it may carry certain physical effects.

— Certain states of consciousness are inherently private (known directly in a way that cannot be overridden by outside observers), whereas all states of the brain are in principle public (open to multiple observers who may sensibly agree or disagree over what they see).

— Some states of consciousness are intentional (inherently 'about' something other than themselves, e.g. beliefs may be about an object), whereas all brain states are non-intentional. Neurons either fire or they don't, but they are not about anything other than themselves.

— Some states of consciousness are transpersonal, for example, near-death experiences and states of mystical union, whereas all brain states are locked in the skull (save perhaps severe epileptic seizure the electrical energy of which may extend several inches beyond the skull).

— Some states of consciousness, such as clairvoyant perception, are 'paranormal' and unexplained (and perhaps unexplainable) by current physics.

The persuasiveness of this dualist way of thinking depends upon being able to show that the 'properties' in question are fundamentally incommensurable, not merely contingently different. For example, one thing can be located in space and have a certain colour; but it can't be both spatial and non-spatial. Or again, being (completely) in a brain/body and being outside one's body at the same time is logically impossible. Dualists do have reasons for their position and it will not do to reject a Cartesian perspective simply because Descartes failed to explain interaction or because dualism is incompatible with certain elements of modern physics. Indeed, an appreciation of the argument above stimulates an appreciation for some of the difficulties of both classical materialism and idealism. *It is not inherently any clearer how consciousness could give rise to matter than it is for matter to give rise to consciousness, so long as we are thinking of these categories in a dualistic manner.*

There are, however, serious difficulties for dualism — probably insurmountable. For example, if I am a nonphysical and thereby non-spatial subject of experience, then where am I? I cannot be said to be 'in' a body, since that implies spatial location. A deeper problem is this.

It's not so much that the above arguments imply a discredited and conceptually challenged position, although that may well be. Rather, the arguments suggesting a dualism of distinct minds and bodies equally well suggest, or at least are consistent with, the kind of multidimensional monism sketched earlier. My experience of joy, for example, suggests an irreducibility to the brain states correlated with it, but is no more inherently a state of 'my' local separate mind than an expression of a universal consciousness that connects us all on a more fundamental level. A serious appreciation for dualism leads us not only away from materialism, but also away from itself — to a larger paradigm.

## *The primacy of energy: matter and the new physics*

I shall take it for granted that readers have some familiarity with the New Physics and can find some stimulating expositions on relevant aspects of it in other sections of this book. However, I do wish to clarify certain elements from the perspective of Energy Monism. For example, the equation that energy equals mass times the speed of light squared is often taken to imply a 'co-equal reality' for both mass and energy. To be sure, each is functionally translatable into the other; we can create matter out of energy and energy out of matter. But such a functional equivalence betrays a deeper asymmetry evident in the thinking of this century's great physicists, notably that fields and forces are the fundamental (physical) reality and matter is its denser by-product. David Bohm offered that matter is simply 'gravitationally trapped light.' In a telling passage, Milic Capek cites Einstein:

> We may therefore regard matter as being constituted by the regions of space where the field is extremely intense ... There is no place in this new kind of physics both for the field and matter, for the field is the only reality. (Capek 1961.319)

Particles in physics are sometimes informally depicted as 'particles of matter,' whereas waves carry more energetic connotations. However, it is useful to remind ourselves that the particles in question — no matter how sub-atomic they may be — are still of an energetic nature; they are not inert corpuscles of hard 'stuff.' They are, more precisely, expressions of field force(s).

An important qualification involves my use of the term 'energy.' I find it linguistically convenient to rely upon this term, especially in labelling my position Energy Monism. However, it should be understood that, as the performance of work or the capacity to create some measurable difference, it is a neutral term that applies across the whole spectrum of physical phenomena and presumably some quasi-physical phenomena, too. Loosely, we refer to kinetic energy, or electrical energy, or thermal energy. However, as Chris Clarke (1997.29) points out, in physics there is technically no plural of 'energy.' So casual reference to difference kinds of energies needs to be appropriately qualified. Underlying different contexts for energy talk are the four primary forces: strong and weak nuclear, electromagnetic, and gravitational all of which appear close to being integrated in a grand unified theory (depending on which physicist you speak to!).

So the question of whether there are so-called 'nonphysical energies' involved with, say, thinking, perceiving a ghost, or healing miracles is really the question of whether there are forces beyond the four recognized by physics, or whether there are special extensions, configurations, or magnitudes of currently acknowledged forces — especially those of an electromagnetic variety — that create extra-dimensional overlays not experienced by current physical means. The 'energy' in Energy Monism fundamentally relies upon an ontology of fields, forces, and frequencies, however far intra- or inter-dimensionally these may extend.

## *Integrating energy and consciousness*

Energy Monism may seem to imply, but does *not* stipulate, that everything is just some form of energy — as may be affirmed in naïve New Age circles. Rather, energy and consciousness are fundamentally understood as aspects of each other and as irreducible to each other. Trying to reduce one to the other, or completely explain the workings of one in terms of the other, in my view is doomed to failure through a ready supply of counter examples or incommensurable properties that just will not disappear. In the language of Vedic spiritual traditions, this 'integrated difference' is reflected in the terms *pranashakti* (the energetic aspect of shakti) and *chitishakti* (the conscious aspect of shakti) — each an aspect of the transcendentally yet imminently pervasive Brahman.

This integrated difference should perhaps not surprise us, for energy and consciousness share some of each other's properties. For example, we attribute to both the capacity to do work or create measurable differences as well as a diaphanous or transparent quality and boundaries that are not strictly defined, but rather, that fade off into other goings-on.

As we move up and down the Great Spectrum of Being, things appear more energetic and less conscious, or more conscious and less energetic (certainly less material!), depending upon the perspectives that govern that level. Rocks, for example, appear to us as densely energetic or material; thus, it seems to us that they are at the lower end of the spectrum. As we explore upper ranges of the spectrum, perhaps through meditation, objects appear less dense and more expressive of the powers of consciousness. How a rock looks to an angel, or an angel to a rock, is presumably quite different. I stress this multi-level perspectivism in order to *counteract* the tendency to separate energy (including its material capabilities) from consciousness. At the level of rocks, everything (from our projected understanding) may appear non-conscious, and from the level of angels, NDEs, or mystical states quite powerfully conscious — where we speak of 'higher states of consciousness' but seldom, if ever, cf 'higher states of energy' (in those contexts). Both are always present, but appear via different filters in disproportionate magnitudes.

The idea of energy-consciousness does imply a polarity. However, this polarity is of subjective and objective or inner and outer. We know consciousness in its various aspects and levels inwardly through ourselves. We know energy in its tangible aspects outwardly through movement, colour, form, and measurement. This polarity is not a dualism of substances or things, much less of mind and matter. It is more akin to the two sides of a plane, or perhaps of a coin. It should not be understood, by analogy, as two coins interacting with each other.

The core foundation of Energy Monism, perhaps its most interesting feature, is that energy is, everywhere throughout the universe and up and down the Great Spectrum of Being, the 'outside' manifestation of consciousness, and consciousness is everywhere the inner aspect or 'inside' of energy. It's common in certain New Paradigm circles to explain various aspects of consciousness in quantum-mechanical terms, in particular the quantum interactions taking place in our brains. That seems as fundamental an explanation as we might hope for. Physicist and American presidential candidate John Hagelin once proposed a series of precise correlations between the radiant, unbounded field of consciousness achieved in higher states of meditation (for him Transcendental Meditation) and the specific equations of a unified string theory in physics unfolded in deductive form! Spinoza would feel vindicated. My point here is that no matter how detailed our correlations become between what we can measure from a third person or external point of view with specific states of consciousness experienced inwardly by the subject, there are nonetheless inner and outer aspects to the process. Push and refine quantum interactions in the brain as far as you wish. On their 'other side' is the experiential aspect. Quantum interactions are perhaps well suited to express states of consciousness. In principle one might even derive a complex quantum picture of what, say, depression looks like on the outside so to speak. But what depression looks like on the outside is not the same as how it feels on the inside. The two perspectives are intimately connected with, but not reducible to, each other.

Energy Monism in fact requires two polarities, an understanding of which will help avoid a common fallacy. Deep within certain New Paradigm discussions, particularly where the importance of being open-minded yet 'scientific' is stressed, there is a tendency, I think, to keep coming back to the brain and states of the brain to explain the evolution of consciousness. Like good holists, the irreducibility of consciousness to brain states is stressed, but how consciousness in all of its many and varied aspects came to be consciousness in the first place, is somehow assumed to be answerable by an evolutionary paradigm that views consciousness as a 'more complex' phenomenon emerging from 'less complex' physical or physically energetic states of affairs. Energy Monism sides with those who, by contrast, understand consciousness to have been present from the beginning, as it were, and the brain as a wonderfully complex tool or filter for the expression of consciousness. Energy-consciousness itself evolves and having a brain, at least for a while, presents many wonderful opportunities for doing so — like seeing through a pair of 'spectrum-restricted' physical eyes. But consciousness did not come from the brain, nor is it simply a higher form or frequency of energy or physical field force. Energy Monism does require a polarity between higher and lower states of energy and of consciousness in the Great Spectrum of Being — at least from a human perspective. (God wouldn't necessarily see it that way, because higher and lower are equally still of God's expressed nature.) What it stresses, though, is that both energy and consciousness parallel each other all the way up and down the spectrum, so to speak. Neither grows out of the other.

The other polarity, as already noted, is between inner and outer perspectives associated with consciousness and forms/fields/frequencies respectively. Consciousness is not the 'higher' part of the higher-lower polarity, but rather, the inner aspect of the inner-outer polarity. Whatever the merits of Energy Monism, an adequate theory of consciousness ought not to conflate these distinctions.

## *Four independent arguments for energy monism*

One neither proves nor disproves a theory as broadly inclusive as Energy Monism. We can, however, point to different areas where independent evidence for certain phenomena supports the kind of thinking Energy Monism incorporates, or to where the application of its principles to those phenomena makes them more understandable or plausible. I propose to do this in four areas.

### THE ARGUMENT FROM OBEs

An independent argument for Energy Monism as against both Cartesian Dualism and Materialism is based upon research suggesting that literal out-of-body ventures take place (Osis and McCormick, 1980). Whatever it is that travels from a body to a target destination and back again has several key features: a sense of self, rudimentary cognitive, emotive, and perceptual abilities, location in space, travel through space, and in some cases the ability to create physical changes in a target area. Thus, this travelling sense of self carries with it both conscious and energetic aspects. Something not normally visible to the naked eye which also occupies space would have to be energetic or force-like — whether or not it is currently measurable by physics.

These considerations rule out Cartesian Dualism, since it defines a mind (the thing that would presumably travel) as both non-physical and non-spatial. Moreover, in principle the right technology some day would allow us to take some kind of picture of that which travels. Cartesian Dualism cannot allow this and still remain what it is. Scientific Materialism, on the other hand, is also ruled out, since it does not allow the existence of anything that could leave the body in the first place. And even an expanded Naturalism which allowed for some kind of travelling force field would still come up short in explaining those aspects of the OBE that relate to consciousness (Woodhouse, 1994). To be sure, a functional dualism is implied ('Consciousness can do some things that brains cannot'), but it is neutral in its underlying metaphysics. It does not imply a dualism of two substances. In sum, the very description of an OBE, much less its ultimate explanation, seems to require a theory that integrates both energetic and conscious aspects of the experience — to wit, Energy Monism.

### The argument from clairvoyant healing

This argument is brief. If you take seriously what clairvoyant healers claim to do, more specifically, identify and remove 'yucky stuff' from clients and replace it with something of a more positive and healing nature, it's hard to see how you could be anything but an Energy Monist — at least by implication. The clairvoyant healer sees something of an energetic nature that is coloured and occupies space. (This may or may not be a fifth force in nature, which current physics cannot explain; it nonetheless appears to the clairvoyant as energetic in nature.) The client, for example, experiences this as, say, anger. The healer facilitates the release of the anger/energy. The client experiences angry expression. There is an inner aspect and an outer aspect to a single process. The healer is not seeing anger *per se,* but rather, the energetic expression of anger. There is a difference. And the integration of this difference leads to Energy Monism.

### The 'I' and the 'Me': identity over time and location in space

Let us think of the 'I' as the ultimate subject of experience, that which has a thought or is aware of its body. Pushed far enough back, it is called the witness self in Vedanta. By contrast, let us think of the 'Me' as the integrated totality of physical and psychological properties and actions that make up my descriptive identity. In Hinduism, these would be sorted as the guna selves. The 'Me' is the person I am (including past lives, if you include them in your cosmology), but it is the 'I' that is aware of 'Me.' Our 'Me's are the dances of life. 'I' is the stage for those dances.

When Hume, Kant, and various other thinkers went looking for their 'I,' they came up empty handed — although in various ways and for somewhat different reasons. According to Energy Monism, the basic reason for this failure is that what they were looking for is universal, not particular; it has no discrete existence as one among many. Hindus call this Brahman, Kant hinted at it with his idea of the transcendental unity of apperception. For Buddhists even the Void is not a mere empty vacuum, but rather, a formless (infinite?) ground without parts upon which the arising and perishing of events plays out. For limited purposes, I dub it generically as Universal Consciousness (Woodhouse,

1990). And what we take to be our individual subject/selves — our individual 'I's — are but the expression of Universal Consciousness through (or as) all the 'Me's in the universe. Vedic thought describes this as the identity of Brahman with Atman.

We often identify, at least by implication, the 'I' with the 'Me' as when we say 'I'm Mark Woodhouse, the author of this essay.' But the mere fact that I could be aware of this identity in difference implies that there is more to the 'I' than can be captured by the 'Me.' This something more, however, not just another spiritualized particular form of 'Me' superimposed over the 'Me' as one among many 'I's. Rather, it's a single 'I' for all of us. Our uniqueness as individual people is found in our 'Me's — not the 'I.' Mystical experience, I suggest, is in part the realization that what we take to be our separate 'I' dualistically locked up in our body is instead something far more universal and potent. When the 'I' (or our sense of I-ness) ceases to identify with the 'Me,' concerns about identity over time (including past or future lives) dissolve. Puzzles about non-locality in human interactions (e.g., distant healing) stem from the fact that a part of us — the discernible, energetic part — is located in space, whereas another aspect, our 'I-ness,' is already spread throughout the universe creating the basis for nearly instant connectedness in ways that appear to violate the laws of physics. Consciousness expresses itself energetically in different places. But consciousness itself is not thereby confined to different places looking for paranormal ways to reconnect with itself over the horizon, as it were.

### The Argument from Psychoneuro-Immunology

Psychoneuro-immunology is an exciting research programme full of therapeutic implications for the mind-body connection. However, it lacks any kind of coherent modelling to help explain how or why it should work. That there is a causal connection between, say, repressed grief and breast cancer mediated by neurotransmitters does not itself explain how this connection works or why grief happens to manifest this way in some women. In the background of PNI is a materialist paradigm which tends to assume that emotions themselves are just complex chemical states of the brain and nervous system. While she herself does not believe this, the title of Candace Pert's book, *Molecules of Emotion,* lends itself to just such an understanding.

The integrated difference of energy-consciousness and the interpenetrating dimensions of human nature in Energy Monism, however, suggest that all physical diseases have roots in unhealthy thoughts and emotions which, as states of consciousness expressing themselves energetically, might naturally be expected to manifest on a physical plane. This is not to say that these psychological roots are the only causes; they are not. Physical triggers abound everywhere in our genes, diets, lifestyles, and environment. However, when we give up the idea of consciousness as some nonphysical substance in our heads in favour of a quasi-energetic field suffused on different levels throughout our bodies and beyond, it should not surprise us that an unhealthy consciousness, if untreated, eventually results in an unhealthy body. Even cancer itself has a distinctive consciousness as theosophists and panpsychists have been telling us for a long time. Energy Monism concurs.

## *Response to criticisms*

### THE IRRELEVANCE OF ENERGY TO NON-LOCAL EFFECTS OF CONSCIOUSNESS

Larry Dossey (1993, 1997) has raised a number of important issues around 'energy talk' particularly in healing contexts. In so far as his criticisms carry implications for Energy Monism, they deserve as much response as space allows. In particular, Dossey argues:

(1) that the idea of 'sending healing energy' does not conform to the definitions of energy associated with the Four Forces (quantitatively measurable, following the inverse square law, etc.);

(2) that calling healing energy 'non-physical' does not add anything to the concept;

(3) that some healing phenomena of a non-local variety actually violate known parameters of energetic transmission and/or effect (a few cases of dramatic healing actually *preceded* prayers offered on behalf of the individual);

(4) that non-local healing phenomena have far more to do with consciousness, e.g., prayerful intent, than with anything of an energetic nature, although consciousness admittedly can be *mediated* by energy at a distance.

I accept all four propositions of concern to Dossey with one qualification in the case of (2).

My reservation is that, while calling healing energy 'non-physical' indeed adds little, if anything, to our understanding, it still signals the fact that in some contexts, for example, clairvoyant inspection, healing does seem to involve some kind of energetic exchange not currently explained by physics. To the best of my knowledge, his extensive writings on the non-local aspects of consciousness in healing contexts fail to address head on what this 'stuff' is that some healers remove and replace. Furthermore, consciousness is already 'built in' to my cosmology and is available for whatever non-local effects, whether instantaneous, non-energetic, or prayer-connected, Dossey wants to ascribe to it for healing contexts. Dossey subscribes to energy (physical and possibly nonphysical) and to consciousness, which is not reducible to energy (or matter). He also rejects Cartesian dualism. And while his ERA-III Medicine model is comprehensive, it does not explain quite how energy and consciousness 'get together.' Energy Monism offers such an explanation.

## Is consciousness more fundamental than energy?

Amit Goswami (1995) answers this question in the affirmative. Indeed, his book *The Self-Aware Universe* is subtitled 'how consciousness creates the material world.' He labels his position 'Monistic Idealism.' Our positions are very close. Certainly we are both monists. The core philosophical difference is this. As noted earlier, while I label my position Energy Monism for convenience, it is technically a double-aspected transcendental monism in which both energy (fields, forces, frequencies) and consciousness are aspects of something even more namelessly primordial. The Tao, for example, is neither consciousness nor energy *per se.* We are thus both opposed to the more scientifically reductive approach of attempting to derive consciousness from energy. Goswami's view might be thought of as 'left wing monism,' its opposite just described as 'right wing monism,' and my view as a transcendentally 'centrist monism.'

Perhaps I am misled by a passion for symmetry. Perhaps Goswami is right and I am better advised to give up the idea that there even is a centrist position to occupy. Still, we are so close perhaps we are both basically correct and separated only by differences of emphasis. He shows us how consciousness creates the *material* world, and I am certainly in agreement that the material world is a reflection of something more fundamental than itself. For him, this 'something' is consciousness, whereas for me it is 'energy-consciousness.' Many of the arguments he offers from quantum physics in support of his view actually appeal to the energy of fields, forces, and frequencies, which he then connects with consciousness. Yet I, too, view consciousness as expressing itself energetically — each being aspects of the other.

Consciousness does not create either energy or matter as something other than itself. So in that, too, we are agreed. The only apparent difference is that I would say that energy across the full spectrum of being expresses itself consciously (that is, reflecting a primordial intelligence, among other things) and I am not certain if Goswami would join me in affirming that. This much is clear, however. No matter how in other respects our accounts converge or differ there is room within his Monistic Idealism for the fundamental polarity of inner and outer by means of which I propose to connect consciousness and energy as different aspects of the same thing.

### A PANPSYCHIST EVALUATES ENERGY MONISM

Christian de Quincey (1997.29) has offered a number of criticisms my brief responses to which might further help to clarify the position. As with Dossey and Goswami, I consider De Quincey an ally in the search for an integrative paradigm of consciousness that moves us beyond the constraints of reductive science. He defends panpsychism, the view that consciousness is to be found all the way up and down the Great Spectrum of Being.

De Quincey seems to interpret me as saying that 'Consciousness is energy.' To the contrary, my proposal is that consciousness expresses itself energetically. An outside perspective never captures the interiority of consciousness which is where most of what is of interest to us resides. He also suggests that I have overlooked the fact that consciousness, considered in itself, has properties that are not of an energetic sort. For example, consciousness in part may be non-spatial or intentional. I fully agree and argue this both here and in *Paradigm Wars.*

He notes that the 'inner-outer' distinction is a spatial metaphor with limited and potentially misleading applicability. I agree that it is a metaphor, one of several ways (together with his own preference for a form-substance unity) to illustrate the idea of difference without separation. But it is one that has some intuitively obvious merit that we all rely upon in referring, say, to our 'inner worlds' of private experience *vis-à-vis* the 'outer' world of tangible things. He also interprets me as saying that energy is a perspective we (can) take on consciousness, then points out (with Dossey) that energy talk adds nothing to our knowledge of consciousness. I wholeheartedly agree with the latter observation and have argued as much, e.g., in my responses to Dossey and Stephen Braude in *Paradigm Wars.* An objective (outside, material, etc.) perspective tells us nothing about the interior subjective nature of consciousness.

De Quincey suggests that my epistemological perspectivism needs to be grounded in an appropriate ontology of energy and consciousness. I agree and perhaps should have been bolder in fleshing all this out. His concern, reflecting that of other philosophers, too, is that I may have committed a fallacy in drawing inferences of an ontological nature from my epistemology. I agree that there is no deductive inference with certainty to be had in this area, but persist in my belief that what we claim exists ought to be connected to how we claim to know this.

He also suggests that I have committed a fallacy in my use of the phrase 'stuff of reality' presumably because I think of consciousness as 'stuff' just like energy. I don't think of consciousness as just like energy and throughout my use of the term 'stuff' is no more than a convenient marker for 'that which exists.' Even that which is in process — which is the case for both energy and consciousness — has being. I agree that I should have done a better job in drawing out the evolutionary and process-oriented implications of Energy Monism. Bergson, Whitehead, and certain schools of Buddhism are complementary allies.

### A final default argument

To philosophical allies and critics of all persuasions, I offer the following argument in closing. If you are convinced that (1) fields, frequencies, and forces in their various multidimensional energetic aspects exist, that (2) consciousness in all of its multidimensional aspects exists and, furthermore, that (3) neither consciousness nor energy is reducible to the other, and that (4) a metaphysical dualism of mind/matter or energy/consciousness ought to be avoided, then the integration I have proposed *à la* Energy Monism, if not compelling, nonetheless will hopefully invite continuing interest.

## *References*

Capek, Milic. 1961. *The philosophical impact of contemporary physics,* New York: Van Nostrand.

Clarke, Chris. 1997. Energy talk. *Scientific and Medical Network.* 64. August.

De Quincey, Christian. 1997. Energy and consciousness. In *Scientific and Medical Network.* 64. August.

Dossey, Larry. 1993. *Healing words.* Harper San Francisco.

—. 1997. Energy Talk. *Scientific and Medical Network.* 63. April.

Goswami, Amit. 1995. *The self-aware universe,* New York: Putnam.

Harman W, and C. de Quincey. 1994. *The scientific exploration of consciousness: toward an adequate epistemology* (research report). Sausalito: Institute of Noetic Sciences.

Osis, Karlis & Donna McCormick. 1980. Kinetic effects on the ostensible location of an out-of-body projection during perceptual testing. *Journal of the American Society for Psychical Research,* 74.319–29.

Wilber, Ken. 1993. *The spectrum of consciousness,* Wheaton: Theosophical Publishing House.

—. 2000. *Integral psychology,* Boston: Shambhala.

Wilber, Ken, and Tony Schwartz. 1996. *A brief history of everything,* Boston: Shambhala.

Woodhouse, Mark. 1997. Why Dossey is an energy monist. *Scientific and Medical Network.* 64. August. 14–17.

—. 1994. OBEs and the mind-body problem. *New Ideas in Psychology.* 12.1–17.

—. 1990. Consciousness and Brahman-Atman. In Robert Forman (ed.) *The Problem of Pure Consciousness.* New York: Oxford University Press.

# Individual Identity: Beyond Identification with the Body

Ravi Ravindra

*Professor Ravi Ravindra, Ph.D., is Professor and Chair of Comparative Religion, Professor of International Development Studies and Adjunct Professor of Physics in Dalhousie University in Canada. He has received many fellowships, awards and research grants and has been visiting professor in a number of universities. He is the author of more than a hundred papers in physics, philosophy and religion and of a number of books including* The Yoga of Christ; Science and the Spirit *(ed.);* Krishnamurti: two birds on one tree; Yoga and the Teachings of Krishna; *and, most recently,* Science and the Sacred.

## *Other worlds, other dimensions, other lives*

My daughter was two years old. One winter evening, well bundled up in parkas, boots, tuques, suitable for a cold Canadian winter, we were lying in the new snow looking up at the stars. Quite out of the blue, deepening the magical profundity of the silence, my daughter announced, 'Daddy, before I was born, I was a star in the sky.' She did not wait for me to say anything or even acknowledge what to her seemed like a casual and obvious statement of a fact among other ordinary facts. I am the one who twenty-seven years later still wonders what to make of such a remark. What would you make of it?

Three years ago I spent some time with a Zen master in South Korea in intensive meditation. This Zen master had not for the previous twenty-five years or so climbed down the mountain on which his hermitage is situated. Occasionally some people would walk up the mountain where a temple had been built. Hardly anyone else came to join us for meditation, except a professor of Physics from a neighbouring university who came occasionally. One evening an antique dealer brought a bronze sculpture of the Buddha from the end of the Silla dynasty (fourth to tenth century CE) for which he wanted US$12,000. I asked the visiting Physics professor to negotiate on my behalf and he was able to talk the price down to $10,000. However all I wanted to pay was $5,000, this being the amount of an award I had just won before coming to Korea. The matter rested there.

The next morning, the Zen master came to my room, bearing a very striking sculpture of the seated Buddha from the middle of the Silla dynasty. He said, 'I was receiving vibrations from you wanting a Buddha image. Take this one. I have had this for a few years. It is a good one, much better than the one you were thinking of buying.' I protested vigorously. 'I cannot take the Buddha image from a monastery. I am supposed to bring gifts here, not take them away.' He said simply, 'This has nothing to do with customary right or wrong. In a previous life you did something for me. It is good if you take this. All this is a play of forces.'

A child and a Zen master: different people, different contexts, different relationships — but each with simple affirmation of other dimensions, other lives. It hardly seems sensible to constrict our view of reality to what can be understood by the narrow aperture of the rational mind.

## *The person is not the body*

It is a universal affirmation of all religious traditions that the person is not the body. The 'body' here includes the mind and the emotions, as in the use of the word 'flesh' in 'The Word became flesh' (John 1:14), and the use of the word *deha* or *sharira,* usually translated as 'body,' in the *Bhagavad Gita.* The person is not the body-mind, and there is something other than what meets the eye (or the scientific instruments as extension of the body-mind) which constitutes the core of the person. There is a spiritual aspect which does not die at the same time as the body-mind dies.

The same is true of the cosmos which also has spiritual aspects. The subtle aspects, whether of the cosmos or of oneself, can be apprehended only by a perception suitable to the task, for 'to any vision must be brought an eye adapted to what is to be seen, and having some likeness to it. Never did eye see the sun unless it had first become sunlike, and never can the soul have vision of the First Beauty unless itself be beautiful.' (Plotinus, *Enneads* I.6.9)

The opening of the subtle eye is the sole *raison d'être* of spiritual disciplines for only a person prepared and transformed can see subtle realities. Even John the Baptist, whose sole mission was to proclaim the coming of the Christ, did not recognize Jesus as such. Only when the Holy Spirit descended as a dove on the head of Jesus, an event which no one else saw, did John recognize Jesus as the Anointed One (John 1:29–34, in this connection, see Ravindra 1992).

In showing his great form to Arjuna, Krishna says (*Bhagavad Gita* 11:7f):

> Here in my body, on one place, now
> the whole world—
> All that moves and does not move—
> and whatever else you wish to see.
>
> Of course, with the ordinary eye
> you cannot see me.
> I give you divine eye to see
> the majesty of my power.

The fundamental question is 'What is the person?' or 'Who am I?' Prajapati, an impartial archetypal teacher of both the gods (*devas*) and the demons (*asuras*), had declared: 'The self which is free from evil, free from old age, free from death, free from grief, free from hunger and thirst, whose desire is the real, whose thought is the real, should be sought, that self one should desire to understand' (*Chandogya Upanishad* 8.7.1, the subsequent story 8.7–12). Both the gods and the demons wished to find the real and their representatives, Indra and Virochana respectively, sought instruction from the great teacher. They brought the appropriate offerings and lived with the teacher for thirty-two years living the disciplined life of students of sacred knowledge. At the end of this training and research, much like our modern day scientists might be after thirty-two years of research, Virochana was satisfied by the notion that the real self is nothing but the body. But Indra was not satisfied by this notion.

Indra then lived with Prajapati for another thirty-two years during which he investigated whether the dreaming self, which does not suffer from the defects of the body, is the real self. Having rejected this notion, he studied with Prajapati for another thirty-two years, inquiring whether the self in the dreamless sleep is the real self. He rejected that notion also owing to the lack of self-awareness in the state of dreamless sleep. Slowly the pupil's understanding ripened. Now he needed only five more years to find the true self. A total of one hundred and one years were spent by Indra in strenuous research and study to come to know — such knowing is not other than becoming — the real self about which Prajapati said, 'He obtains all worlds and all desires who finds the self and understands it.'

'I am Brahman,' says a great sage in the *Brihadaranyaka Upanishad* (I.4.10).* Jesus Christ said, 'The Father and I are one.' (John 10:30) Simone Weil quotes Madame Jeanne de Salzmann saying, 'Identify yourself with nothing less than God.' Here is a part of Sri Aurobindo's song of liberation (1952):

> I have become what before time I was
> A secret touch has quieted thought and sense:
> All things by the agent mind created pass
> Into a void and mute magnificence.

## *Reincarnation is not being born again*

There are many levels of the self, and it is good to be clear that 'reincarnation' is not the same as 'being born again.' The classical scriptural references for these two notions, that of reincarnation and of being born again are the *Bhagavad Gita* (chapter 2), and the Gospel according to St John (Chapter 3). Krishna says (*BG* 2:27; 2:22):

> Whoever is born will certainly die,
> and whoever dies will certainly be born.
> Just as a person discards worn-out clothes,
> And puts on others, that are new,
> The embodied leaves behind worn-out bodies
> And enters others, new ones.

* This is one of the four 'great utterances' (*mahavakyas*) of the Indian tradition. The other three are: 'Thou art that' (*Chandogya Up.* 6:9ff), 'This atman is Brahman' (*Mandukya Up.* 2), and 'Consciousness is Brahman.' (*Aitareya Up.* 5:3)

> Jesus said: 'In truth, in very truth I tell you, no one can see the kingdom of God unless he is begotten from Above.' 'How can a man be born again once he is old?' asked Nicodemus. 'Can he return to his mother's womb and be born over again?' Jesus replied: 'In truth, in very truth I tell you, no one can enter the kingdom of God without being begotten of water and Spirit. Flesh begets flesh, Spirit begets spirit. Do not be surprised that I tell you that you must all be begotten from Above. The wind blows where it will. You hear the sound it makes but you do not know where it comes from, or where it goes. So it is with everyone begotten of the Spirit.' (John 3:3–8)

Being born again, refers to being born from Above. It is not a repetition of physical births, as in *reincarnation* in which one re-enters another womb and is reborn biologically. It is rather a birth in a new dimension, subtler and spiritual, an emergence at a different level of being. Reincarnation has to do with continuation in time, more or less as one is, whereas being born again has nothing to do with time; it speaks of a radical transformation of being. The one refers to everlasting life; the other to eternal being. One has to do with an extension in time, the other with transcending time.

## *Is the eternal everlasting?**

The *everlasting* is generally understood to refer to an unlimited extension of the time coordinate allowing a temporal entity to last forever. When a person hopes for *everlasting life,* a sort of quantitative extension in time is commonly hoped for. However, this projection is based on a fear of the loss of personal ego whose continuation, in the known form, is wished for because the ego is not related to a larger and more cosmic dimension of the Self and of Reality. This profounder relationship, which is possible only in heightened states of consciousness, defines the *eternal.* The *eternal* is not opposed to *time,* nor is it a continuity in time; it is rather orthogonal to time. The eternal is an aspect of the quality of being rather than of temporality.

* The remarks that follow are based on Ravindra & Murray 1996.

## *The everlasting: extending time*

The *eternal* cannot be approached except by sacrificing the wish for the *everlasting.* When I wish to have a life without end, it is in fact a wish for a continuity of my personal identity, my own ego-self, throughout time. This wish arises out of a fear of the loss of my ego. It is difficult for me to imagine life, or the cosmos, without my ego being present. Because I am self-occupied, I regard myself as the centre of the universe and, in my ego-centred imagination, I believe that the whole universe would collapse if I were to cease existing in the form I know. I project my fear of the loss of the known onto the unknown and I devise whole systems of consolation which would vouchsafe an everlasting life for me.

The wish for continuity, the tendency to repeat myself and the inertia of a psychological momentum prevent my transformation — being born of the Spirit. This feature of the mind is what is called *abhinivesha* by Patanjali in the *Yoga Sutras* (2:9). The usual interpretation of this notion is that this is 'a wish for continuation of life,' which in turn is often interpreted as 'a fear of death.' However, *abhinivesha* is any desire for the continuation of the status quo which results in a fear of change. The wish for everlasting life is a consequence of *abhinivesha* and it stands in the way of the spiritual transformation necessary to find eternal life. The spiritual masters have said — see for example, Matthew 10:39, Luke 11:33, John 12:25 — that only the person who is willing to sacrifice the superficial life (or self, or ego, or Samsara) can find Life (or Self, or God, or Nirvana) . 'He that loveth his life shall lose it; and he that hateth his life in this world shall keep it unto life eternal.' (John 12:25*)*

The spiritual traditions do speak about the continuation of personal identity in time, but their concern is primarily with the quality of life — here and now, and not only after the physical death.

In the *Bhagavad Gita,* Krishna declares:

> I proclaimed this imperishable teaching (yoga) to Vivasvan
> He taught it to Manu, and he, to Ikshvaku.
> Handed down in this way from one to another,
> This yoga was known by the sage-kings,
> But, Arjuna, it became lost on earth with the lapse of time.
> This very yoga of old is being taught by me to you today.
> For you are devoted to me and my friend,
> And this yoga is, indeed, the supreme secret. (*BG* 4:1–3)

Arjuna has not yet realized the true nature of Krishna and he is quite understandably puzzled about Krishna's relationship with time. He asks:

> Later was your birth, earlier was the birth of Vivasvan:
> How am I to understand this,
> That you proclaimed this teaching in the beginning?
> [Krishna replies:]
> Many are my past lives and yours, Arjuna;
> I know them all, you do not, Foe-Destroyer.
> Though I am unborn and of changeless self,
> Though I am Lord of beings,
> having taken my stand over my own *prakriti*
> I am born by my own self's power (*maya*). (*BG* 4:4–6)

Earlier (*BG*.2:12) Krishna had said:

> Never was there a time when I was not,
> Nor you nor these rulers of men;
> And never hereafter shall there be
> A time when any of us will not be.

Here is a clear statement about the continuity of personal identity through time across the boundaries of life and death. Even though Arjuna and, like him, most human beings are not aware of their previous births nor of their future existences, the sages know of them, for 'whoever is born will certainly die, and whoever dies will certainly be born.' (*BG* 2:27) Each human being is assured of, or even condemned to, immortality, to a continuity in time for ever in which one is imprisoned everlastingly in one's own selfhood.

If we move from the Eastern perspective to a Christian one, in spite of many differences we find a similar situation in this important aspect, namely, that a person is condemned to immortality. A person does not disappear after death into total annihilation, but continues. And therein lies the dread — as well as the hope — for one may be cast into everlasting hell, though one hopes for everlasting heaven.

> Nor dread, nor hope attend
> A dying animal;
> A man awaits his end
> Dreading and hoping all. (W.B. Yeats)

It is important to emphasize that, contrary to the general popular impression, religious traditions do not refer to the mere continuity of personal identity in time across the boundary of physical death, as a promise. Such a quantitative extension of the duration of one's existence, without a change in the quality of life, is rather a threat. Death does not lead to final extinction, as some might even wish and hope, and cannot therefore solve anything. Each of us is obliged to face the consequences of our personal actions precisely because of the continuity of the person after death. There is no escape from oneself, for as one sows so shall one reap. The realization of a continuity of identity in time is rather a sobering fact. A philosophic life or a good life can be a preparation for life after death because of this continuity.

The Indian tradition says that life after death, in another incarnation, will be more or less a repetition of this life, with superficial changes. The body is changed just as the clothing which is worn out might be (*BG* 2:22). Unless there is a radical transformation in the being of the person, unless the wearer changes deeply and essentially, only the clothes will be different. Those who see below the surfaces — as does Yama, the god of death and of law, and as one sees oneself in the mirror of one's own conscience — are not fooled by appearances. The changes in the physical body as it ages, or the change of bodies through different incarnations, do not mean that there have been changes in the essential nature and the persistent tendencies which identify the person.

Similarly, in the Christian tradition, the life after death will depend on the quality of life before death, for no one can come to God who is not radically transformed by the Spirit. Christ said, 'In truth, in very truth, I tell you, no one can see the kingdom of God unless he is begotten from Above ... no one can enter the kingdom of God without being begotten of water and Spirit. Flesh begets flesh, Spirit begets spirit.' (John 3:3–6) If a person loses the opportunity for transformation in the incarnated state — as is also understood in the Indian traditions where incarnation is said to be necessary for spiritual evolution — then one continues for ever in the untransformed state of being. Trapped in one's own selfhood, in self-occupation which is the exact opposite of the state of true love, a person remains exiled from the presence of God. Those who are aware of the fact of their exile, because they have sometimes experienced a different state of being, suffer the torments of hell. Only those who have sometimes sensed the possibility of vastness can truly suffer in the prison of their smallness, just as only those who have sometimes seen know the agony of blindness.

## *The eternal: transcending time*

If the everlasting continuity of personal identity is not what the spiritual seeker wishes, what is aspired for? There is an ancient Vedic prayer, quoted in the *Brihadaranyak Upanishad* (I.3.28), which says:

> From the unreal lead me to the Real
> From darkness lead me to Light
> From death lead me to Life.

This state of Non-death, of Life (*amrita*), presumably is not the state in which one is born again and again, endlessly, for this requires no effort and is guaranteed to all. Such a state cannot be the goal of spiritual life, any more than death can be such an aim, for the simple reason that everyone will undergo this fate in any case. On the contrary, the desired end is a state of being which does not come about automatically; it requires strenuous effort and discipline, a yoga, from below and grace from Above.

A spiritual seeker wishes for a transformation of being so that the quality of the relationship with higher energies and levels could be radically altered. This transformation results in a life which is not ego-centred but is rather centred in God, who because of his omnipresence lives in the deepest recesses of the seeker's heart as well as in every other person and in every other thing. A mark of this inner reorientation in the aspirant is a shift from being in a state of occupation with acquisition and self-advancement to one of love for others and of wishing to be of service. (In this connection, see Ravindra 1974 and 1984, Chap.1.)

The highest form of sacrifice is the renunciation of the ego-self. Our one individual and personal possession is the sense of 'I'; all other possessions are accidental and subject to external loss. This self which is occupied with itself is what the spiritual aspirant undertakes to surrender. The saints achieve only this: they succeed in doing nothing. Nothing, that is, which is their own. They have no project, no point of view, no ambition of their own; they do what they must under the guidance of the will of God, as a service and as an offering. 'In truth, in very truth I tell you, the Son can do nothing by himself; he does only what he sees the Father doing: what the Father does, the Son does ... The teaching that I give is not my own; it is the teaching of him who sent me. Anyone whose teaching is only his own is bent on self-glorification.' (John 5:19; 7:16,17) And St Paul said, 'I live, yet no longer I, but Christ liveth in me.' (Gal.2:20)

The greatest fear of the saints is that of dying without being self-annihilated, without having died to their ego-selves. Without this death they would be condemned to the prison of their own egos. As the *Theologia Germanica* (Chapter 34) says, 'Nothing burneth in hell except self-will.' The sage strives for a discontinuity of the ego-self in time and not for its everlasting perpetuation. Very different sorts of questions about life after death arise for those who wish to be free of their own self-will than for those who fear the extinction of their egos. The sage fears dying without the extinction of the ego, without self-naughting, without having entered into the state of Eternal Life, of Nirvana.

Krishna says in the *Bhagavad Gita* (14:19f):

When the seer perceives no doer
other than the gunas (constituents of nature)
And knows what is higher than the gunas,
Such a one attains to my being.
Having gone beyond these three gunas springing from the body,
The embodied one, released from birth and death, old age and unhappiness,
Attains immortality (*amritam).*

This state of 'immortality,' of being freed from the cycle of birth and death, is certainly not a continuation of personal identity in time. This state is rather one of freedom from the limiting self — and therefore from fear and ambition which are the marks and supports of the ego — as well as from the limitations of time.

The sun does not shine on it, nor the moon nor fire;
Those who come to this, my supreme dwelling-place,
They do not return. (*BG* 15:6)

Only those can come to God who do not bring themselves. One who is anyone is not fit to be one with God. As Christ said, 'And no one has gone up to Heaven except he who came down from Heaven.' (John 3:13) Krishna declares as a summation of his entire teaching in the *Bhagavad Gita* (18:53–58):

> Having forsaken the sense of I, might, insolence
> Desire, anger, possession; Unselfish and at peace,
> One is fit to become Brahman.
> Having become Brahman, tranquil in the self,
> One neither grieves, nor desires;
> Regarding all beings as equal,
> One attains supreme dedication to me.
> Through this dedication,
> One knows me in essence;
> Then having known me essentially,
> One forthwith enters into me.
> Ever performing all actions,
> Taking refuge in me, By my grace,
> One reaches the eternal, imperishable abode.
> Renouncing all action to me with your mind,
> Intent on me, relying on the yoga of understanding.
> Become constantly mindful of me.
> Mindful of me, you will cross all obstacles by my grace.
> But if, due to your sense of I, you will not pay heed,
> You will perish.

As long as we confine ourselves to our egoistic selves, we restrict our consciousness to a small aperture in the vast spectrum of consciousness. If we widen the doors of our perception, we will be able to see more clearly than we ordinarily do. One who is awakened to the Spirit dwells both in time and in eternity. Although in time, such a person is then not restricted by it. Eternity is a quality of being, rather than an extension of temporality, and it is neither an infinite extension of time nor is it in opposition to it. Eternity is quite orthogonal to time in the mathematical sense: it intersects with the dimension of time, but is not at all contained in it. No description exclusively in terms of time can adequately comprehend eternity, just as no combination of lines in two dimensions can produce a cube. In that sense, the eternal is timeless. Another dimension of consciousness is needed to live in eternity. As long as we remain confined to our ordinary consciousness, we experience and move only in time, having only vague and occasional hints of eternity.

> Men's curiosity searches past and future
> And clings to that dimension. But to apprehend
> The point of intersection of the timeless
> With time, is an occupation for the saint —
> No occupation either, but something given
> And taken, in a lifetime's death in love,
> Ardour and selflessness and self-surrender.
> (T.S. Eliot, 'The Dry Salvages' in *Four Quartets)*

In order to experience the realm of the eternal or the timeless, a re-orientation of the ego is needed — not a physical death. When one is awakened, one is freed of the tyranny of time; then one does not live in the past or in the future, but in the present, now, radically open. Eternity contains time within it, just as a cube includes a square. A consciousness viewing our temporal world from an eternal and universal point of view is not limited by our notions of temporal or causal sequence. To it, past and future events are as clearly comprehensible as the present ones; events far away are as clearly visible as near ones. In his sermon titled *Adolescens, tibi dico: surge!,* Meister Eckhart says, 'Yesterday I said something that would seem truly incredible. I said: 'Jerusalem is as near to my soul as the place where I am now standing. Yes, in all truth; what is even more than a thousand miles farther than Jerusalem is as near to my soul as my own body; and I am as sure of this as I am of being a man.'

The temporal order — past, present and future — does not describe or limit the eternal. Whatever is eternal is always present, without beginning or end in time — unborn and undying. 'Everything stands in a present now.' (Eckhart) Those who live in the present, which is to say those who are alive and awake to the moment — which has to do with a quality of awareness rather than with any external time — have a possibility of contacting the eternal order. As Wittgenstein said: 'If we take eternity to mean not infinite temporal duration but timelessness, then eternal life belongs to those who live in the present.' (*Tractatus Logico Philosophicus,* proposition 6.4311)

A person for whom the ego-identity, which claims 'I am this' or 'I am that,' is no longer the central motivating force of life, but who is cleansed in the supreme identity of oneness with Brahman or God or

Suchness, can say simply 'I AM.' 'I AM' is a sacred name of God and the experience of this is the same as an experience of 'God IS.' (For a discussion of the importance and meaning of 'I AM,' see Ravindra 1992, Chaps.4,7,8.) Even though our ordinary rationality experiences this as a transgression, the sage can truly say as Christ did: 'In truth, in very truth, I tell you, before Abraham was, I AM.' (John 8:58) No wonder the text adds, as a contemporary text might add about our rationalist scientists and philosophers, then the crowd 'picked up stones to throw at Jesus ...'

## *References*


Aurobindo, Sri. 1952. The Self's Infinity. In *Last poems.* Pondicherry: Sri Aurobindo Ashram.

Ravindra, R. 1974. Self-surrender: core of spiritual life. In *Studies in Religion/Sciences Religieuses.* 3.357–63.

—. 1984. *Whispers from the other shore: spiritual search east and west.* Wheaton: Quest. (An updated version 2000. Halifax, NS: Shaila Press.

—. 1992. *The yoga of the Christ.* Shaftesbury: Element. (Reissued 1998 as *Christ the Yogi.* Rochester, VT: Inner Traditions International.

—. 1998. *Yoga and the teaching of Krishna.* Adyar: Theosophical Publishing House.

Ravindra, R. and P. Murray. 1996. Is the eternal everlasting? In *The Theosophist.* 117.140–6. Reprinted in R. Ravindra. 1998.

# The Sleeping Beauty: The Awakening of Instinct into Consciousness

ANNE BARING

*Anne Baring is a member of the Association of Jungian Analysts in London and author, with Jules Cashford, of* The Myth of the Goddess: evolution of an image; *a children's book,* The Birds Who Flew Beyond Time *and, with Andrew Harvey,* The Mystic Vision *and* The Divine Feminine. *She is passionately interested in the way in which consciousness seems to be guiding its own expansion towards a greater understanding of itself through the human psyche.*

I'd like to start on a personal note — with an experience that I had when I was eleven — an experience of leaving my body. I was dozing on my bed one hot summer day when I became aware of an intense purple light in the room. Suddenly, I felt my eyes closed by what felt like an irresistible power. The bed beneath me opened as if it were cut by a knife. In terror I struggled to open my eyes, shout for help, move my arms and legs, but my body refused to respond. I was pushed down through the opening and the bed closed over me. I found myself going through a long tunnel with a rushing and roaring noise like an avalanche or a waterfall which absolutely terrified me. Suddenly, I was ejected from this tunnel into total silence. I heard a voice say to me: 'I Am.' It was going to say something else but my fear cut it short and I shall never know what the rest of the sentence might have been. I found myself re-entering the tunnel and plunged once more into the roaring, deafening vortex of sound, emerging from it to find myself lying in my bed, thankfully alive in a familiar world. As you can imagine, this experience set the trajectory of my life in terms of trying to find out what that voice was, what that experience meant — and eventually, what consciousness was. So, it was that experience, so long ago, which has ultimately brought me to this conference.

Looking back now, I can see that this event precipitated me into a dimension of consciousness that other people did not know about and that I might never have discovered if it had not happened to me. This secret knowledge became the foundation of my own individual myth — what throughout my life has held supreme meaning for me. I am coming to this talk from this inner experience, from an awareness that a wider, deeper consciousness than our own may be trying to reach us, trying to make itself known to us.

I have chosen as an opening slide this picture of a man putting his head beyond the edge of a familiar universe, going beyond the space/time barrier and gazing in wonder at another dimension of reality. So here is an image of exploration, an image of breaking through, an image of quest and discovery. I think we are today in our understanding of reality where the Portuguese explorers were in the fifteenth century when they set out on their great sea voyages — that is to say — we are moving from a flat earth to a round earth image of reality.

As I was preparing this talk, I came across a sentence in a book by Bede Griffiths called *Return to the Centre*. This is what he wrote:

> The evolution of matter from the beginning leads to the evolution of consciousness in man; it is the universe itself which becomes conscious in man ... It is the inner movement of the Spirit, immanent in nature, which brings about the evolution of matter and life into consciousness. (1976.31f)

I find this an immensely exciting idea because it revolutionizes our view of nature and of spirit. I believe this understanding, so beautifully expressed by him, is the basis of a new paradigm that is coming into being. Consciousness seems to be like a plant, an organic growth, which has its roots in an unknown depth. Its flowering is a potential within us — a potential that we have still to experience, that only a few pioneers of consciousness have experienced. As we evolve, so we become intelligible to ourselves; as we grow, so we experience the true nature of reality.

## *Origins of our dualistic view*

So the great questions in my mind over the last twenty years have been: where did our present dualistic view of reality originate? When did we split life into two polarities, the one masculine, the other feminine? I believe our view of reality has been formed by two powerful myths, which I shall come to in a moment. Because of their profound influence on previous civilizations and, through them, our own, we have come to divide life or reality into two aspects — spirit and nature, mind and matter. But, as I hope to show in this talk, I believe these are arbitrary divisions, whose origin may be found in the far older experience of our separation from nature, which has been a painful but necessary phase of our evolution. Partly because of this experience of separation and partly because of the accelerated development of the mind in the last five thousand years, human consciousness has also come to be divided in two — into mind and soul, head and heart. We are now virtually unconscious of our soul and our connection to the greater matrix of nature out of which we have evolved. It is difficult for us to speak to each other as people spoke to each other in the past, because of our fear of appearing non-rational. A part of ourselves is almost speechless, autistic. Today we live in our head, in our mind, in what we believe is the supremely conscious, most interesting and powerful part of ourselves. Nature, soul and heart — the realm of the non-rational — have been left out of the equation.

If I were to ask, 'What is beyond the brain?' I would answer, 'the lost realm of soul.' In the past, the word 'soul' carried meaning in a culture and the greatest artists, poets and mystics were engaged in connecting people with their soul. Today, however, the word may convey nothing to a culture which is focused entirely on the external world and knows nothing of an inner life, an inner, imaginal life. For such a culture, which might be described as a purely sensate one, in the sense that the philosopher Pitirim Sorokin (1992) used that word, focused on the experience of the senses alone, the soul is asleep, dissociated, unable to communicate with the surface consciousness that directs our lives. Our brilliant technological culture with its ruthlessness and its brutality and ugliness inflicts intolerable stress on us and it reflects, I think, a dissociated, unbalanced consciousness and a loss of soul.

The great image of reconnection which flows from the hidden life of the soul is the sacred marriage, so important to fairy tales and alchemy. Myths and fairy tales reconnect us with soul. They take us into a mythic realm where we can respond to the guidance of the imagination. The imagination can reconnect us to our instincts, to the flow of life in ourselves and the universe, giving meaning and value to our brief lives on this planet. I have chosen the story of the Sleeping Beauty to illustrate the theme of marriage, the marriage between the masculine and feminine aspects of the soul: between thinking and feeling — between our head and our heart. The Sleeping Beauty is the imaginal mind as opposed to the literal mind. Through this imaginal mind we are connected with a reality beyond the reach of rational intellect; it acts rather like a plug connecting us to the socket of that deeper reality. When we are not in touch with the imagination, it is as if a vital part of us is asleep; it cannot communicate with us, cannot help us. I believe that in the story of the Sleeping Beauty, the Prince and the Sleeping Beauty, symbolize these two aspects of our consciousness which belong together as bridegroom and bride.

## *The Sleeping Beauty*

I am sure you will remember the story of the princess who explored the unused rooms of the castle on her fifteenth birthday and came across an old woman turning and turning her spinning wheel. Attempting to take the spindle from the old woman, she pricked her finger on it and at once fell into a deep sleep, so fulfilling the curse placed on her by the uninvited thirteenth fairy at her christening — a curse that was mitigated by another fairy who remitted that death sentence to a hundred years' sleep. The whole court fell asleep with her. A great forest of rambler roses — an impenetrable hedge of thorns — grew up around her and for a hundred years, legends were told about the Sleeping Princess who lay hidden at the heart of the forest until the day when a prince, hearing of the legend, determined to set out to find her. Many suitors had perished in the attempt to penetrate the hedge of thorns but, the story says, the thorns turned to roses for him, the way through the hedge opened and he came to where she lay sleeping and awakened her with a kiss. As she awoke, the whole court came to life and preparations began for their marriage — for all the best-loved fairy tales end in marriage.

Fairy tales are very old: they portray the landscape of the soul; they speak with the voice of the soul and carry many levels of meaning. Who can say where the story of the Sleeping Beauty originated and how it was transmitted from generation to generation? It may be descended from long-forgotten Bronze Age rituals — rituals that celebrated the sacred marriage of heaven and earth and others which mourned the annual death of the life of the earth and its regeneration in spring. The sacred marriage of king and queen, prince and princess is an image that is also woven into the rich tapestry of hidden or lost mystical traditions — alchemy, gnosticism and Kabbala.

I see this magical story as a metaphor for our own time and the urgent need for a marriage between our head and our heart, between our too-literal, linear mind which knows nothing of a deeper ground of consciousness, and our imaginal, instinctual, creative soul. This deep instinctual part of ourselves which is the matrix of our ability to imagine and create, works through the principle of attraction. It is through our instinctual soul and its longing for relationship with what is 'other' that we are most closely connected to nature and the Kosmos. It is imagination and instinct which draw us into connection with a reality beyond the reach of mind, acting rather like a plug connecting us to the socket of that deeper reality.

The Prince, I suggest, stands for the solar principle of consciousness — the questing human mind which seeks to explore, discover, understand, penetrate to the heart of reality and who, in this story, is seeking the lost feminine counterpart of himself. The Sleeping Beauty carries the lunar principle of soul, the neglected feeling values *(eros)* which are undeveloped or inarticulate in relation to mind, and have, so to speak, lain under a spell for centuries. From another perspective, the story can be seen as a metaphor of the reconciliation of spirit and nature or the reunion of the masculine and feminine aspects of spirit which have been progressively sundered during the last four thousand years.

## *Loss and recovery of soul*

The hedge of thorns shows what an impenetrable barrier lies between our head and our heart, between our analytical, literal mind and the deep, feminine ground of our soul, and how difficult it is to get through it. I suggest that the hedge of thorns symbolizes all the belief systems we have built up over hundreds, if not thousands of years: deeply rooted religious beliefs about the nature of God and our fallen and sinful human nature and scientific beliefs about what we call matter: beliefs about what spirit is and beliefs about what nature is. These belief systems, deeply imprinted on us over generations, stand between us and our soul and make it almost impossible for us to reach below the surface of our everyday consciousness and relate to and value the dimension of feeling. Instinctive consciousness does not communicate primarily through words, through language, but rather through feelings, intuitions, images of all kinds, and through emotions and dreams. If we do not pay attention to these, there will be no way in which these feelings, intuitions and images can reach our surface mind that is so focused on the external world. They will be shut away behind a hedge of thorns. The journey in search of the soul, back the way we have come, is difficult and even dangerous because it requires that we relinquish the certainty of what we think we know and what we have been taught to believe. It means surrendering the desire to be in control and opening ourselves to the journey. Many myths and fairy tales emphasise the need for surrender and trust in the strange non-rational guidance offered by animals or shamans on the quest. As the hero follows their guidance, so the hedge opens, the way unfolds. Following the guidance of the non-rational, intuitive wisdom of the instinct is the royal road into the realm of soul.

Following this intuitive, non-rational wisdom is also the theme of Greek mythology as well as fairy tales, if you remember the story of Theseus and Ariadne. Looking at this image (of Perseus, Andromeda and the dragon), I am reminded of a story told to me by Richard Tarnas.*

If the soul had two suitors and one of them said to her: 'You are of some interest to me as an object for clinical analysis. I want to see whether you exist and whether you conform to a theory I have about you. If you fit my theory, I might consider you as a suitable partner

*Author of *The Passion of the Western Mind.*

but I will set the terms of our contract.' And the other said, 'I have fallen passionately in love with you and want to know you better. I cannot conceive of life without you. Will you marry me?' Which of these suitors do you imagine she would choose? Supposing Perseus had approached Andromeda with the first offer. Might she not have chosen the dragon as a preferable fate? It is most unlikely that nature and our instinctual soul will yield their secrets to an analytical suitor; only to the one who loves them and wishes to discover what they *want.*

## *The split between mind and soul*

Now I would like to explore with you in more detail how I believe the separation between mind and soul may have come about. Reflecting on this image of the human brain, I see it as part of nature and as an organ that it has developed to further the evolution of consciousness; an organ which connects us to our immediate environment but which also connects us to a wider and deeper invisible field of consciousness — something like a still undiscovered field of incredibly fine energy which binds together many different levels and forms of life and functions at many different rates of vibration. The physical brain and all the interrelated systems that we call body and which form an organic whole have come into being over millions of years of the Earth's life. The brain (which cannot really be considered as separate from the rest of the body) has been the organ for a consciousness that has moved infinitely slowly from unconscious instinctual responses programmed through the life experience of countless species through millions, if not billions of years, to the time where one species out of many — our species — developed self-awareness and the ability to focus attention through reflective, analytic and directed thought.

This miraculous evolutionary process was focused relatively recently through the reptilian and mammalian brain system and then, only very recently in relation to planetary evolution, through the neocortex or new mammalian brain. Infinitely slowly, as if in response to an innate directing impulse, the consciousness latent or present within nature and matter, as the form of an oak is present within an acorn, has slowly become conscious. We carry all this immense evolutionary experience — this memory bank — in the cells of our body. We carry both the older and the newer brain systems co-ordinating as a single entity. However, as the ability of our species to develop a sense of self,

*The winged and crowned mermaid.*
*From Solidonius. Bibliothèque de L'Arsenal, Paris, Ms.973, f.12.*

to inhibit instinctive reflexes and increasingly to be able to control the environment evolved, so we became cut off from the immense network of relationships in which we were once embedded — that we call nature, the planetary matrix out of which we have evolved. This was in no sense our fault. We have simply instinctively followed the gradient of our evolution and have not been able to understand until now what has happened and why it has happened.

This image of a winged and crowned mermaid, surrounded by symbols of the four elements, taken from an alchemical text, describes this evolutionary process rather well. We can see how the older and newer systems of consciousness are brought together in the figure of the mermaid. Her tail could represent the older, instinctual stratum of consciousness; her body and head the more recently developed levels and her crowned head and wings a potential of consciousness that has not yet been realized by us as a species. The development of a sense of self, and the ability to focus and direct consciousness towards specific goals seems to have brought about a dissociation between the older and the newer aspects of our nature, between mind and soul, between rational intellect and the greater matrix of nature which functions instinctively. Nature has been emptied of numinosity and divinity as human consciousness gathered that divinity and numinosity to itself. This inner dissociation in our own nature has been projected onto the belief that spirit and nature are something intrinsically *different* from each other. Spirituality has always been presented as a movement away from nature, upwards towards spirit. Only the Taoists among the religious systems of the last three thousand years seem to have understood that in order to discover the ground of our being within nature and within ourselves, we need to be connected to the instinct as something of great value. A part of consciousness that has been split off from its ground like a child from the mother, needs to rejoin that ground. We are part of what we observe around us because we have evolved from the same matrix or root as everything we observe. In moving to an exploration of our own consciousness as the key to understanding both ourselves and the universe, we are, I believe, moving towards an extraordinary revelation.

## *The role of instinct*

But the dissociation in our nature is becoming increasingly dangerous for ourselves and the planet because, although we believe that we are in control of our instincts, we are in fact controlled and directed by the older part of our nature in ways that we are simply not aware of. Although thinking seems to be so conscious, so rational, it is inseparably tied to feelings and instincts that come from the older levels of consciousness. Our belief systems, whether religious or scientific, as well as our ways of relating to each other as individuals and nations are profoundly rooted in unconscious instinctive responses which have their origins in earlier phases of our evolution. The unconscious responses of the reptilian/mammalian brain system are immensely conservative and immensely powerful. They fear change as an overwhelming threat. Once a belief system or a pattern of behaviour has been established over several thousand or even several hundred years, the instinctual response to any new idea is to attack it and to defend the old position with all the power that is available to it. Hence the ridicule and furious resistance provoked by ideas which run counter to the general belief system of the age. In defending an established belief system, we can behave with all the instinctive aggression of an animal defending its

*The Great Mother. Found in a rock shelter at Laussel, in the Dordogne. Now in the museum of Aquitaine in Bordeaux.*

territory. (Analytical work also encounters the fear of losing the safety of what is familiar).

From another perspective mythology can also throw some light on how the dissociation between mind and soul came about and also on the evolution of consciousness. This is the earliest known image of the Great Mother, dating to about 22000 BC.

The Great Mother or the Great Goddess stands for the maternal ground, the older layers of consciousness, the deeper reality we know so little about and the whole instinctual network of invisible relationships that we call nature. She also stands for the phase in our evolution when we lived in greater participatory union with the ground of life, contained, so to speak, in its womb. Owen Barfield (1988) describes this earlier phase of our evolution as 'Original Participation.' Duality in the sense of feeling ourselves to be separate from nature, had not yet come into being. For some fifteen thousand years and maybe far longer, the image of the Great Mother was the focus of human consciousness. One might call this phase of unknown length the phase of lunar consciousness. Throughout this time, life was experienced as an organic, living and sacred whole, and the Great Mother was the whole, the matrix of being, the womb or source of all life, both visible and invisible. The earth was peopled with unseen entities, a 'thou' not an 'it,' as it is today. We can relate this phase to that phase in our own lives when we are contained in the maternal womb and closely associated with our mother during our early years. This sense of participatory consciousness lasts far into the Bronze Age and beyond — until about 2000 BC.

But suddenly, around 2000 BC, we can see from the texts and mythic imagery of the time that there is a dramatic shift of focus from the feminine to the masculine principle, from goddess to god. This is reflected in a Babylonian myth which tells how the god Marduk murders the mother goddess Tiamat (who is portrayed as a dragon) and creates heaven and earth from the two halves of her dead body. An Assyrian relief of a thousand years later, now in the British Museum, describes the earlier Babylonian myth. Here is the earliest image of a god separate from creation who brings it into being not as a natural, organic process but by a conscious act of will. Here is an image of duality, an image that suggests the separation of consciousness from the maternal ground of instinct, the beginning of the differentiation of mind from soul, and the emergence of a conscious ego which sees itself as the creator of the world. Marduk exults in his power to destroy the mother goddess and to create the universe, setting the stars in their courses. This late Bronze Age myth had an immense influence on later cultures and is the prototype of Greek myths describing a hero's struggle with the dragon. It establishes the paradigm of the fundamental split between spirit and nature that was to lead, via Hebrew and Christian culture, to the belief (first expressed in theology and then, much later, in science) that nature and matter are something separate *from* and inferior *to* spirit, fundamentally different from spirit, something passive and inert, without consciousness, something that can be controlled and dominated by the human mind and made subject to the human will. Inheriting these concepts by a quite fascinating transmission of mythology from culture to culture, it seems as if the human mind today has modelled itself on Marduk, believing with all the hubris of an ego cut off from its roots, that it can manipulate nature and matter as it chooses. The end-result of this transmission of ideas has led ultimately to the creation of the atom bomb, splitting and using the elements of nature to destroy life in the same way that Marduk used the elements of nature to destroy Tiamat. (Marduk used the wind to blow her up). Nothing illustrates the dissociation between mind and soul better than this recent event. Five thousand years after Marduk, the ethos of Western culture is still one of conquest, whether the conquest of enemies or the conquest of nature or space and I believe it originates with this powerful Babylonian myth.

We are only just becoming aware of unconscious mythological programming that has profoundly influenced and directed our religious beliefs and our scientific research. In Western civilization, God has been presented or imagined in the masculine mode for nearly three thousand years and the feminine dimension of the divine has been deleted from our definition of spirit. God has been conceived as an intelligence or being beyond creation rather than as the life of creation and the hidden intelligence within it. Four thousand years ago, with the myth of Marduk, divinity began to be identified with the heavens, with the sky, with spirit, and then with creative mind, ultimately with our mind — all imagined in the masculine gender. The Great Mother and the goddess, who once stood for the ground of being and for the whole Kosmos prior to the separation of heaven and earth, gradually became identified with the earth alone, then with nature and matter and eventually (with the myth of the Fall), with sin and sexuality. Nature was reduced to the role of servant supplying humanity with the material for a better life. I hope I have managed to convey to you how we may have accepted things without sufficiently exploring the root of how ideas and beliefs have come into being.

## *The goddess tradition and the Fall*

If we go back to the older paradigm, inherited from the earlier goddess tradition, we see that it survived wherever the worship of the goddess survived. Through the focus of this image, life was still experienced (albeit for the most part unconsciously) as an organic, living and sacred whole. This different understanding or perception of reality mediated through the soul, through instinct and feeling, was enshrined in the image of the sacred marriage — the principal religious ceremony of the Bronze Age — which celebrated the union of heaven and earth, goddess and god and also, as we can understand now, the union of the two aspects of our consciousness. For the goddess symbolized the older matrix of the instinctual soul and the god became the focus for the developing power of the ego, the emergence of the individual from the collectivity of the tribe and the faculty of conceptual, abstract thought, or what today we call rational mind. The image of the sacred marriage, essential for keeping alive the bond between the two aspects of consciousness, between goddess and god, was transmitted to alchemy and to all those myths and fairy tales which end in a marriage. And so we return to the Sleeping Beauty as one of the most famous of these.

Now I would like to look at another crucially important myth — the Hebrew myth of the Fall — because it also describes the separation of consciousness from its instinctual ground. This myth seems to elaborate feelings that accompanied the experience of no longer being contained in the womb of nature. With the development of the conscious ego and of analytical, reflective thinking came an awareness of suffering and of profound guilt, responsibility and choice. The incredible fear of no longer feeling contained in the womb of nature, of feeling expelled from the Garden, and the belief that humanity was responsible for incurring this catastrophe through some primordial sin pervade the pages of the Old Testament. (Anyone who has worked with patients knows how deeply this feeling of guilt and sin is imprinted on the Christian psyche, particularly the psyche of woman). The need for control and power that is so much a feature of Iron Age culture and, indeed, of our own, may be understood as a compensation to the feeling of vulnerability in an alien world.

This myth, like the earlier one of Marduk, tells the story of how consciousness became divided into two parts — the one associated with the god and with spirit, reason, mind and the masculine principle; the other with the goddess and with soul, nature, feeling, instinct and the body as the feminine principle. Adam and Eve stand for these two aspects of our own nature. The division of a unified cosmos into the two parts of heaven and earth, mind and body, spirit and nature is an image of human consciousness entering a dualistic phase of its evolution. The duality we have projected onto life is not intrinsically real although, understandably, we have constructed our lives on the premiss that it is real. It is a provisional interpretation of an overwhelmingly difficult evolutionary experience. The image of a god transcendent to creation was perhaps necessary for our evolutionary growth and for the development of a strong sense of self and the development of individuality. But it has had tragic effects on humanity. Only as a therapist have I gained insight into the terror that the experience of separation and loss evokes and into the corrosive guilt that men and women who have experienced these carry in their soul.

The Expulsion from the Garden is a myth that marks the birth of modern consciousness, and the winning of some small measure of freedom from the overwhelming power of instinct and the dawning awareness of choice and responsibility. But it also marks the beginning of fear of the instincts and feelings, their repression and a loss of relationship with the soul. All this is told in the drama of Adam, Eve and the serpent. The serpent, symbol of the older instinctual consciousness, was blamed for tempting Eve. Eve was blamed for bringing death and suffering into the world. Woman through Eve was blamed for being the lure that led men into sexual relationships. Woman's sexuality in particular was associated with the primal sin which brought about the Fall. I think you can see what a disastrous and quite unnecessary amount of human suffering has come from this myth — all due to belief, fear and repression. The separation from nature and the emergence of the ego is the beginning of conflict within our own nature. This conflict, projected onto myriad situations in the world over thousands of years is the root of enmity between individuals and tribes that has led to the terrible carnage of this century. So, in a sense, the hedge of thorns is within us. The greatest problem in the world today, as Jung said, is how to heal the dissociation in our consciousness by bringing the masculine and feminine aspects of our nature together.

It looks to me as if the instinctive soul needs to be put into intensive care. It needs our attention. It has suffered terribly during the last three thousand years, first from repression and persecution by religion, lately from repression by the scientific attitude which insists that the non-rational, the unprovable, must be excluded from our view of reality. The rigorous repression of anything outside orthodoxy in religion and the exclusion of the non-rational from science amounts to the same thing — the strangulation or suffocation of the soul. In modern dreams the soul appears as a wounded animal, an emaciated or starving woman, a weeping or anorexic child. In a thousand ways, some acceptable to us, others unacceptable, it tries to get through to us, it tries to tell us its story, make us aware of its need for relationship with us. It tries to tell us that something is gravely amiss, out of balance. But it can't get through to the rational mind. This is why Jung in the last year of his life (1960) wrote these words: 'I have failed in my foremost task:

to open people's eyes to the fact that man has a soul, and that there is a buried treasure in the field and that our philosophy and religion are in a lamentable state ...' (Adler 1979.92).

## *Alchemy*

Now I want to turn to Alchemy and to how this situation might be changed. A sixteenth century painting (in *Splendor Solis* by Salomon Trismosin in the British Library) shows an alchemist holding in his hand an alchemical flask and standing barefoot in a landscape surrounded by a border of exquisite flowers and birds. He is wearing the royal purple robe which reflects an awakened consciousness and the integration of mind with soul. The alchemists called themselves the Sons of Wisdom because wisdom was the philosopher's stone, wisdom was the end-result of a long process of transformation. I believe that certain alchemists discovered that the dissociation between mind and soul could be healed and that through that healing, consciousness could evolve further, eventually reaching that state described by the great mystics of all cultures — the experience of the reunion of our nature with the ground of being. They knew, long before us, that matter was energy or spirit. They discovered that there was a hidden spirit, a hidden consciousness that was active within nature and human nature and that it was possible to work with that spirit, so bringing about an astonishing transformation. They called this spirit Mercurius. It was androgynous. They observed matter in their alchemical vessel; it came alive before their eyes. They saw it undergo a transformation and they began to speak to it through their imagination. Their understanding was transformed by that dialogue. The mystery drew them into the midst of itself, step by step. They became vehicles for the further evolution of consciousness. What we are discovering now — what the scientists present at this conference are discovering — rests on foundations they laid centuries ago. But the greatest alchemists regarded themselves as the servants, not the masters of life. They set their work in the context of a quest for a priceless treasure. 'Our gold is not the common gold.' They gave this treasure names like the wondrous stone, the philosopher's gold, the elixir of life. They discovered that the essential preparation for the experience of the treasure was a marriage between the solar and lunar, masculine and feminine aspects of our nature. They called these the king and the queen.

*The alchemist.*
*From* Splendor Solis.

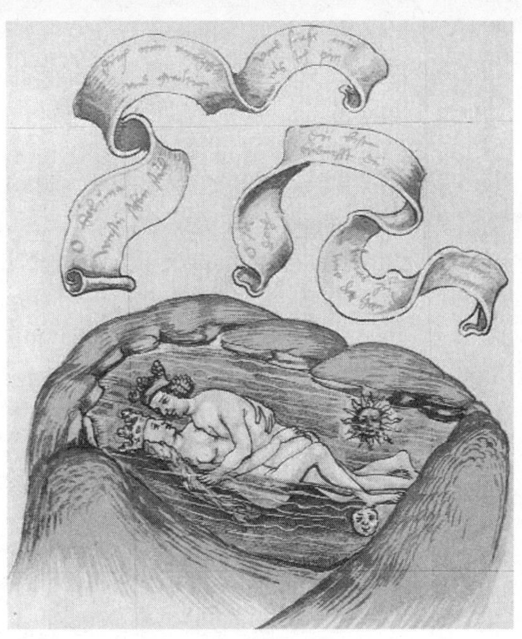

*The king and queen in union.*
*From* Rosarium philosophorum, *Stadtbibliothek Vadiana, St Gallen, MS 394a, f.34.*

Water and the sea have always been a symbol of the soul — remember that image of the mermaid — so in this alchemical image we see the king and queen immersed in the water of the soul, united in sexual union. The king enters the alchemical waters of the matrix of consciousness. There, he encounters a different kind of consciousness symbolized by the queen. This union of which the alchemists recorded many phases symbolized the process of psychic transformation whereby king and queen come to know each other intimately, entering into a dialogue with each other. The king becomes aware of his feelings, his instincts, not as something inferior to himself, something he has to dominate and subject to his will, but as something like his own mother, something that he has been born out of, that he has separated from and that he now needs to relate to and reunite with as his bride. The queen responds and changes as the king learns how to value and relate to this feminine and royal counterpart of himself. Translated into our modern understanding, the union would mean that our logical, analytical masculine mind begins to develop a different way of perceiving reality, a different, more feminine, participatory and empathic way of relating to life. Bathing in the maternal waters restores a sense of trust in life, taking away that fear that has so long dominated us. It leads to trust in the support and guidance of instinct, for instinct also undergoes transformation. As the king learns how to relate to the queen, he develops insight and follows a different, intuitive logic. As he differentiates himself from the archaic and unconscious power drive of his instinctual nature derived from the genetic programming of the older brain system, so that power becomes available to him to be used not against life but on behalf of life, on behalf of nature, on behalf of something that he begins to realize with amazement, is of the same essence as himself. He grows in moral stature through insight. In this one image there may be concentrated a lifetime of alchemical work.

This is how the alchemists pictured the ancient reflexes of the dragon that still have us in their grip. The dragon is the primordial life instinct in its unconscious state: the will to survive, the instinct to procreate, the territorial and tribal instinct, the fight/flight response, the maternal instinct to protect the young, the instinct for predator to attack and kill its prey. The dragon in mythology has long been a symbol of the immense power of instinct, power so great that our still immature conscious ego is like an ant compared to a dinosaur. The power of the dragon today is reflected in our terrible weapons of destruction, our

*The dragon feeding on its own tail.*

*From Pelecanos,* Synosius, *Bibliothèque National, Paris, Ms. grec 2327, f.297.*

*The Mighty Ethiopian.*
*From* Splendor Solis.

*The Slayer.*
*From* Splendor Solis.

drive for power and control and the horrifying pattern of predator attacking and destroying its prey as in the ethnic cleansing taking place in Bosnia and Rwanda. But the dragon is also the power to heal, to create, to transform; it is the colossal energy that impels our lives, the courage of human endeavour, the source of our extraordinary technical skills, our passionate longing to alleviate human suffering. The dragon is the root of our imagination, the energy that empowers it which has flowered in so many marvellous creations of the human soul. But an unconscious dragon acts blindly, following the pathways that are familiar to it through millions of years. Its energy and creativity can be harnessed to goals that injure and destroy life. An alliance between our technological skills and the power drive of the dragon can be very dangerous if there is no awareness of what is directing us.

## *Transformation and integration*

The alchemists gave supreme importance to the transformation of these archaic instinctual drives. They gave us a picture of this heroic achievement in an image of a dark man emerging from muddy waters, being welcomed by an angel holding the red robe which symbolizes a new, regenerated consciousness (in *Splendor Solis).* The alchemists called this dark figure the Mighty Ethiopian — a term which originates in Egypt with the god Osiris and the mythology of death and regeneration. So, applying this to ourselves, we ourselves would have to die to our old way of living in order to be born into a new understanding of life.

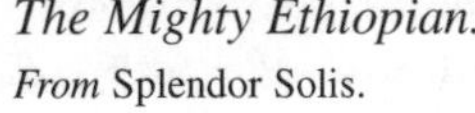

Here, in this image of integration king, queen and dragon are now related to each other. The three aspects of our nature are able to function in unity rather than in conflict with each other. The dragon wears a crown signifying that it too has become conscious, awake, and can no longer act blindly. It is an image of a unified soul, where all parts are related to each other and in harmony.

And here is an image of what we have to go through in order to effect this transformation. It is an image (of a man holding a severed head and standing in front of a dismembered body) that takes us back to the Dionysian mysteries of death, dismemberment and regeneration that is one of the most powerful themes of alchemy (in *Splendor Solis)*. The solar consciousness by which we live, focused only on the external world, is dismembered, dissolved, in order that a deeper understanding may come into being through reconnection with our lunar consciousness. The alchemists said that their art was not a method of metallic transmutation, so much as a true and solid science which teaches us how to know the centre of all things, which is called the spirit of life — the consciousness which permeates all forms of life. We cannot know this spirit with the limited, intellectual knowledge of the head. We need to know it with the heart, as an experience, and this is the beginning of wisdom. So dismemberment is an image of letting go of old beliefs and changing the patterns of behaviour in which the life spirit has become imprisoned or buried. Psychic growth is a very painful process and this image of dismemberment reflects it. But again you see the beautiful border round the edge which symbolizes bringing oneself into relationship with nature and the flowering of nature within us.

Other images of transformation are focused on water and fire as agents of transmuting the lead that we are into the gold of the final treasure. Water washes, cleanses, renews, gives life. Fire burns, purifies, transmutes. By these processes the matter of our psychic life is refined, cleansed, rendered more subtle and translucent to the divine ground. By these methods the quintessential gold of the life spirit is separated out from the rust or verdigris that has accrued to it over the millennia of human evolution. The alchemists called themselves washerwomen and cooks. Reaching ever deeper into the heart of their psychic life, they perceived the unity of everything; they saw that matter was not dead, inert. They felt the aliveness of matter, worked with the spirit hidden in matter, entered into a dialogue with it and were struck with wonder and amazement at what they discovered. Their growing insight worked a profound transformation of their consciousness, their understanding. They hid their discoveries in obscure symbols for fear of persecution. Fortunately for us, a few of their books with their amazing illustrations have survived.

The peacock with its many-eyed tail is, in alchemy, an image of the flowering of the new kind of consciousness, the hundred eyes that we begin to see with once we move into a deeper relationship with life (in *Splendor Solis).* It reflects the flowering of the imagination and the capacity to feel related to the whole of creation.

Being a therapist has taught me something that I didn't know before and that I could have learned in no other way. It has taught me how infinitely vulnerable we are, how infinitely sensitive, how courageous, how noble, how tragic our lives are when in the grip of a complex that can create a negative fate, a fate we cannot comprehend, and how deeply intelligent we are once we have begun to understand what our symptoms are trying to convey to us about the suffering of our soul. There is no doubt that the chief longing of human consciousness is to know itself, to understand itself, to discover its purpose on this planet. I don't think suffering by itself teaches us anything at all. If it did, we would have come to our senses centuries ago. It is only through insight into our behaviour that we can radically alter our fate, change our behaviour. The excitement and wonder that comes with the realization that we can transform our psychic life, that we can change our fate by changing our consciousness is deeply moving. The joy and energy released is phenomenal. Instead of living from the mind, from surface of our being or from the collective beliefs and values of the culture, we begin to live from a deeper level. And this is where synchronicity comes in: as if responding to our effort to live differently, life indicates its awareness of this shift of consciousness by helping us in some tangible way. It's as if it's saying: 'Yes, you're on the right track. Trust that intuition. Follow that path.' Books fall out of shelves. Unexpected meetings take place. This in turn encourages trust and further effort to let go of an obsolete pattern of living. We begin to perceive how intimately linked our lives are with the lives of others, how we are all one essential life at the root. This is intensely moving — at times a revelation. As we move closer to the heart of our own being, so we are attracted to others who are on the same path as ourselves, experiencing this process of awakening, and we can share with them the discoveries and experiences which have enriched our lives.

*The Alchemical Wedding.*
*From* Splendor Solis.

So here, to end, is an image of the alchemical wedding (in *Splendor Solis),* the final stage of the alchemical work, which actually takes place in all the phases of this process of awakening but here is shown as an image of completion. King and queen, the solar and lunar aspects of consciousness are united, in relationship with each other; neither one repressing, threatening or in conflict with the other. There is balance, integration and creative expansion in the service of life. There is no need for forced sacrifice as in many religious traditions, no need for the punishing ritual of ascetic self-denial. I feel very strongly about this because the body has suffered terribly through these practices and still carries the memory of that suffering. The alchemists were careful to say that their union included body, soul and spirit. They also said that this union could only be brought about gradually and gently and that, although their work was apparently 'against' nature, against continuing in bondage to unconscious instinctive patterns, the awakening of instinct could only be accomplished with the assistance of nature. The way to its consummation would be revealed step by step. It could not be hurried or forced.

Alchemy is a psychic experience that is impossible to describe or teach. The symbols yield their secret to those who contemplate them.

The process of transformation is unique for each one of us yet intrinsically the same for all. This is the slow creation of the wondrous stone, the vision of the Holy Grail, the tasting of the elixir of life, the healing with the alchemical gold. It is the blazing revelation of the divinity of life in the reunion of body, soul and spirit and the service of that life with whatever creative gifts it has bestowed on us. The gradual creation of the treasure is an experience of great suffering and sacrifice on the one hand and illumination, wonder and inexpressible joy on the other as the light of the unified consciousness dawns.

No-one, the alchemists said, may accomplish this work except through affection, humility and love for it is the gift of God to his humble servants. To return to the ground from which we have come, so completing our evolutionary journey on this planet and bringing the consciousness of the planet with us, is one of the most exciting quests that I can imagine. To discover that spirit, so long projected onto a God remote from ourselves and creation, is the quintessential consciousness which is awaiting discovery both in nature and ourselves is one of the greatest revelations that it is possible for the human spirit to experience. The other revelation, no less overwhelming, is that we have the extraordinary privilege of helping this divine consciousness to achieve its evolutionary goal. In awakening to our soul, in discovering how to relate to it, transform it, to heal its wounds and listen to its guidance, to receive its dreams and acknowledge its visions, we help to bring about the marriage between the Sleeping Beauty and the Prince and eventually also, that sacred marriage with the ground of being which is the tremendous destiny of the human race.

## *References*


Adler, Gerhard. 1979. *Dynamics of the self.* London: Coventure.

Barfield, Owen. 1988. *Saving the appearances.* Middletown, Conn.: Wesleyan University Press. (Originally published 1957. London: Faber & Faber.)

Griffiths, Bede. 1976. *Return to the centre.* London: HarperCollins.

Klossowski de Rola, Stanislas. 1973. *Alchemy, the secret art.* London: Thames & Hudson.

Sorokin, Pitirim. 1992. *The crisis of our age.* Oxford: Oneworld.

*Splendor Solis.* Manuscript by Salomon Trismosin in the British Library.

## *The Scientific and Medical Network*

The Scientific and Medical Network is an informal international group consisting mainly of qualified scientists and doctors, together with engineers, psychologists, philosophers, therapists and other professionals. The Network came into existence in 1973 and now has over 2,000 Members in more than fifty countries. It questions the assumptions of contemporary scientific and medical thinking, so often limited by exclusively materialistic reasoning. By remaining open to intuitive and spiritual insights, it fosters a climate in which science as a whole can adopt a more comprehensive and sensitive approach. Anyone interested may join the Network as an Associate Member and receive our publication *Network,* while qualified professionals are welcome to join as Full Members.

Further details:
The Scientific and Medical Network,
Gibliston Mill, Colinsburgh, Leven, Fife KY9 1JS, Scotland.
Email: info@scimednet.org Web: www.scimednet.org

## *Institute of Noetic Sciences*

The Institute of Noetic Sciences is an international non-profit organisation with nearly 50,000 Members. Founded in 1973 by Apollo 14 Astronaut Edgar D. Mitchell, the Institute of Noetic Sciences supports research and education on consciousness, human potential, and personal and social transformation. Members receive subscriptions to the *Noetic Sciences Review,* the *Noetic Sciences Bulletin,* and *An Intelligent Guide to Books and Tapes.* Members also have the opportunity to participate in Institute-sponsored travel programmes, dialogue groups, conferences and special events. Members enjoy discounted prices on books, tapes and conferences.
To receive a free information pack about the Institute, write to
The Institute of Noetic Sciences,
101 San Antonio Road, Petaluma, CA 94952-9524, USA.
Tel: (415) 331 5650. Web: www.noetic.org

# Index